CROP ADAPTATION AND DISTRIBUTION

A SERIES OF BOOKS IN AGRICULTURAL SCIENCE

Plant and Soil Science Editors: *Iver Johnson and M. B. Russell*

CROP ADAPTATION AND DISTRIBUTION
Carroll P. Wilsie

Animal Science Editors: *G. W. Salisbury and E. W. Crampton*

APPLIED ANIMAL NUTRITION: The Uses of Feedstuffs
in the Formulation of Livestock Rations
E. W. Crampton

REPRODUCTIVE PHYSIOLOGY: Comparative Reproductive
Physiology of Domestic Animals, Laboratory Animals and Man
A. V. Nalbandov

THE SCIENCE OF MEAT AND MEAT PRODUCTS
American Meat Institute Foundation

FUNDAMENTALS OF NUTRITION
E. W. Crampton and L. E. Lloyd

PHYSIOLOGY OF REPRODUCTION AND ARTIFICIAL
INSEMINATION OF CATTLE
G. W. Salisbury and N. L. VanDemark

CROP ADAPTATION

AND DISTRIBUTION

CARROLL P. WILSIE *Iowa State University*

W. H. FREEMAN AND COMPANY

SAN FRANCISCO AND LONDON

Preface

Although a high degree of specialization is accepted as essential in training students in various branches of the biological sciences, some effort toward integration appears to have merit. In studies of environmental biology, whether the subject be called crop adaptation, ecological crop geography, or crop ecology, there is ample opportunity to effect such integration. Crop ecology is concerned with the ways in which plants adapt to their environment; the many factors of the habitat, considered individually and collectively; the differential responses of species, varieties, and individuals; and the effects of natural selection on a group of interacting plants occupying the same general habitat.

The development in this book treats first the basic principles of ecology and plant geography, progresses through a consideration of the important factors of the plant's environment, and finally considers generally the distribution of important world crops on a climatic basis.

Crop adaptation—crop ecology itself—is closely related to genetics and plant physiology. Thus, knowledge of the basic concepts of biological evolution and genetics is essential for an understanding of crop adaptation. Natural selection, the fundamental basis of adaptation, has been of utmost importance in determining the characteristics of present-day crops, and it is still of great significance in modern plant breeding.

There is a close relationship between the plant's behavior pattern (or response to its environment) and its physiology. The influences of individual environmental factors, such as temperature, moisture, and light, as well as the more complex interrelationships inherent in the whole ecosystem, play important roles in the establishment of a behavior pattern. Genotype-environmental interactions, so important in plant breeding, suggest that there is a high degree of specificity in physiological requirements.

In a consideration of geographical distribution of plants the important contributions from other disciplines, particularly climatology, geology, geography, and soil science are evident. Although man's influence—from the standpoint of historical, political, and economic factors—has been great, climatic factors still are basic in determining where most crops are grown. This concept is emphasized in considering some of the world's important crops, and particular attention is given to their adaptation to the major types of climate found over the earth.

Since 1945 the author has taught a course in Crop Adaptation to seniors and graduate students at Iowa State University. Though the majority of these students has been from the Department of Agronomy, other departments have been represented nearly every year, especially Botany and Plant Pathology, Horticulture, Forestry, Economics, and Education. In the course the author has attempted to emphasize broad principles having application to crop production throughout the world. Though many of the students have come from foreign lands and have had highly divergent backgrounds, interests, and training, the course assumes introductory courses in agronomy and botany. Additional prerequisites for the course are general genetics, plant physiology, and senior or graduate classification.

Satisfactory textbooks are difficult to find. For many years Klages' *Ecological Crop Geography* was used as a standard reference. Other texts used extensively are Daubenmire's *Plants and Environment,* Odum's *Fundamentals of Ecology,* and Whyte's *Crop Production and Environment.* Some material for class use has been taken also from the more recent texts on economic geography by Shaw, Jones, and Darkenwald and by Bengtson and Van Royen.

This book has been written to fill the need for a general text on principles of crop adaptation and distribution. It is designed for a one-semester course, but it may also be used satisfactorily for a one-quarter course if portions are shortened or omitted. The broad, general coverage may possibly not appeal to everyone teaching a course in Crop Adaptation, Crop Ecology, or Crop Geography; however, the viewpoint has been kept broad in order that the book will not appear to be provincial in outlook. It is assumed that this book will be used to supplement and strengthen agronomic training which includes basic courses in genetics, plant physiology, soils, botany, and plant breeding. Furthermore, it is hoped that this book will be of interest not only to students in agronomy, but also to students in other areas of agriculture and in economic botany and forestry.

December 1961   CARROLL P. WILSIE

Contents

PART III   CROP DISTRIBUTION ON A CLIMATIC BASIS

GENERAL PRINCIPLES
AND CONCEPTS

Ecological Approach to the
World Food Problem

The problem of world food supply directly or indirectly affects people in every occupation and in every social and economic status. Patterns of world crop distribution have developed which are based on natural principles of biological evolution and ecology, but which may be influenced greatly by man's ambition and ingenuity. These patterns are largely taken for granted, and we seldom stop to reflect seriously on why we grow crops where we do.

The study of the relationships between crop plants and their environment is known as *crop ecology*. It implies studies of: (1) climatic factors, such as moisture, temperature, and light; (2) edaphic factors, including parent material and soil; and (3) biotic factors, such as the effects of other organisms, as all these relate to plant adaptation, distribution, and production. Klages (1942) has included also some of the social factors brought into the picture by man, and has called the entire area of study *ecological crop geography*. He has shown how the natural patterns of crop production have been greatly influenced by historical, political, economic, and social forces. This has resulted in situations in which crops are not always grown where they are best adapted nor where they can be grown most economically.

The farmer is concerned with principles of adaptation when he chooses the crops he plants. He knows that some varieties mature early, whereas others mature late. If he lives in the northern region, he is aware that early frosts in the autumn constitute a hazard which he must face each year. Consequently, he chooses varieties which will take advantage of the full growing season, yet offer only a slight risk of not coming to full maturity. He knows the importance of soil moisture and light, and realizes that when he plants alfalfa or red clover with a small grain crop, competition may determine the success or failure of the legume.

The agricultural economist may look at the ecology of crops primarily from the viewpoint of production efficiency. Here, the principle of comparative advantage may become paramount. The natural factors of environment may determine which crops can be grown effectively, but economic factors may decide what and how much will be grown.

The geneticist or plant breeder has a different, and perhaps a more complete, concept of crop adaptation. To him a species or variety may appear as a population, more or less infinite in size, possessing a range of genetic diversity dependent largely on its origin and mode of reproduction. The opportunity for selection of biotypes better adapted to present or potential production areas may appear to him as the most important aspect of adaptation.

POPULATION AND WORLD FOOD SUPPLY

During the past few decades, the people of the United States have begun to realize the necessity of a world viewpoint on food problems. Agricultural production in this country reached an unprecedented peak at the end of World War II, and again at the time of the Korean conflict. After the cessation of hostilities, drastic adjustments in production were not made, with the result that huge surpluses of wheat, corn, cotton, and other agricultural commodities were accumulated in the United States. By 1950, Europe had largely regained its prewar status in food production, and less of some of these staple commodities were imported. Also, other countries had come into a more favorable competitive position. For these two reasons the export of agricultural products by the United States declined. Through government financed programs of storage, of price supports and production controls, attempts were made to compensate for this loss of export market. These attempts were not particularly successful, and it was apparent that too many agricultural resources were being used for the population that had to be fed. Even though the increase in population has been rapid since 1945, it appears that with our present production capacity there are still too many people engaged in producing food. A more rapid shift from farming into other occupations would seem to be the only way in which the agricultural economy can be brought up to the level of the general economy. A background for this concept of our present agricultural situation is presented in detail in recent studies by Kutish, Kaldor, Heady, Timmons, *et al.* (1957).

However, even though we in the United States face the present dilemma of too much food, it is possible that from the world point of view all of our productive capacity may be needed in the future. In many areas of the world, large elements of the population suffer from some form of malnutrition. Because of the current rapid rate of worldwide population increase, the ability of man to feed himself adequately in the near future often is questioned.

Huxley, in 1950, estimated that during the next 50 years the population of the world would increase from 2.5 billion to 3 billion. It seems obvious now that this figure will be exceeded greatly, for it was estimated at 2.8 billion in 1958 and predicted to pass 3 billion by 1962 (United Nations, 1959). Estimates of Putnam (1953) and Brown (1954) indicate something like 6 billion to 8 billion for the world, and 375 million for the United States by the year 2050. Luck (1957) has projected the present trend in population increase and has arrived at the astounding possible figures of 9 billion for the world and 600 million for the United States in another 100 years.

In general, there are two constrasting views on the problem of population and world food supply, the pessimistic and the optimistic. The pessimistic view at its most extreme goes back to Malthus (1798), who remarked that the power of population to increase was infinitely greater than the power to provide food. Actually the Malthusian theory is a prediction of eventual famine. In more recent times the possibility of population growth outstripping food supply has been called to our attention by Jacks and Whyte (1939), Vogt (1948), Cook (1951), Osborn (1957, 1958), and others. These writers point out the serious implications of our present rapid rate of population increase, and urge that we consider immediately the practical problems we will face in the future. As Osborn suggests, if we cannot keep up in increasing the facilities of our schools and colleges to accommodate the influx of pupils, if we cannot meet the increasing demands for more adequate housing and better social services, we had better take positive steps to cut down on the rate of population growth. This may be the only way in which we can maintain our present standard of living.

Living space itself is becoming a problem of increasing importance, according to Sears (1958). He has noted that "no known form of life has been observed to multiply indefinitely without bumping against the limitations imposed by the space it occupies." Further, he has suggested that at the present rate of population increase in the United States, the aggregate volume of human bodies will be doubled in 41 years. Sears points out that cities, industries, and highways in the United States alone absorb a million acres of land each year. These acres are not always waste acres, but often represent some of the better agricultural lands in the country.

A more optimistic view of this problem is that a rapid rate of population increase is inevitable and must be taken for granted. Some physical scientists, engineers, agricultural experts, and government employees have indicated that the situation can be met through greatly expanded food production whenever needed. It has been suggested that this be accomplished through (1) technological advances, (2) expansion of production into colder areas, and (3) expansion of production into the humid tropics.

We cannot quarrel with the first point, for technology has changed agricultural production tremendously during the last few decades, and it appears quite likely that continued application will meet future needs adequately, at least in the United States. However, there may be some question on the merits of the second and third points. Such expansion, while within the realm of possibility, offers many obstacles difficult to overcome.

Possibly an intermediate view is more realistic than either of the extremes. In the first place, as has been pointed out by Bennett (1954), the world famine predicted by Malthus has not yet arrived. The world's population has increased tremendously, it is true, but the general level of consumption also has increased. Bennett indicates that although population has the power to increase more rapidly than land or food supply, history has shown repeatedly that this power is not always used. It lies within man's control to regulate his population.

POPULATION TRENDS AND MAN–LAND RATIO

During the past thirty years, the world's population has increased at the rate of approximately 12 persons per thousand per year (Whelpton, 1958). This compares with a rate of about 8 persons per thousand per year for the preceding thirty-year period. At the present time the population is increasing at the rate of approximately 45 millions per year, which is about 15 persons per thousand per year.

In the United States the rate of population increase is now about 16 persons per thousand per year, as compared with 13 per thousand a generation ago. Whelpton (1958) has suggested that this marked increase in rate may be a short-term fluctuation rather than a long-time trend. Canada, Australia, New Zealand, and the USSR have similar rates of natural increase, while those of Central and South America tend to be still higher. The rate of population increase in most European countries is about half the rate of the world average.

In Whelpton's view, there is some indication in the United States that the rate of population increase may have reached or passed the peak, and some decline is likely in the near future. Only time will prove whether or not this is more than a logical prediction. Since the birth rate in the United States is largely under voluntary control, the rate and magnitude of decline will likely depend on economic considerations as well as on the attitudes of our millions of young people toward marriage patterns and optimum size of family.

In other countries, particularly in South America, there is no evidence that the rate of population increase has reached a peak. In India and Japan, which have been plagued for generations with overpopulation problems, there is growing evidence of increasing interest in positive controls of population growth. Such interest has been developing in China also, but apparently cannot make much headway under the present governmental policy on population.

The necessity for providing more food usually is the incentive for more intensive cultivation of crops. In primitive societies the size of the population is largely dependent on the stage of culture. As Wissler (1923) noted, "the tribal group expands until it reaches the limit of its food supply. Then, if it does not succumb or remain static, it evolves a new mechanism for feeding itself, only to repeat the phenomenon over once more."

The density of population is expressed on the basis of number of persons per square mile, or in a more realistic manner, as the number of persons per unit of arable land. Distribution of arable land throughout the world is, unfortunately, far from uniform, as is indicated roughly in Figure 1-1.

Harberger (1958) has emphasized important differences between countries with regard to population pressure and food supply. Under a well-developed industrial and agricultural economy, such as we have in the United States, he believes that the population possibly could increase at the rate of 6% per year without causing an early decline in living standards. In contrast, an under-developed country might suffer a reduction in living standards with a population growth of only 2% per year.

From the short-term viewpoint there seems to be little doubt that in the United States the food requirements of our rapidly increasing population can be met, at least for the next generation or two. However, from the long-time view, unless the rate of population growth declines, all of our available resources are likely to be needed to maintain a satisfactory living standard.

Optimum man-land ratios are rather nebulous terms, because the very concept varies with the economic and cultural standards of different peoples. Broek (1958) has pointed out how religious and social customs exert powerful influences on attitudes toward the most effective use of land. Until very

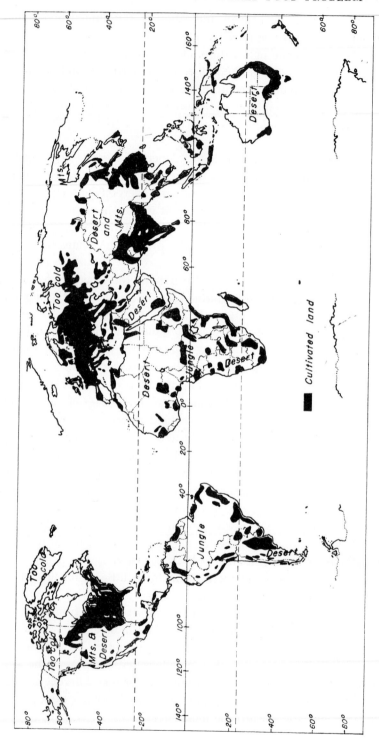

FIGURE 1-1.

Approximate cultivated land area of the world. [Courtesy U. S. Department of Agriculture, Foreign Agricultural Service.]

recently at least, Indian villagers would rather lose their crops than kill cattle or monkeys. In Great Britain the social prestige of hunting has kept extensive lands out of effective agricultural production. Present man-land ratios can be determined, but optimum ratios may still be undefined. Hunting and gathering economies support only sparse populations, estimated by Deevey (1958) to be possibly one person per 9 or 10 square miles. In contrast, an agricultural economy in the tropics or subtropics, with intensive cultivation, may support 3000 or more persons per square mile.

The ecological concept of equilibrium populations has been applied to the world's human population by Deevey (1958). At equilibrium a population is in a state of balance between the forces of procreation and those of destruction. The ecologist is familiar with all sorts of biological populations at, above, or below equilibrium.

A model for determining the flow of energy through an ecosystem at equilibrium has been developed by Lindeman (1942), Odum (1959), and others. Essentially, the standing crop of the biological components is measured, estimates are made of their various rates of turnover, and the input and use of energy by the whole community is computed. Plants are considered to be approximately 0.1% efficient in their use of solar energy, the herbivores are about 10% efficient in utilizing the plants, and the carnivores are about 10% efficient in utilizing the herbivores. Through this kind of analysis it becomes obvious why meat is more expensive than vegetables.

Deevey (1958) computed the gross productivity of human beings, basing his calculations on the present standing crop and the normal growth rate. He found that this value was similar to that of the estimated gross productivity of all of the plants on the earth. Deevey noted further that if the human crop were increased ten times, not only would meat eating become impossible, but the whole land area of the earth would have to be brought into production and made to produce as much edible carbohydrates as it now produces of all forms of vegetable tissue, including wood. To bring about a tenfold increase in population would require only an average rate of increase of 1% per year for a period of 230 years. However, it is believed by Deevey that the equilibrium population may be reached before this tenfold increase occurs, through the self-regulation of numbers.

MAN–LAND RATIO AND NUTRITION

Russell (1954) proposed a working basis for considering the relationship between arable land and adequate nutrition. In countries having 2.5 or more acres of cultivated land per person, the people can enjoy an adequate mixed diet. The United States, Canada, Argentina, Australia, and the USSR are in this category. New Zealand also may be included because much of its pasture land is highly productive, but is not normally included in the figure for arable land. Countries having between 1 and 2.5 acres of arable land per capita, such as France, Spain, Portugal, Australia, Poland, and Czechoslovakia may be approximately 80% self-sufficient, but the diet may be a monotonous one, lacking in variety in animal foods such as meat, milk, and butter. With less than 1 acre of arable land per person, a vegetable diet only is possible, excepting through the importation of food. The United Kingdom, Netherlands, Belgium, Switzerland, Italy, and West Germany are in this category, but enjoy an adequate mixed diet through importation of food, made possible by the development of international trade. Other countries,

TABLE 1-1.   MAN–LAND RATIOS IN VARIOUS COUNTRIES, 1959*

Country	Approximate Population Density (persons per square mile)	Approximate Amount of Arable Land (acres per person)
Congo	15	8.9
Canada	5	5.4
Australia	3	5.3
Argentina	19	3.7
United States	49	2.7
USSR	24	2.6
Uruguay	37	2.0
Ghana	73	1.9
Spain	204	1.7
Nigeria	103	1.5
Denmark	274	1.5
Poland	243	1.4
Mexico	45	1.4
France	213	1.2
Sweden	42	1.2
Brazil	21	0.8
Cuba	146	0.8
India	330	0.8
Italy	436	0.8
New Zealand	23	0.8
Norway	28	0.6
Philippines	213	0.6
West Germany	573	0.4
United Kingdom	550	0.3
Egypt	66	0.3
China	180	0.3
Puerto Rico	680	0.3
Belgium	773	0.3
Netherlands	880	0.2
Japan	650	0.2

* Source: United Nations, Demographic Yearbook, New York, 1959.

usually nearly self-sufficient on the basis of a vegetable diet, include India, China, Japan, Egypt, and most of those in southeastern Asia.

Countries exporting large quantities of agricultural commodities include the United States, Canada, Australia, New Zealand, Argentina, and Brazil. In the last two countries the potential production of many agricultural commodities is many times greater than present production.

Data on population density for a representative number of countries of the world, expressed on the basis of both total land area and arable land, are given in Table 1-1.

National differences in patterns of food consumption have been discussed at length by Bennett (1954). These differences may be based on income per capita, and, within similar income groups, on food preferences, price differentials and basic differences in natural resources. In countries of relatively high income per capita, such as the United States, Canada, Sweden, the United Kingdom, Australia, and New Zealand, a much lower proportion of the total calories consumed is obtained from carbohydrates than is true of countries of low average income. Also, of the protein portion of the diet of people from nations of low income per capita, such as Mexico, Burma, India, China, and Indonesia, most of it is of vegetable origin, whereas the people from countries of high income per capita obtain more than half of their protein from animal sources.

Within similar income brackets there are many interesting differences in food consumption. For example, the Swiss consume more milk, cream, and vegetables than do the Canadians, but the Canadians use more poultry and eggs than do the Swiss. Likewise, Norwegians consume more milk and cream than are consumed by the French, but in France more fruit and vegetables are eaten than are consumed by Norwegians. Figure 1-2 shows a map of the world indicating estimated national income per capita for various countries.

Another factor of importance, which has been brought to our attention recently by Pollock (1956), is that eating habits of people change. While such changes may be slow, almost imperceptible at times, they have marked effects over a long-term period. Though Americans consume approximately the same number of calories as they did a half-century ago, the per-capita consumption of grain products and potatoes has dropped 40%. Also, the per-capita consumption of eggs has increased 40%, green vegetables 60%, citrus fruit and tomatoes 80%, and meat, poultry, and fish about 2%. One of the striking changes in the United States has been the increase in consumption of margarine to approximately three times the pre-World War II average, while butter consumption has dropped 50%.

In considering present and potential population density, it seems likely

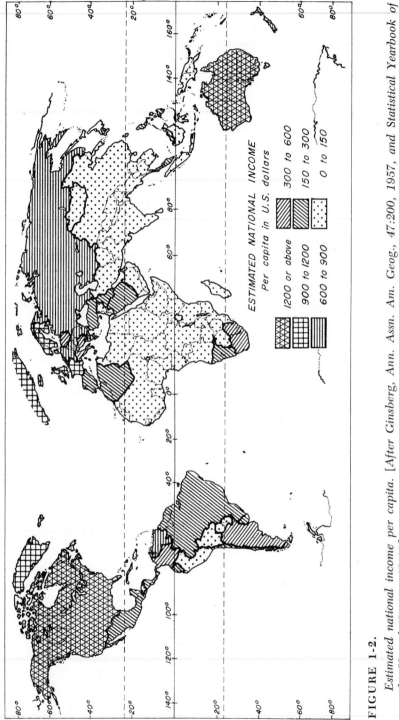

FIGURE 1-2.

Estimated national income per capita. [*After Ginsberg, Ann. Assn. Am. Geog., 47:200, 1957, and Statistical Yearbook of the United Nations, N. Y.*]

that there are three areas in which environmental conditions favor a greater population. These are the West Coast area of North America, the southeastern part of Australia, and the favorable parts of Brazil and Argentina. Some years ago Taylor (1922) predicted that the five great world centers of white settlement in the future would be London, Chicago, Sydney, Buenos Aires, and Durban. The inclusion of Durban today seems doubtful, but all of these cities are located in regions possessing high climatic energy, a factor cited by Klages (1942), Huntington (1951), and Markham (1944) as being of great importance. This concept of high climatic energy is based on the fact that most human beings work more efficiently in temperatures in the range of 60° to 65°F than in higher or lower temperatures. Also, variability in the weather is considered an asset, and the occurrence of frequent cyclonic storms tends to assure this variability. According to Huntington (1951), seasonal changes in climatic conditions are desirable. A study of factory workers in the northeastern part of the United States showed a peak of efficiency in October. By January or February workers' efficiency dropped 10%, rose again to another peak in May or June, then dropped again in midsummer. The lack of climatic energy may have been a factor in the decay of early centers of civilization in tropical and subtropical regions. It was probably a factor in the limited degree of development and accomplishments of the Polynesian and Melanesian peoples of the Pacific area.

LAND USE AND SOCIAL FACTORS

Ecological land use refers to the utilization of land for those particular crops and enterprises for which the area is well suited. In 1946, Ackerman, in discussing the geographical meaning of ecological land use, gave a classification of natural land types in the world and considered problems inherent in development of satisfactory ecological land use in each type. His classification is shown in Table 1-2 and in Figure 1-3.

Ackerman noted that progress toward better ecological land use has been made in areas of Type 1. In areas of Type 2 and Type 3 there is a great population burden for the limited resources offered. Much of India, China, and Japan are included in these types, and here the problem is not simply one of educating people to the use of new methods. These may be most impracticable, as has been discovered in many instances in conducting work of technical assistance in the Point-Four programs. In Type 4 areas, careful management is essential. Over long periods, careless management of semiarid lands may result in eventual reversion to desert. In Type 5 areas, the

TABLE 1-2.   WORLD CLASSIFICATION OF NATURAL
LAND TYPES *

Natural Land Type	Percent of	
	World Area	World Population
1. Humid, middle latitude lands	9	25
2. Humid subtropics	4	25
3. Seasonally dry tropics	13	20
4. Semiarid and subhumid	18	10
5. Rain forest, low latitude	8	4
6. Other	48	16

* Data from Ackerman, *Jour. Soil and Water Cons.* 1 (2): 63–66, 76–80,
1946.

humid tropics, there will always be a heavy demand for fertilizers. Erosion
may be serious and nitrogen losses heavy, but Ackerman suggests that the
eventual lack of sufficient phosphorus and potassium may be even more
limiting.

Examples of good and poor ecological land use can be found close at
hand. In the heart of the Corn Belt in the United States, on deep prairie
soils where erosion is not a problem, the production of corn represents good
ecological land use. In colonial days, much cotton was grown in Virginia
and Kentucky. Today this crop is of only minor importance in those states,
for it has found a much more suitable environment in the alluvial soils of
Mississippi and in the rich irrigated valleys of California and Arizona.

During the first 25 years of this century, plantings of citrus fruit in Florida
and California were extended far beyond tolerance limits for these crops.
Heavy frosts, lack of water, and poor soil caused many failures. In more
recent years, the citrus industry has achieved greater stability because of
greater attention to environmental requirements in locating orchards and
the added protection from frost hazard reduction through use of heaters
and wind machines.

Wheat is another crop which has been planted extensively outside of its
tolerance limits. During World War I, many Great Plains areas of grassland
were plowed and planted to wheat. Because of lack of sufficient moisture
there were many failures. Still worse, perhaps, was the general effect of
disturbing these large acreages of sod, contributing no doubt to the "dust
bowl" conditions of the early 1930's. Even today, as shown by recent studies
of Herves and Schmieding (1956), hail, drought, and winter-killing constitute a great hazard in the production of wheat in Nebraska and other
Great Plains areas.

The endeavor to grow temperate-zone crops in the tropics is likewise

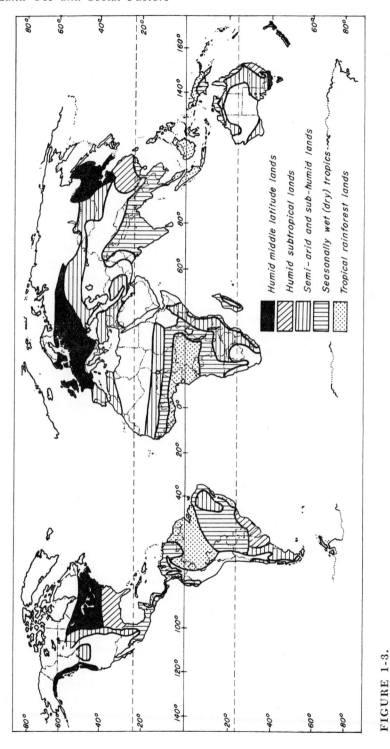

FIGURE 1-3.

Distribution of natural types of agricultural land. [After Ackerman, Jour. Soil and Water Conser., 1:63–76, 1946.]

Humid middle latitude lands

Humid subtropical lands

Semi-arid and sub-humid lands

Seasonally wet (dry) tropics

Tropical rainforest lands

doomed to scant success. During both World Wars, the people of Hawaii made serious efforts to produce more of the food they consumed instead of depending on Mainland shipments. For the most part these efforts were of little avail, for most of our temperate-zone crops are poorly adapted to tropical environments.

These examples, which suggest poor ecological land use, illustrate the influence of what Klages (1942) has called "social factors." In this broad context, social factors are those historical, political, economic and socio-logical influences which affect crop distribution, but are not inherent in the conditions of the natural environment.

The sugar industry furnishes a classic example of an agricultural enter-prise operating under a high degree of control by social factors. Sugarcane is a tropical crop, demanding for its best performance a high level of soil fertility, a relatively warm temperature throughout the year, and large amounts of water and sunshine. Such conditions are found in Cuba, Puerto Rico, Hawaii, Philippines, Java, India, and other tropical regions. In por-tions of Florida and Louisiana, under subtropical conditions, sugarcane can be grown as an annual crop, but yields of sugar are considerably lower than in the more favorable tropical areas.

Sugar beets furnish the other large source of sugar. During World War I, sugar beet production in Europe was interrupted, and a serious shortage developed in the United States, as well as in other parts of the world. By the time the beet industry had recovered, the cane industry had forged ahead and Cuba was in a position to supply much of the sugar needed by the United States. However, because of the strategic importance of sugar in times of war, domestic production of both sugarcane and sugar beets in the United States was encouraged. A tariff was imposed on imported sugar, with Cuba enjoying a preferential rate. In 1934, the Jones-Costigan Sugar Act established quotas on raw and refined sugar for each area supplying sugar to the United States and provided subsidies to cane- and beet-sugar producers. These measures resulted in further stimulation to domestic sugar-cane and sugar beet production.

Other nations too saw the importance of an adequate supply of sugar and instituted tariff policies for the protection of their own producers. By 1930, the world sugar market was in a rather chaotic state and serious efforts were made to adopt some kind of international control of sugar pro-duction. In 1937, the International Sugar Agreement was adopted by 22 major sugar-producing and sugar-consuming countries, 90% of the world's production and 85% of the world's consumption being involved.

Since 1934, sugar legislation in the United States has fostered domestic production through the following: marketing quotas, a tariff, an excise tax, and compliance payments. Within the sugar industry, competition may be quite intense. In the West Coast area, where Hawaii has refined and marketed most of its sugar, major development of production in the beet industry has resulted in sharp competition for the western market. While sugar yields in Hawaii are much higher than sugar yields from mainland beets, the disadvantages of spiraling labor costs and greater distance from the market have largely offset this natural advantage.

In general, crops should be grown where they are well adapted and where efficient production is the rule. This means that favorable conditions for international trade must be present in order that proper distribution of products can be made. For example, the United States has no climate favorable for large-scale coffee production. Brazil has an abundance of land and climate favorable for coffee, but also has great areas favorable for cotton, a crop which we too produce for export. Europe has little or no satisfactory climate for cotton production, but does have export possibilities for industrial products. These examples are given merely to show the complexity of the problem of the world's food and fiber. Stamp (1952) has suggested the use of an important principle in expanding or contracting food supply. In time of war, when greatly increased supplies are needed, the most efficient way of accomplishing this is to intensify production in the more favorable areas rather than through expansion into marginal areas. This calls for an equal adjustment in the opposite direction when the need has declined.

Recent studies by Fuller (1956) have shown evidence of an ecological approach to some of California's farm problems. He has pointed out that farm population stabilized, while the general population increased 53% between 1940 and 1950. Only 6% of the state's people live on farms, yet California is one of the most productive agricultural states in the Union. As the population increased, cattle, wheat, butter, and eggs shifted from an export to an import category. California's unique export commodities, however, including fruits, nuts, vegetables, and specialized seed crops, have continued to be important without regard to the size of the state's market. The dominating influence governing the agricultural output of California has been the demand from outside the state rather than within it. If this principle of producing those commodities which an area is uniquely fitted to produce could be applied more completely throughout the world as a whole, it might be exceedingly helpful to the world's food economy.

Regardless of the degree of optimism or pessimism of our own views on the problem of population and the world's food, we are likely to become increasingly aware of our responsibility in the United States in assisting in a solution of world food problems. One important aspect of these problems is the adaptation of the numerous crops and varieties throughout the world. A more complete understanding of the specific environmental requirements of our present crops is basic to a sound ecological approach. Also, greater attention should be given to the ecological aspects of the great range of genetic and breeding materials now available in our major crop plants as a source of future varieties for presently known and possible new uses. Even when plagued with overproduction of certain crops, we cannot condone inefficiency. For a continued rise in standards of living, an ever greater efficiency is essential. Greater efficiency is attained through utilization of the best varieties and the best production practices. As technological advances in crop production are made, relatively fewer people are needed in food production. This releases workers for other occupations in producing goods and services—a healthful situation for an expanding general economy.

References

1. Ackerman, E. A. 1946. The geographical meaning of ecological land use. *Jour. Soil and Water Cons.* 1 (2): 63–66, 76–80.
2. Bennett, M. K. 1954. *The World's Food.* Harpers, New York.
3. Broek, Jan O. M. 1958. The man-land ratio. In Francis, R. G. (ed.), *The Population Ahead.* Univ. Minn. Press, Minneapolis.
4. Brown, H. 1954. *The Challenge of Man's Future.* Viking, New York.
5. Cook, R. C. 1951. *Human Fertility: the Modern Dilemma.* W. Sloane, New York.
6. Deevey, E. S. 1958. The equilibrium population. In Francis, R. G. (ed.), *The Population Ahead.* Univ. Minn. Press, Minneapolis.
7. Fuller, Varden. 1954. Farm population in California. *Cal. Agr.* 8 (11): 2, 16; 8 (12): 2, 16; 9 (1): 2, 15.
8. Harberger, A. C. 1958. Variation on a theme of Malthus. In Francis, R. G. (ed.), *The Population Ahead.* Univ. Minn. Press, Minneapolis.
9. Herves, Leslie, and Schmieding, A. C. 1956. Risk in the central Great Plains. *Geog. Rev.* XLVI (3): 375–387.
10. Huntington, Ellsworth. 1951. *Principles of Human Geography.* 6th ed. (Rev. by Earl Shaw), Wiley, New York.
11. Huxley, Julian. 1950. Population and human destiny. *World Rev.* (New Ser.), London, 11: 7–14.
12. Jacks, G. V., and Whyte, R. O. 1939. *The Rape of the Earth.* Faber and Faber, Ltd., London.
13. Jones, C. F. and Darkenwald, G. G. 1954. *Economic Geography.* Macmillan, New York.
14. Klages, K. H. W. 1942. *Ecological Crop Geography.* Macmillan, New York.
15. Kutish, F. A., Kaldor, D. R., Heady, E. O., Timmons, J. F., *et al.* A Basebook for Agricultural Adjustment in Iowa. Part I. Agriculture in the mid-fifties. Spec. Rept. 20, Iowa State Coll., Ames, Iowa. Oct. 1957.

16. Lindeman, R. L. 1942. The trophic-dynamic aspect of ecology. *Ecol.* 23: 399–418.
17. Luck, J. M. 1957. Man against his environment: the next hundred years. *Science* 126: 903–908.
18. Malthus, T. R. 1798. *An Essay on the Principle of Population.* Reprinted, 1872. Ward Lock and Co., London.
19. Markham, S. F. 1944. *Climate and the Energy of Nations.* Oxford Univ. Press, London.
20. Odum, E. P. 1959. *Fundamentals of Ecology.* 2nd ed. Saunders, New York.
21. Osborn, F. 1957. Our reproductive potential. *Science* 125: 531–534.
22. ———. 1958. Optimum rates of population growth. In Francis, R. G. (ed.), *The Population Ahead.* Univ. Minn. Press, Minneapolis.
23. Pollock, E. O. 1956. The change in our eating habits. *Co-op. Grain Quart.* 14 (2): 22–23.
24. Putnam, P. C. 1953. *Energy in the Future.* Van Nostrand, New York.
25. Russell, E. John. 1954. *World Population and the World's Food Supply.* Allen and Unwin, Ltd., London.
26. Sears, P. B. 1958. The inexorable problem of space. *Science* 127: 9–15.
27. Stamp, L. Dudley. 1952. *Land for Tomorrow.* Ind Univ. Press, Bloomington, Ind.
28. Taylor, G. 1922. The distribution of future white settlement. *Geog. Rev.* 12: 375–402.
29. United Nations. 1959. *Demographic Yearbook of the United Nations.* United Nations, New York.
30. Vogt, Wm. 1948. *The Road to Survival.* Sloane, New York.
31. Whelpton, R. K. 1958. A generation of demographic change. In Francis, R. G. (ed.), *The Population Ahead.* Univ. Minn. Press, Minneapolis.
32. Wissler, C. 1923. *Man and Culture.* Crowell, New York.

Plant Distribution and
Limiting Factors

Basic principles and concepts relating to the natural distribution of plants throughout the world are useful also in their application to crop adaptation. The plant geographer studies spatial relationships of plants in the present and in the past, and attempts to explain their origins, development, and distribution. Such studies may furnish the basis for an understanding of the relationship between environment and present patterns of crop distribution.

The distribution of plants has resulted from both natural causes and the activities of man. Through the ages there have been changes in geographic and climatic values. These changes have been associated, at least in the last 10,000 or more years, with repeated human migrations which have shaped the patterns of human development. Man's activities have resulted in a widespread distribution of exotic species, especially in areas such as temperate North America. They have contributed also to the development of deserts, in some instances almost as useless as those of natural origin (Good, 1953).

HISTORICAL ASPECTS

To understand the problems of plant distribution today, it is necessary to consider conditions and events of the past. During the course of geologic time, the vegetation of the earth has gradually developed through the processes of organic evolution. These evolutionary processes have been so

ERA	PERIOD	EPOCH	BEGINNING OF INTERVAL (Million years)	EVENTS
CENOZOIC	QUATERNARY	Pleistocene		Development of man. The great ice age.
CENOZOIC	TERTIARY	Pliocene	13	Development of mammals (horses, deer, cats, dogs, apes).
CENOZOIC	TERTIARY	Miocene	25	Modern trees and birds.
CENOZOIC	TERTIARY	Oligocene	36	Elevation of Rocky, Sierra Nevada and Cascade Mts.;
CENOZOIC	TERTIARY	Eocene	58	Colorado and Columbia plateaus.
CENOZOIC	TERTIARY	Paleocene	63	
MESOZOIC	CRETACEOUS UPPER	Maestrichtian	72	Extinction of dinosaurs. Uplift of Rocky Mts. began;
MESOZOIC	CRETACEOUS UPPER	Turonian	90	much vulcanism. Rise of mammals and birds.
MESOZOIC	CRETACEOUS LOWER	Cenomanian	110	Last great submergence;
MESOZOIC	CRETACEOUS LOWER	Albian	120	Gulf of Mexico to Alaska.
MESOZOIC	CRETACEOUS LOWER	Neocomian	135	Rise of angiosperms.
MESOZOIC	JURASSIC UPPER / MIDDLE / LOWER	Bathonian	166 / 181	Giant reptiles; first birds and primitive mammals. Many insects. Vulcanism on Pacific Coast; submergence.
MESOZOIC	TRIASSIC UPPER / MIDDLE / LOWER		200 / 230	Many large reptiles. Complex marine animals. Large land area-arid. Coniferous forests.
PALEOZOIC	PERMIAN UPPER / MIDDLE / LOWER		260 / 280	Decline of fern trees and rise of conifers. Many reptiles and insects. General emergence; folding of Appalachian Mts.
PALEOZOIC	CARBONIFEROUS PENNSYLVANIAN			Vast fern forests. Rise of reptiles and insects. Interior seas and swamps.
PALEOZOIC	CARBONIFEROUS MISSISSIPPIAN	Visean	320	Widespread submergence. Many fish and amphibians.
PALEOZOIC	CARBONIFEROUS MISSISSIPPIAN	Tournaisian	345	Forests of ferns. Primitive conifers.
PALEOZOIC	DEVONIAN UPPER / MIDDLE / LOWER		365 / 390 / 405	First forests (ferns). First amphibians. Submergence; mountain uplift and vulcanism in New England.
PALEOZOIC	SILURIAN		425	Development of fishes. First land plants and animals.
PALEOZOIC	ORDOVICIAN UPPER / MIDDLE / LOWER	Trenton	445 / 500	Abundant mollusks. Early forms of fish. Sediments deposited. Mountain building in New England and Canada. No land plants or animals.
PALEOZOIC	CAMBRIAN UPPER / MIDDLE / LOWER		530	Widespread submergence and deposition of sedimentary rocks. First abundant fossils (shelled marine invertebrates). Primitive marine life.

Vertical time scale (Million years, left axis): 0, 50, 100, 150, 200, 250, 300, 350, 400, 450, 500, 550, 600

FIGURE 2-1.

Geologic time scale with notations on some important geographical and biological events. [After Kulp, Sci. 133:1111, 1961, and Finch, Trewartha, Robinson, and Hammond, Elements of Geography. N. Y.: McGraw-Hill, 1957.]

important that they comprise the whole background of plant distribution, or, as so aptly stated by Good (1953), "evolution is the medium in which the picture of plant distribution is painted."

All plants in the world today have come from earlier forms. The periodic production of new biotypes, ecotypes, species, genera, and families has given us the vast number of forms of today's plant world. The evolutionary processes have operated against a background of alternating "normal" and "revolutionary" climates (Zeuner, 1952). Normal climates (continents relatively small, relief gentle, temperatures fairly high and rather uniformly distributed, humidity high, and rainfall moderate) have prevailed a greater percentage of the time. Revolutionary climates (continents more extensive, relief contrasts sharper, and temperatures widely varied with differences in latitude and altitude) have prevailed a lesser portion of the time. Geologists consider that we are in a period of revolutionary climate today.

According to the geological time scale, the earth has existed through five major eras, varying greatly in duration, the Archeozoic, Proterozoic, Paleozoic, Mesozoic, and Cenozoic. The use of the new isotopic geochronometers based on the radioactive decay of rubidium-87 and potassium-40 has made possible the time scale developed by Kulp (1961) and shown in Figure 2-1.

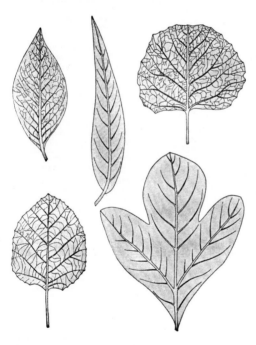

Through studies of rock layers and fossil remains of plants, paleontologists and geologists have determined a chronology of the appearance on the earth of various animal and plant groups. The Angiosperms (flower and seed bearing plants) are believed to have appeared for the first time during the lower Cretaceous period of the Mesozoic era (Dunbar, 1960), Many of the evergreen conifers appeared considerably earlier. Before the end of the Cretaceous period, the flowering plants were widely distrib-

FIGURE 2-2.

Leaves of Cretaceous deciduous trees. From left to right; top: Magnolia; Salix, a willow; Populus, a poplar; bottom: Betula, a birch; Sassafras. [*After Berry, in Dunbar: Historical Geology, N. Y.: John Wiley and Sons, 1960.*]

uted and had, in fact, become the dominant plants of the world. Fossils of Cretaceous flora, especially woody plants, were abundant in several parts of the world including Greenland and North America (Berry, 1911). Leaves similar to those of modern species of trees are represented in Figure 2-2.

Revolutionary geologic events, destined to exert a great influence on climate and vegetation, took place in the late Cretaceous period. A great inland sea, stretching from Alaska to Mexico, began to disappear. The whole area was subjected to folding and thrust-faulting on a colossal scale. From this activity there arose the great Rocky Mountain system, extending from Alaska to South America (Dunbar, 1960). With the development of the whole Cordillera chain, there was a gradual climatic shift, toward a drier climate east of the mountains.

The Tertiary period witnessed gradual climatic changes from temperate conditions at the beginning, through a long period of warm-temperate to tropical conditions to cooler and drier climates at the end of the period. Temperatures dropped rather drastically over widespread portions of the earth, especially at higher latitudes, culminating eventually in the glacial ages of the Quaternary period.

In the Pleistocene subperiod, which lasted possibly a million years, there were four distinct Ice Ages, known as the Nebraskan, Kansan, Illinoian, and Wisconsin (Deevey, 1949). The approximate extent of glacial drift in the United States is shown in Figure 2-3. Ice advances of a somewhat comparable nature occurred in Europe during the same period.

It has been suggested by Dillon (1956) that during periods of maximum glaciation there probably was a clinal depression in temperature which amounted to 5°F at the equator, to 10°F at latitudes 35° to 40°N, and to 25° at the edge of the ice sheet. This change in temperature gives a logical basis for marked changes in vegetation (Seward, 1941; Good, 1953). Many plants at the higher latitudes were faced with frost problems for the first time. Potential areas for various species shifted with climatic changes. Milder climates shrank in extent, with the consequence that many species, and perhaps genera, became extinct or persisted only in isolated niches as glacial relics.

There is little actual evidence on the nature of the vegetation of the early Pleistocene. Studies of peat deposits in Iowa by Wilson and Kosanke (1940), however, indicate that in the Aftonian interglacial period, between the Nebraskan and Kansan stages, vegetation changed from boreal forest of spruce and fir, to a mixed pine-oak forest with much grass, to mixed hardwoods, and back to spruce-fir forest.

In the Sangamon interglacial period, between the Illinoian and Wisconsin glacial stages, Voss (1939) reported that the sequence in Illinois was from

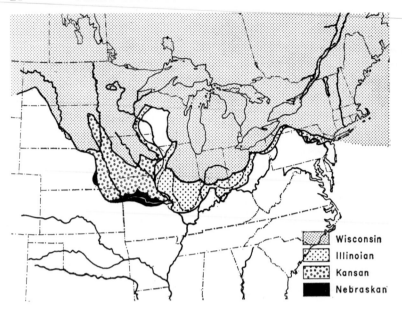

FIGURE 2-3.

Approximate extent of glacial drift in the United States. [After Flint, Glacial and Pleistocene Geology. N. Y.: John Wiley and Sons, 1957.]

spruce-fir, to pine, to oak, and to beech, while in Iowa, according to Lane (1941), the sequence was from spruce-fir, to pine, to oak, and to grass. The development of the radiocarbon dating method, Libby (1952), has made possible a rather accurate chronology of recent geological events.

The beginning of the Wisconsin glacial stage has been dated about 25,000 years ago (Karlstrom, 1956). Much has been written concerning the substages of the Wisconsin, but there is still some lack of agreement on their exact chronology. Recent detailed accounts have been given by Suess (1956), Leighton (1957), Wright (1957), Ruhe, Rubin and Scholtes (1957), and others. Table 2-1 suggests the chronology of the principal substages in Iowa as simplified from Ruhe and Scholtes (1959).

Following the Cary substage, a readvance known as the Mankato (or perhaps a late phase of the Cary) occurred about 12,000 to 13,000 years ago (Wright, 1957). By 11,400 years ago the ice had receded to the Straits of Mackinac outlet of Lake Michigan, which allowed the lake to drain to the north (Curtis, 1959). This interstadial period is known as Two Creeks, because of the extensive forest beds dating to that time which were found at Two Creeks, Wisconsin (Wilson, 1932). Shortly thereafter, about 11,000

TABLE 2-1. SUBSTAGES OF WISCONSIN GLACIAL STAGE,
RADIOCARBON DATES AND VEGETATION IN IOWA*

Substage or Advance	Time before Present	Vegetation
Postglacial	6,500 ± 200	Grass
	8,140 ± 200	Oak
	11,660 ± 250 ⎫ 11,790 ± 250 ⎭	Spruce
	11,952 ± 500 ⎫ 12,200 ± 500 ⎭	Hemlock
Cary		
	12,970 ± 250 ⎫ 13,030 ± 250 ⎭	Larch
Tazewell-Cary	13,820 − 14,470	Fir, spruce, hemlock
Tazewell	14,700 − 16,370	Hemlock
	16,700 − >17,000	Yew, spruce, hemlock
Farmdale	24,500 ± 800	Larch
	>29,000	Hemlock
Iowan	>35,000	Spruce
	>37,000	Spruce, larch
Pre-Iowan	>38,000	Hemlock

* After Ruhe and Scholtes, 1959. *Jour. Geol.* 67:592.

years ago, there was a readvance of ice in eastern Wisconsin known as the Valders substage (Wright, 1957). This ice sheet receded approximately 9,000 years ago. A still more recent advance, called the Cochrane, occurred about 5,800 years ago. It took place in Canada, but did not extend into Wisconsin (Curtis, 1959).

In the postglacial period it is known that there was a considerable shift in climate toward continentality. According to Sears (1942), a peak of a drier, or "Xerothermic," period was reached about 3,500 years ago. Pollen analyses in Wisconsin bogs show that at this time there was a dominance of oaks and mixed hardwoods, a negligible number of conifers, and a high proportion of grasses. Mixed forest and savannas and areas of interspersed prairie were common.

In northern Wisconsin, north of the division between the northern conifer-hardwood forest and the southern area of hardwood forest, oak savanna, and prairie, a uniform pattern of vegetation development has been shown by bog pollen analyses. As noted by Curtis (1959), pine became codominant with oak at the peak of the driest period (3,500 years ago). There was a decrease in spruce-fir, which was also true in the southern part of the state. Since the Xerothermic period, however, there appears to have been a shift southward of climatic belts. The northern bogs show a resurgence of spruce-fir in the northwest and an increase in hardwoods in the north-central area.

In summary, Curtis believes that vegetation has undergone little change in postglacial times in northern Wisconsin, but that in the southwestern

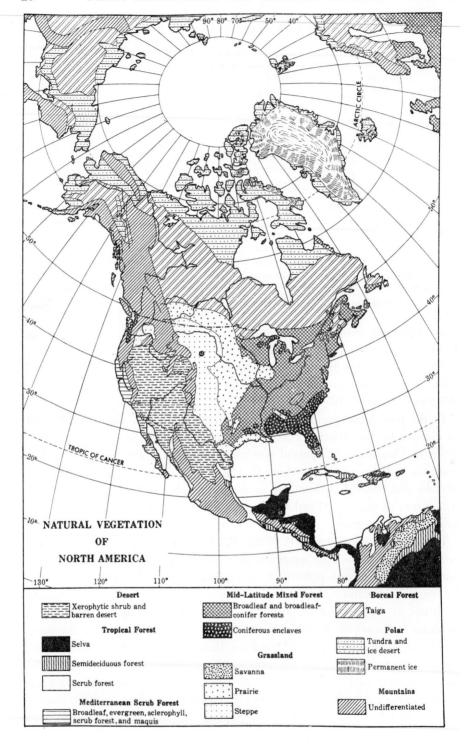

NATURAL VEGETATION

OF

NORTH AMERICA

Desert	Mid-Latitude Mixed Forest	Boreal Forest
Xerophytic shrub and barren desert	Broadleaf and broadleaf-conifer forests	Taiga
Tropical Forest	Coniferous enclaves	**Polar**
Selva	**Grassland**	Tundra and ice desert
Semideciduous forest	Savanna	Permanent ice
Scrub forest	Prairie	**Mountains**
Mediterranean Scrub Forest	Steppe	Undifferentiated
Broadleaf, evergreen, sclerophyll, scrub forest, and maquis		

part of the state a retrogression has taken place. This retrogression was caused by an increased continentality of climate, and possibly also by forest destruction by fire. These fires probably were the result of man's activities. In the last few thousand years there has been a reversal, a trend toward a more moist climate or a decreased incidence of fire or both, resulting in more stable forests having a higher content of terminal hardwoods. A map showing the natural vegetation of North America in recent post-glacial times is presented in Figure 2-4.

THE NORTH AMERICAN GRASSLAND

Extensive studies of the great grassland biome have been made by Gleason (1922), Transeau (1935), Carpenter (1940) and Weaver (1954). East of the Rocky Mountains, from Texas on the south to Saskatchewan on the north, and eastward in the shape of a wedge to Indiana and Ohio, this grassland region developed. Climatic changes, brought about primarily through the uplift of the Rocky Mountain system, are considered to be responsible for the development of the steppe and prairie vegetation which characterized the region. Moisture-laden winds from the Pacific Ocean dropped much of their moisture on the west side of the mountains. Winds blowing eastward became drier and great areas of low summer rainfall and dry winters resulted.

Carpenter (1940) has considered three somewhat distinctive areas in the grassland biome: (1) eastern tall-grass prairie, (2) western short-grass plains, and (3) central mixed-grass area. By plotting mean monthly temperatures against mean monthly precipitation, he developed a series of polygonal figures which could be used to characterize climatic conditions and associated vegetation types. Figure 2-5 illustrates Carpenter's concept of the grassland biome, indicating the three grassland subdivisions and the prairie-forest ecotone.

The eastern part of this region is often called the "Prairie Peninsula." It extends from southern Manitoba diagonally through Minnesota and southwestern Wisconsin, and includes the northern two-thirds of Illinois and part of northwestern Indiana. Also included are Iowa, northern and western Missouri, southeastern Kansas, northeastern Oklahoma, and portions

---

FIGURE 2-4.

Natural vegetation of North America in recent post-glacial times. [From James, A Geography of Man. Rev. Ed., Chicago: Ginn and Co., 1959.]

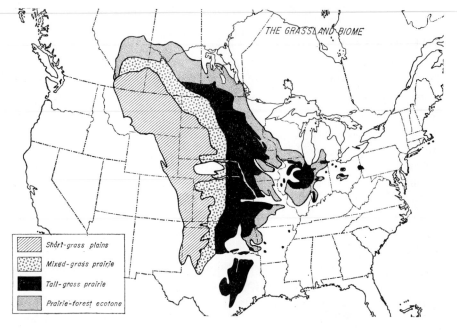

Short-grass plains

Mixed-grass prairie

Tall-grass prairie

Prairie-forest ecotone

FIGURE 2-5.

The North American Grassland Biome, illustrating the three grassland subdivisions and the prairie—forest ecotone. [*After Carpenter, Ecol. Monog. 10:617–684, 1940.*]

of Texas (Transeau, 1935). This portion of the prairie has a climate which ranges from subhumid-moist to moist. Borchert (1950) indicates that this area now has a forest climax climate, but a subclimax vegetation of grass maintained by soil conditions and by fire. This view is shared by McComb and Loomis (1944), who have cited evidence that in central, and even western, Iowa the forest is increasing. The absence of mycorrhizal fungi in prairie soils is apparently somewhat unfavorable to tree growth. Fire retards forest development, but does not necessarily result in prairie. Periodic fires over wide prairie regions, however, undoubtedly aid the persistence of prairie vegetation, as has been emphasized by Curtis (1959).

It appears quite unlikely that all of the prairie has been in grassland continuously since Tertiary times. On the contrary, there is considerable evidence, presented by Voss (1939), Lane (1941), Simonson (1941), and Ruhe and Scholtes (1956), to indicate that in Iowa and Illinois many grassland areas have been occupied alternately for varying periods of time by forest and grassland.

THE PLANT ENVIRONMENT

The natural environment of a plant is dynamic and everchanging. It presents a complexity which is difficult to comprehend. The intensity of its factors vary with the hour, the day, and the season. The rates of change of intensities, the time of their duration, and the extreme values reached are all important aspects of an environment (Daubenmire, 1959).

Environment has been classified in a number of ways. One of the simpler classifications was that given by Tansley (1923), who recognized four groups of factors: (1) climatic, (2) physiographic, (3) edaphic, and (4) biotic. A more recent and more detailed analysis of plant environment was given by Billings (1952). He states that environment includes all the external forces and substances affecting the growth, structure, and reproduction of the plant. In an analytical approach to an understanding of relationships, Billings subdivided environment into five large groups of factors: climatic, edaphic, geographic, pyric, and biotic. Each of these groups is broken down into individual factors and subfactors, with important aspects of each one listed. His outline is presented here because of its completeness for reference purposes (Table 2-2).

PRINCIPLES OF PLANT DISTRIBUTION

Environmental factors in all of their complexity appear to be highly influential in determining the natural distribution of plants. The plant geographer Good (1931, 1953) formulated certain basic statements, or principles of plant distribution, which he believes have broad and general application. The first of these is evolution, which has already been emphasized in this chapter under "Historical Aspects." In addition to evolution, the master factor which underlies all others, Good lists six principles of plant distribution:

"(1) That plant distribution is primarily controlled by the distribution of climatic conditions.

"(2) That plant distribution is secondarily controlled by the distribution of edaphic factors.

"(3) That great movements of floras have taken place in the past and are still continuing.

"(4) That species movement (plant migration) is brought about by

**TABLE 2-2.   FACTORS OF A TERRESTRIAL PLANT
ENVIRONMENT**[*]

Groups	Factors	Factor Subdivisions	Aspects
Climatic	Radiation	Solar radiation	Wavelengths
			Intensity
			Photoperiod and other cycles
		Cosmic radiation	Wavelengths
			Intensity
			Cycles
		Terrestrial radiation	Wavelengths
			Intensity
			Cycles
	Temperature	Air temperature	Degree
			Cycles
			Lateral variation
			Vertical variation
		Soil temperature	Degree
			Cycles
			Freezing and thawing
			Lateral variation
			Vertical variation
		Rock and parent material temperature	Degree
			Cycles
			Freezing and thawing
			Lateral variation
			Vertical variation (geothermal gradient)
	Water	Water vapor	Amounts
			Vapor pressure
			Vapor pressure deficit
			Evaporation
			Transpiration
		Condensed water	Cloud
			Fog
		Precipitation	Types
			Amounts
			Frequency
			Snow cover
		Soil water	Soil moisture
			Hygroscopic water
			Capillary water
			Water table
	Atmospheric gases	Composition	CO_2 content
			O_2 content
			Other gases
		Pressure	Altitude
			Local pressure differences
			Cyclones
		Wind	Frequency

TABLE 2-2. (Continued)

Groups	Factors	Factor Subdivisions	Aspects
Climatic (continued)			Force Direction Abrasive agents
Edaphic	Parent material	Acid materials	Minerals present Structure Weathering susceptibility
	Soil	Physical properties	Profile Structure Texture Soil moisture Soil air
		Chemical properties	Clay minerals Base exchange properties pH Anions Organic compounds
		Biotic properties	Soil flora Soil fauna Litter and humus Antibiotic effects
Geographic	Gravity	Internal effects	Hormone effects Translocation
		External effects	Isostasy Fruit and seed dispersal Runoff Landslides
	Rotational effects	Coriolis force	Works through other factors
	Geographic position	Latitude Longitude Distance and direction from coast	Work through other factors
	Vulcanism	Thermal effects Mechanical effects	See temperature Ash cover Lava flows Gas explosions
	Diastrophism	Folding Faulting	Work through other factors except very locally
	Erosion and deposition	Water Snow (avalanches) Ice (glaciation) Wind	May affect plants directly or through changing other factors
	Topography	Slope direction Slope angle Elevation	Work through other factors
Pyric	Fire	Climatic effects	Temperature (air and soil) Intensity

TABLE 2-2. (Continued)

Groups	Factors	Factor Subdivisions	Aspects
Pyric (continued)			Postburning microclimatic effects
		Edaphic effects	Organic matter destruction
			Soil structure changes
			Erosion
		Biotic effects	Community composition
			Animal populations after fire
Biotic	Other plants	Competition	Light competition
			Water competition
			Nutrient competition
			Antibiotic effects
			Autotoxic effects
		Dependence effects	Litter and humus
			Physical effects
			Chemical effects
			Cover
	Animals	Destructive effects	Use of plant as food, etc.
			Effects on soil
		Beneficial effects	Fruit and seed dispersal
			Nutrient effects
	Man	Can change almost any factor, at least locally	

* After Billings. *Quart. Rev. Biol.* 27:251–265, 1952.

the transport of individual plants during their motile dispersal phases.

"(5) That there has been great variation and oscillation in climate, especially at higher latitudes, during the geological history of the Angiosperms.

"(6) That at least some, and probably considerable, variation has occurred in the relative distribution and outline of land and sea during the history of the Angiosperms."

Good believes that these principles are so evident as to be incontestable. In defense of the first he states that plant geography everywhere points to the basic influence of climate on plant distribution. Climate is regarded as comprising four aspects: temperature, moisture, light, and wind.

Good's second principle states that edaphic factors are secondary. These factors may be assumed to include parent material, soil, and physiography. They are secondary because they are influenced in no small degree by climate itself. Climatic factors determine largely whether a given plant (or crop) is potentially suitable for an area, but soil factors may actually determine whether it actually is found there and in what abundance.

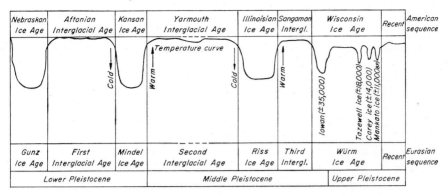

FIGURE 2-6.

Temperature variations in glacial time. [*After Dunbar,* Historical Geology. *N. Y.: John Wiley and Sons, 1960.*]

The third principle relates to movements of species and floras. The fossil record shows evidence of a succession of different floras from the earliest times to the present. This is a recognition of plant migration which is made possible through individual plant dispersal and transport (the fourth principle).

The fifth principle refers to variations in climate, especially at higher latitudes, brought about in revolutionary geological periods due to mountain building, glaciation, and so on. This principle may be considered the basic cause of the third (plant migration). Figure 2-6 illustrates an approximation of temperature variations (an important aspect of climate) during the Pleistocene Epoch.

Good's final principle states that variations in relative distribution of land and sea areas have occurred in geological time. This one is clearly associated with the fifth principle and exerts a high degree of control over the third. Many examples could be given to illustrate this point, such as the representation of the great Rocky Mountain Seaway in mid-Cretaceous time in Figure 2-7.

THE TOLERANCE THEORY

As a part of his principles of plant geography, Good developed a concept of specific tolerance to explain why climatic and other environmental changes resulted in plant movement and migration. He stated his tolerance theory as follows:

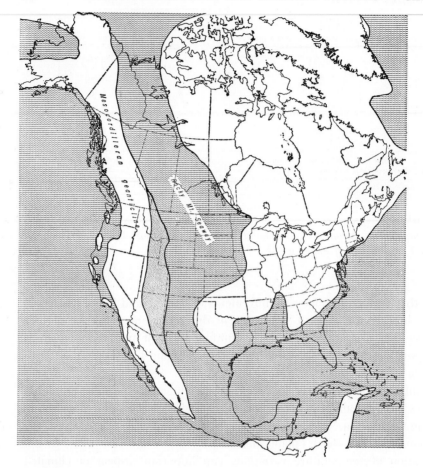

FIGURE 2-7.

Paleographic map of North America showing Rocky Mountain Seaway in Mid-Cretaceous time. [After Dunbar, Historical Geology. *N. Y.: John Wiley and Sons, 1960.]*

"Each and every plant species is able to exist and reproduce successfully only within a definite range of climatic and edaphic conditions. This range represents the tolerance of the species to external conditions (Figure 2-8).

"The tolerance of a species is a specific character subject to the laws and processes of organic evolution in the same ways as is its morphological characters, but the two are not necessarily linked.

"Change in tolerance may or may not be accompanied by morphological change, and *vice versa.*

"Morphologically similar species may show wide differences in tolerance, and species with similar tolerances may show little morphological similarity. The relative distribution of species with similar tolerance is finally determined by the result of competition between them.

"The range of tolerance of any larger taxonomic unit is the sum of (or the total range or extent of) the ranges of tolerance of its constituent species."

Shelford (1913) proposed a general law

FIGURE 2-8.

Ecological concept of the range of tolerance. [After Shelford, Animal communities in Temperate America. *Chicago: Univ. Chicago Press, 1913.]*

of tolerance at a considerably earlier date. Essentially this law included the following concepts:

1. Organisms with wide ranges of tolerance for all factors of the environment are likely to be widely distributed.

2. Organisms may have a wide range of tolerance for one factor and a narrow range for another.

3. When conditions are not optimum for one factor, the limits of tolerance may be reduced with respect to another factor.

4. The period of reproduction usually is critical, when environmental factors are likely to be limiting.

A generalized concept of limits of tolerance is illustrated in Figure 2-9. With respect to temperature it is noted that species "A" has a narrow range of tolerance and is tolerant to low temperatures. Species "B" also has a narrow range of tolerance, but is tolerant to high temperatures. A third species, "C," has a wide range of tolerance for temperature, including the total range of "A" and "B" plus a broad area of intermediate temperatures between.

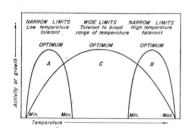

FIGURE 2-9.

Comparison of the relative limits of tolerance of organisms of narrow limits to low and to high temperatures and those having broad limits of tolerance. [After Ruttner, Fundamentals of Limnology. *Toronto: Univ. Toronto Press, 1953.]*

Good's Tolerance Theory was proposed in 1931 and has been the subject of considerable comment by plant geographers and ecologists since that time. Mason (1936) accepted Good's major thesis on principles of plant distribution, but suggested certain minor variations: (1) the extremes of climatic conditions are more significant than the means, which emphasizes the periphery or limits of range where extremes of climatic factors are most likely to be limiting; (2) both dispersal and establishment are essential to plant migration; and (3) the tolerance theory should emphasize the factor-function relationship. Further, Mason stated that there are times in the life history of the plant when it is in a critical phase which has a narrow tolerance range for a particular factor of the environment. This addition gives added emphasis to differences in tolerance ranges as the plant progresses through its ontogenetic phases from germination to maturity.

In 1944, Cain devoted an introductory chapter of his book, *Foundations of Plant Geography,* to a consideration of Good's principles plus modifications suggested by Mason and by himself. Cain listed thirteen principles, six relating to the environment, three to plant responses, two to migration, and two to perpetuation of species and evolution. The principal additions were three: (1) that biotic factors may be important, (2) that the environment is holocoenotic, and (3) that tolerances have a genetic basis.

It is true that biotic factors are important in the plant environment, but Good believes that they exert their influence mainly as they influence edaphic factors. However, some biotic factors appear to exert direct influences on plant distribution, namely, obligate insect pollination, seed dissemination by animals, and grazing by livestock.

Cain's second addition was that the environment is holocoenotic. His concept, however, appears to go much further than that suggested by Allee and Park (1939) who introduced this term to convey the idea of the dynamic interrelationships among environmental factors, and the "wholeness" of their effects on living organisms. Cain states that "the plant is conditioned simultaneously and collectively by all factors of the environment." One may question whether this is to be interpreted literally, especially unless the statement is qualified to include "at any specific time." Preclusion of the independent action of one factor also may be questioned, because at times a single factor appears to be the one which definitely limits distribution. However, the general idea of an interdependent and interacting system, including the environment and the plant, is an important concept.

Billings (1952) illustrated the holocoenotic concept with a circular diagram, showing 15 factors in direct relationship to the plant as well as interrelationships to one another (Figure 2-10).

The holocoenotic idea does emphasize the complexity of the environment, and Cain has expressed the belief that many ecological problems may be insoluble in the mathematical sense. Attempts to develop quantitative expressions of these interacting plant-factor relationships, however, have been and are being made. Major (1951) proposed a formula for solv-

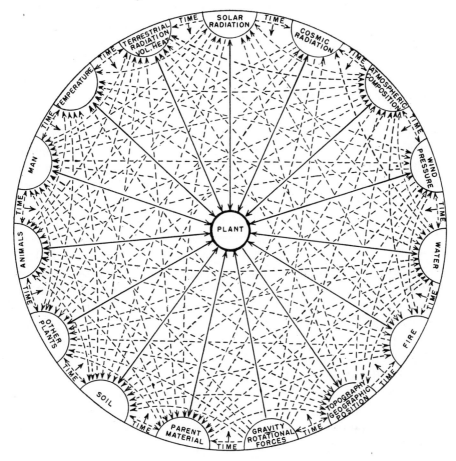

FIGURE 2-10.

Factor interaction in the holocoenotic environment. [*From Billings, Quart. Rev. Biol. 27:251–264, 1952.*]

ing quantitative environmental interrelationships. Such efforts may be highly rewarding in the future. Rapid progress has been made, in recent years, in determining more precisely the effects of individual factors of the environment on plant development. With better facilities for complete environmental control, several factors may be studied simultaneously. Particularly notable in this area of research has been the work of Fritz Went and his associates at the Earhart Laboratory at California Institute of Technology (Went, 1950).

Cain's third addition to Good's principles was that tolerances have a genetic basis. This calls particular attention to a concept implicit in the Tolerance Theory that "the tolerance of a species is a specific character subject to the laws and processes of organic evolution, etc."

LIMITING FACTORS

The central idea expressed in Good's principle of specific tolerance is in many ways similar to, but broader than, that implied in the concept of "limiting factors." The chemist, Liebig (1840) expressed his "Law of the Minimum" by stating that "growth is dependent on the amount of food-stuff (or element) presented to it in minimal quantity." This law was expanded by Taylor (1934) to include not only plant nutrients, but all of the environmental factors. Furthermore, he stressed the importance of the condition of the organism at the time the factor was applied. This was expressed in terms of limiting factors at the most critical season of the year or the most critical year of a climatic cycle. This was an important concept, for it emphasized critical stages of development when the organism may have narrower tolerances for certain factor intensities. For example, the importance of adequate moisture at the time of seed germination and again at the time of anthesis is well known.

In 1905, Blackman developed his "Theory of Optima and Limiting Factors," in which the rates of reactions were emphasized. The theory stated that "when a process was conditioned as to its rapidity by a number of factors, the rate of the process was limited by the pace of the slowest factor." As usually interpreted, both Blackman's and Liebig's laws are rather rigid, offering little opportunity for the degree of interaction of factors and possible replaceability of factors now believed probable. This was pointed out by Lundegardh (1931) who emphasized that as a factor increases in intensity its relative effect on plant growth decreases. This principle, sometimes called the "Law of Relativity," will be considered later in connection with correlation of environmental factors and crop yields.

Livingston and Shreve (1921), in their concept of "physiological limits," suggested that "for every vital function there is a maximum and a minimum zero point with respect to any conditioning factor, beyond which the function ceases. Further, for every distinct climatic area there appears to be a corresponding type of vegetation, and this principle is probably of primary importance in the study of plant distribution."

All of these theories or laws relating to tolerances of a species toward the environmental factors were developed in attempts to explain the reactions of plants of different genetic constitutions to the complex and interacting factors of their environments. Odum (1959) attempted to combine these several theories by noting that under natural conditions plants appear to be controlled mainly by three kinds of forces: (1) quantity and variability of materials for which there are minimal requirements, (2) physical factors which are critical, and (3) limits of tolerance of the plants themselves to these and other factors of the environment.

In accepting the tolerance theory we recognize that environmental relations have a foundation in genetics and that variations in tolerance to environmental factors are likely to be as great as are variations in morphological characteristics. It was Cain (1944) who noted that "the capacity of the species to tolerate or respond to its environment is governed by the laws of evolution and genetics, and the range of tolerance is the direct result of the diversity of the species." This statement carries much the same implication as Darwin (1859) had implied by the comment that "widely ranging species vary most."

EXAMPLES OF FACTORS LIMITING
PLANT DISTRIBUTION

Temperature is one of the most common limiting factors in plant distribution. Many tropical crops, such as rubber (*Hevea braziliensis*), cacao (*Theobromo cacao*), and banana (*Musa sapientum*) will not withstand freezing temperatures. Of these, rubber probably has the narrowest tolerance range, and banana the widest, for temperature. It was emphasized by Mason (1936) that extremes probably were more important than means in controlling plant distribution. He cited the example of observations of McGinitie (1933) on redwood (*Sequoia sempervirens*) in California. This species has a restricted distribution, limited on the south by low rainfall and low humidity. On the north it had extended its range into the northern coastal counties and across the Oregon line. In December 1932 a period of eight consecutive days with minimum temperatures of 32° to 22°F (15° to 18° below normal) caused much frost damage in Del Norte and Humboldt Counties. The trees looked as though they had been browned by fire. McGinitie believed that occasional severe weather conditions, such as occurred in 1932, effectively limited the northern range of this species.

In many localities in the Midwest a similar event occurred in 1940. The autumn had been warm, without any cold weather until November. A sudden blizzard swept down from Canada and the northwest, and the temperatures throughout Iowa (as well as other states) dropped to zero in a few hours. Many kinds of vegetation were killed, including hardy shrubs, forage crops, and apple trees, which are normally considered well adapted to Iowa conditions. Only those apple orchards in which trees had been grafted to extremely hardy roots, such as the Russian crabapple, came through without widespread killing.

Jones (1951) has presented data to illustrate the application of the tolerance theory (the moisture factor in this instance) in the control of an insect pest. The wireworm, *Limonius* spp., is destructive to sugar beets, but experiments have shown that the larvae and prepupae have a narrower range of tolerance for moisture than do eggs or adults. On irrigated soils, therefore, flooding may be used to control wireworms. On nonirrigated lands, planting alfalfa or wheat so as to dry out the surface soil to a point beyond the tolerance of the larvae is a method of control. In one instance, the maximum tolerance is exceeded, in the other instance the minimum tolerance.

Another agricultural pest, the western cutworm, is widely distributed throughout the plains region and survives in the marginal parts of its range during periods of normal rainfall. During a series of dry years, Cooke (1924) found that the area inhabited by the cutworm was decreased by hundreds of square miles. Moisture appeared to be the limiting factor.

Edaphic factors have been known to limit plant distribution in a number of instances. Serpentine soils, found in a number of locations in the Appalachians and more widely in the central Coast Range of California, are highly infertile to most agricultural crops. This appears to be caused in the main by their low content of calcium, nitrogen, phorphorus, and sometimes molybdenum. On the other hand they are high in magnesium, chromium, and nickel. The serpentine soils are characterized by a unique endemic flora, in general quite different from that in nonserpentine soils of the same region (Kruckberg, 1954; Whittaker, 1954; Walker, 1954).

Other edaphic factors limiting distribution of plants have been discussed by Beadle (1954). In the Sydney district of Australia investigations have shown three distinct limiting factors: (1) content of NaCl, (2) claypan in B horizon, and (3) deficiency of phosphorus. In some soils, phosphorus is completely limiting to most crops, but some trees, *Eucalyptus* species, can thrive. On soils of very low fertility a number of common weeds do not persist, including *Amaranthus viridis, Euphorbia peplus, Bidens pilosa,* and *Setaria glauca.*

Some aspects of the interplay between variable climatic conditions and the range of tolerance of plant species have been considered by Dansereau (1957). He has called attention to the importance of climatic stress in the establishment of limits of range. The typical environment of the spruce-fir forest is a cool, moist climate. If, through a period of years, the climate tends to become warmer, these species may show a greater vitality at the upper latitudinal limit of their range. In Alaska and in the Hudson Bay region there have been indications of a recent warming trend, at least locally, with a resulting northward spread of certain tree species (Marr, 1948; Lawrence, 1950).

The sugar maple (*Acer saccharophorum*) has been studied extensively by Dansereau (1957), who has pointed out how the boundaries of its range have been determined by interacting climatic influences (Figure 2-11). Toward the east, the sugar maple is limited by the Atlantic Ocean,

FIGURE 2-11.

Bioclimatic limits of the sugar maple Acer saccharophorum, *showing coincidence with meterological elements. 1, 30-inch annual rainfall; 2, −40°C mean annual minimum; 3, B/H boundary; 4, ten-inch mean annual snowfall; 5, −10°C mean annual minimum.* [*After Dansereau,* Biogeography. *N. Y.: The Ronald Press, 1957.*]

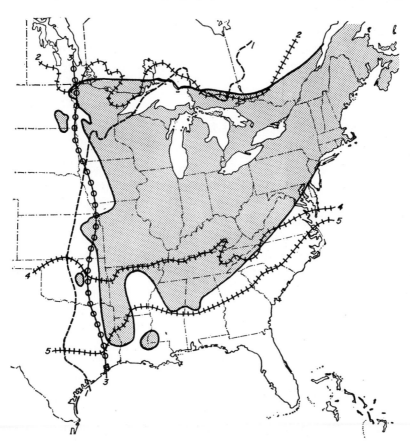

to the north by the $-40°C$ mean annual minimum isotherm, and to the south by the $-10°C$ mean minimum; to the west it coincides with the 20-inch isohyet in the north and the 30-inch isohyet in the south. Actually, the western limit is nearly identical with the limit of the forest itself. In certain portions of the Great Lakes region, the maple codominates with beech (*Fagus grandifolia*); in somewhat drier areas in Wisconsin and Minnesota it codominates with basswood (*Tilia glabra*); to the north and east, especially in eastern Canada, it is found codominating with hemlock (*Tsuga canadensis*).

Another aspect of tolerance suggested by Dansereau, is what might be called avoidance. This may be accomplished through a rapid completion of the life cycle, dormancy in seeds to avoid effects of the hottest and driest periods, dormancy in vegetative parts or roots of hardy perennials, water accumulation in succulents, and extremely deep root systems to avoid moisture deficiency. The requirements and tolerances of a species may be considered as complimentary. Species with low requirements and high tolerances can make use of the resources of the environment to a high degree of advantage. The common dandelion (*Taraxacum* spp.), for example, has relatively low requirements and high tolerance toward variations in light, soil fertility, and biotic factors.

FACTOR REPLACEABILITY

Factor compensation, or replaceability, has been studied by many workers. Often, near the periphery of the range of a species, this phenomenon may allow the species to persist in what does not seem to be its proper environment. Rubel (1935) has shown that an amount of a factor normally considered to be limiting can be reduced still further when compensated for by another factor. He has discussed several kinds of compensating factors:

1. Elevation can be substituted for latitude. Altitude, because of its temperature effects, induces a zonation of vegetation similar to that found through a wide range of latitude. In tropical latitudes, crops requiring a frost-free climate, such as rubber, cacao, and bananas, give way to subtropical crops, including rice, maize, sugarcane, and citrus, at elevations where light frosts occur. These crops, in turn, are replaced by temperate-zone species at elevations of possibly 4000 to 6000 feet, where climatic conditions resemble those at latitudes of 35°–45°.

2. Slope angle and direction may be substituted for latitude. This also

is mainly a temperature adjustment, dependent on angle of exposure to solar radiation, wind exposure, and possibly other factors.

3. Parent material may compensate for climate. The upper limit of the desert creosote bush, *Larrea* spp., was found by Shreve (1922) to extend 900 to 1500 feet higher in altitude on limestone soils than on granite soils. In the White Mountains, California, dolomites between 10,500 and 11,500 feet above sea level are covered with pure stands of *Pinus aristata*, while adjacent quartzite is occupied by subalpine sagebrush vegetation.

Similarly, some species favor soils derived from acidic rocks. Billings (1952) reported that several species of Sierran conifers and subalpine herbs extended into sagebrush steppe areas at some distance from the mountains on islands of highly acidic and infertile altered andesite. Most grasses and shrubs do not grow on these altered rocks, so the little moisture available supports a scattered population of conifers.

4. Rainfall may be replaced by fog and to some extent by dew. Rubel (1935) found that on the rainless coasts of Chile and Peru thick fog makes a grassland vegetation possible. In California, the redwood, *Sequoia sempervirens*, occurs in great forests made possible by the moisture of Pacific fogs. In Switzerland, in heavy mist belts, the beech, *Fagus* spp., grows in relatively dry areas. In Great Britain, with an annual rainfall of from 24 to 40 inches, forests thrive which in North America would require 45 to 60 inches of precipitation. Hodgson (1950) reported that in Alaska, bromegrass (*Bromus inermis*) produced 6,000 pounds of dry matter per acre with a precipitation from January 1 to November 1 of about six inches. The soil is only 24 to 36 inches deep and could not store enough moisture to compensate for the deficiency caused by only six inches of rainfall. Days are long, 20 hours on June 21, humidity usually is high, and dews and mists often are heavy.

5. Soil texture may be substituted for moisture. Asparagus thrives in sandy soils in areas where heavy soils would be much too wet for it. On the other hand, in dry seasons in the corn belt, corn on fine textured silty-clay loams and clay loams shows much less severe conditions of stress than on coarse textured sandy soils.

References

1. Allee, W. C. and Park, Thomas. 1939. The holocoenotic environment. *Science* 89: 166–169.
2. Beadle, N. C. W. 1954. Soil phosphorus and the delimitation of plant communities in eastern Australia. *Ecol.* 35: 370–375.

3. Berry, E. W. 1911. The lower Cretaceous flora of the world. Maryland Geol. Survey.

4. Billings, W. D. 1952. The environmental complex in relation to plant growth and distribution. *Quart. Rev. Biol.* 27: 251–265.

5. Blackman, F. F. 1905. Optima and limiting factors. *Ann. Bot.* 19: 281–298.

6. Borchert, John. 1950. The climate of the central North American grassland. *Ann. Assoc. Am. Geog.* 40: 1–39.

7. Cain, S. A. 1944. *Foundations of Plant Geography.* Harpers, New York.

8. Carpenter, J. R. 1940. The grassland biome. *Ecol. Monog.* 10: 617–684.

9. Cooke, W. C. 1924. The distribution of the pale western cut-worm, *Porosogrotis orthogonia* Morr: a study of physical ecology. *Ecol.* 5: 60–69.

10. Curtis, J. T. 1959. *The Vegetation of Wisconsin.* Univ. Wis. Press, Madison.

11. Dansereau, P. 1957. *Biogeography—an Ecological Perspective.* Ronald, New York.

12. Darwin, Chas. 1859. *On the Origin of Species by Means of Natural Selection.* Reprinted by Philosophical Library, New York.

13. Daubenmire, R. F. 1959. *Plants and Environment.* Wiley, New York.

14. Deevey, E. S., Jr. 1949. Biogeography of the Pleistocene. *Bul. Geol. Soc. Amer.* 60: 1315–1416.

15. Dillon, L. S. 1956. Wisconsin climate and life zones in North America. *Sci.* 123: 167–176.

16. Dunbar, C. O. 1960. *Historical Geology.* Wiley, New York.

17. Gleason, H. A. 1922. The vegetational history of the middlewest. *Ann. Assoc. Amer. Geog.* 12: 39–85.

18. Good, R. 1931. A theory of plant geography. *New Phytol.* 30: 149–171.

19. ———. 1953. *Geography of the Flowering Plants.* Longmans, Green and Company, London.

20. Hodgson, H. 1950. Personal communication.

21. Jones, E. W. 1951. Laboratory studies on the moisture relations of *Limonius* (Coleoptera; Elateridea). *Ecol.* 32: 284–293.

22. Karlstrom, T. N. V. 1956. Radiocarbon-based Pleistocene correlations and world-wide climatic change. *Sci.* 124: 939.

23. Kruckberg, A. R. 1954. Plant species in relation to serpentine soils. *Ecol.* 35: 267–274.

24. Kulp, J. L. 1961. Geologic time scale. *Sci.* 133: 1105–1114.

25. Lane, Geo. H. 1941. Pollen analysis of interglacial peats in Iowa. *Iowa Geol. Serv.* 37: 233–262.

26. Lawrence, D. B. 1950. Glacier fluctuation for six centuries in southeastern Alaska and its relation to solar activity. *Geog. Rev.* 40 (2): 191–223.

27. Leighton, M. M. 1957. Radiocarbon dates of Mankato drift in Minnesota. *Sci.* 125: 1037–1038.

28. Libby, W. F. 1952. *Radiocarbon Dating.* Univ. Chicago Press, Chicago.

29. Liebig, J. 1840. *Chemistry in Its Application to Agriculture and Physiology.* 3rd ed., Peterson, Philadelphia.

30. Livingston, B. E. and Shreve, F. 1921. *The Distribution of Vegetation in the United States, as Related to Climatic Conditions.* Carnegie Inst. Publ. 284, Washington, D. C.

31. Lundegardh, H. 1931. *Environment and Plant Development.* Edward Arnold and Company, London. (Translated by Eric Ashby.)

32. Major, Jack. 1951. A functional, factorial approach to plant ecology. *Ecology* 32: 392–412.

33. Marr, John W. 1948. Ecology of the forest-tundra ecotone on the east coast of Hudson Bay. *Ecol. Monog.* 18: 117–144.

34. Mason, H. L. 1936. The principles of geographic distribution as applied to floral analysis. *Madrono* 3: 181–190.

35. McComb, A. L. and Loomis, W. E. 1944. Subclimax prairie. *Bul. Torrey Bot. Club* 71: 46–76.

36. McGinitie, H. D. 1933. Redwoods and frost. *Sci.* 78: 190.

37. Odum, E. P. 1959. *Fundamentals of Ecology.* 2nd ed. Saunders, Philadelphia.

38. Rubel, Edward, 1935. The replaceability of ecological factors and the law of the minimum. *Ecol.* 16: 336–341.

39. Ruhe, R. V., Rubin, M., and Scholtes, W. H. 1957. Late Pleistocene radiocarbon chronology in Iowa. *Amer. Jour. Sci.* 255: 671–689.

40. Ruhe, R. V. and Scholtes, W. H. 1956. Age and development of soil landscapes in relation to climatic and vegetational changes in Iowa. *Soil Sci. Soc. Amer. Proc.* 20: 264–273.

41. ———. 1959. Important elements in the classification of the Wisconsin Glacial Stage: a discussion. *Jour. Geol.* 67 (5): 585–593.

42. Sears, P. B. 1942. Postglacial migration of five forest genera. *Amer. Jour. Bot.* 29: 684–691.

43. Seward, A. C. 1941. *Plant Life Through the Ages.* Cambridge University Press, England.

44. Shelford, V. E. 1913. *Animal Communities in Temperate North America.* University of Chicago Press, Chicago.

45. Shreve, F. 1922. Conditions indirectly affecting vertical distribution on desert mountains. *Ecol.* 3: 269–274.

46. Simonson, R. W. 1941. Studies of buried soils formed from till in Iowa. *Soil Sci. Soc. Amer. Proc.* 6: 373–381.

47. Suess, Hans. 1956. Absolute chronology of the last glaciation. *Sci.* 123: 355–357.

48. Tansley, A. G. 1923. *Practical Plant Ecology.* Dodd, Mead, New York.

49. Taylor, Walter P. 1934. Significance of extreme and intermittent conditions in distribution of species and management of natural resources, with a restatement of Liebig's law of the minimum. *Ecol.* 15: 274–379.

50. Transeau, E. N. 1935. The prairie peninsula. *Ecology* 16 (3): 423–437.

51. Voss, John. 1939. Forests of the Yarmouth and Sangamon interglacial period in Illinois. *Ecol.* 20: 517–528.

52. Walker, R. B. 1954. Factors affecting plant growth on serpentine soils. *Ecol.* 35: 259–266.

53. Weaver, J. E. 1954. *North American Prairie.* Johnson, Lincoln, Nebr.

54. Went, F. W. 1950. The response of plants to climate. *Sci.* 112: 489–494.

55. Whittaker, R. H. 1954. Vegetation response to serpentine soils. *Ecol.* 35: 275–288.

56. Wilson, L. R. 1932. The Two Creeks forest bed, Manitowoc County, Wisconsin. *Trans. Wis. Acad. Sci. Arts Lett.,* 27: 31–46.

57. ——— and Kosanke, R. M. 1940. The microfossils in a pre-Kansan peat deposit near Belle Plaine, Iowa. *Torreya* 40: 1–5.

58. Wright, H. E. 1957. Radiocarbon dates of Mankato drift in Minnesota. *Sci.* 125: 1038–1039.

59. Zeuner, F. E. 1952. *Dating the Past. An Introduction to Geochronology.* Methuen, London.

Adaptation Through
Natural Selection

An adaptation may be defined as any feature of an organism which has survival value under the existing conditions of its habitat. Such a feature or features may allow the plant to make fuller use of the nutrients, water, temperature, or light available, or may give protection against adverse factors, such as temperature extremes, harmful insects, and diseases (Daubenmire, 1959). Plants may have morphological adaptations such as growth habit, strength of stalk, radial symmetry, or rhizomes; they may have physiological adaptations which result in resistance to parasites, greater ability to compete for nutrients, or ability to withstand desiccation. Actually, there may be little difference between many of the so-called morphological and physiological adaptations because both represent the expression of physiologic processes.

According to Dansereau (1957), adaptation implies an adequacy to cope with conditions of the natural environment, and to so utilize its resources as to maintain an ecological position. In considering the environment, we must recognize that it refers not only to the prevailing conditions of the moment, but to the sequence of environments surrounding an organism throughout its life cycle. This means that an organism can reproduce itself from a certain range of food materials under a variety of environmental conditions. It follows then, that every organism is adapted to live in a certain variety of environments. We shall consider how this varies with the genetic makeup of the organism.

Every living thing is a product of its biological heredity and its environment. In using the term environment in connection with human beings, we mean both physical and cultural aspects. The cultural aspect refers to the social legacy, or total way of life of a people, the important basis for which is man's true speech and ability to make value judgments. With other animals and with plants, obviously, only the physical aspect of their environment need be considered.

Two terms introduced by Johannsen (1903), genotype and phenotype, should be clarified at this point. By **genotype** is meant the heredity received by the organism, which is relatively constant throughout life. **Phenotype** refers to the appearance of the organism—what it looks like— which is subject to change throughout life.

Gross differences in adaptation are recognized by everyone. We say that birds fly because they have developed a good flying mechanism, that a fish is adapted to living in water because of its form and its modified breathing apparatus. The source of this adaptability, however, has been a puzzle for many generations. It has long been recognized that there is apparently some relationship between form and function in all organisms. This has led to some widely differing views on how adaptations come about.

Early workers in biology were inclined to views which were dominated by teleology and anthropomorphism. Teleology implies purposive adaptation, a need to be fulfilled by changing form or structure as is necessary. Anthropomorphism involves giving human traits to nonhuman organisms, such as saying that a plant "avoids" acid soils, or "stores food" in its roots.

The French biologist Lamarck (1835–1845) was an exponent of the theory of evolution, and developed a concept relating to evolutionary changes which may be summarized in four general laws:

1. Life, by its inherent forces, tends to increase the volume of every living body, and to extend the dimensions of all of its parts, up to a limit determined by its own needs.

2. The production of a new organ in an animal results from a new need, and from new movements which this need originates and sustains.

3. The degree of development of organs and their force of action are always in proportion to the use made of these organs.

4. All that has been acquired, imprinted on, or changed in the organization of the individual during the course of its life is preserved, and if present in both sexes, is transmitted to the succeeding generations.

The first two laws are highly teleological in character. While, in a general sense, the first one tends to be partially correct, evolution can go also from large to small, indicating that the law is not universal. The statement of the second law gives no clue as to how adaptations actually arise due to the supposed need. The third law is, at least, logical, but is of no value in evolution unless the fourth law is true. This last one is the basis for the great controversy which has persisted to this day, relating to possible inheritance of acquired characters. As Carter (1959) has noted, "no incontrovertible evidence in favor of it has been put forward, and it is very difficult to bring its truth into line with our knowledge of genetics." Nevertheless, the Lamarckian concept of a permanent change caused by molding or altering of structure, function, or form in direct response to the environment, still has its adherents. The Russian agriculturist Lysenko (1946) developed this idea to the point where, with the aid of political expediency, it became (for many years) the dominant belief among biologists in the U.S.S.R. Even among some of the followers of the older ecology in the United States, there were those who favored the concept of direct adaptation. Clements, Martin and Long (1950) stated that "adaptation is brought about by responses to direct physical factors and is expressed both in function and form. . . . There is no evidence that adaptation arises through the selection of genetic strains or variations." It seems possible that through 40 or more years of field botanical work, Clements was unduly impressed by the effect of environment in modifying the appearance of plants, and so came to the belief that new forms arose directly through the action of the environment.

In contrast to the Lamarckian view, the genetic concept of adaptation is that adaptations arise through the selective action of the environment *on the genetic variations which are available.* The basis for this idea is to be found in Darwin's theory of the origin of species. Shortly after he had completed his education at Edinburgh and Cambridge, Charles Darwin was appointed naturalist on the *Beagle* which was embarking on a cruise around the world. During the five years of this voyage, Darwin observed and collected plants, animals, and birds at various points where the ship stopped, making especially complete studies on the Galapagos islands and in the coastal regions of South America.

Upon his return to England, he published several papers of a geological nature, and at least two on morphology and systematics. At heart, Darwin was a naturalist, however, and he began to write a more general work relating to evolution. It is believed that Malthus' essays on population had an influence on Darwin's thinking. The idea that population could soon outrun food supply could be applied to any organism. Darwin reasoned that any animal would become too numerous for the earth to support, unless some force kept the population in check. He noted that many progeny die before maturity, and that predators, parasites, and diseases operate to keep populations down.

In 1858, as reported by Carter (1958), Darwin received a letter from

A. R. Wallace, including an essay which expressed views on evolution similar to his own. Then, a little later that same year, both Darwin and Wallace presented their views before the Linnean Society. During the following year, 1859, *On the Origin of Species* was published.

The essential points in Darwin's theory can be expressed rather simply:

1. He accepted from Malthus the fact that the reproductive powers of animals are much greater than is required to maintain their numbers. Only if a large proportion of the offspring are destroyed will the numbers remain relatively constant.

2. If many individuals are being destroyed, there must be a "struggle for existence" both between members of the same species, and between members of different species.

3. Animals vary, and their variations are inherited.

4. In the struggle for existence the favorable variations will survive and the unfavorable ones will be exterminated. Favorable variations will accumulate, and this "natural selection" will lead to a gradual change toward better adaptation. This gradual change, when it has proceeded far enough, will result in origin of a new species. Thus, the means by which evolution, or the origin of species, is produced in nature is explained.

Darwin's theory was supported by a wealth of evidence. He demonstrated that variation is universal both among plants and animals in nature and under domestication. He then proceeded to cite evidence of the struggle for existence, which he believed he had observed in his experience. Later in the book he discussed geographical distribution, showing that the facts agreed with his belief.

Darwin's belief that natural selection was effective was a logical conclusion to draw from the many facts of the life of plants and animals as he had observed them. He believed further that natural selection acted primarily on small variations, since these are found everywhere in natural populations.

It is interesting to note that Darwin's concept was highly materialistic, susceptible to analysis by the scientific method. Also, it should be emphasized that while most biologists of his time were interested primarily in morphology or systematics, both Darwin and Wallace were mainly interested in the organism as a whole, as it lived its life in its natural surroundings. They were concerned with the effects of the external conditions on organisms, or the ecology of plants and animals.

The geneticist Dobzhansky (1951) has suggested that we may consider adaptive value (or Darwinian fitness) as the reproductive efficiency of a given genotype in a certain environment. If a population is a mixture of genetically distinct types, some of them may produce more surviving

progeny than others. Certain genes and genetic recombinations will become more, and others less, frequent in succeeding generations. Dobzhansky noted that "the essence of selection is that carriers of different genotypes in a population contribute differentially to the gene pool of succeeding generations. . . . The relative capacity of carriers of a given genotype to transmit their genes to the gene pool constitutes the adaptive
value of that genotype."

Adaptive value in a plant is determined by many factors, including the
individual's somatic vigor, its viability, the duration of its reproductive
period, the number of seeds produced, and the efficiency of its pollinating
mechanism. It is not necessary, therefore, to think of natural selection only
in terms of struggle or competition in the usual sense.

If one genotype, in a freely interbreeding population, leaves 100 living
offspring, on the average, and another leaves 90, the adaptive value of
the first may be considered 1.00, the second .90. The second genotype is
opposed by a selection coefficient of .10 or 10%. Huxley (1942) pointed
out that if a mutation occurs which increases survival by only 1%, it
will become established in half of the population in 100 generations.

To survive and reproduce, a species must be at least tolerably well
adapted to the environments with which it regularly comes in contact.
Dobzhansky (1950a) has suggested that when faced with this necessity,
it may not attain maximum efficiency in any one of the environments
occupied. There is a premium placed on versatility, rather than perfection.
This is an important aspect of the adaptation of crops because of the variable climatic and soil conditions to which most of our crops are subjected.

It has been shown through the application of the Hardy-Weinberg
formula, which was developed independently by Hardy (1908) and Weinberg (1908), that in a random cross-breeding population at equilibrium,
the relative frequencies of each gene allele tend to remain constant from
generation to generation, unless the carriers of the different gene alleles
survive or reproduce at different rates. This may be expressed mathe-
matically through the use of the binomial $(p + q)^2$, where $p + q = 1$. If
a dominant gene A has the frequency p, and its recessive allele a the frequency q, in the gene pool of a sexual random-breeding population, the
succeeding generations will consist of genotypes with frequencies expressed
by the expansion of the binomial $(p + q)^2$, or $p^2AA + 2pqAa + q^2aa$.
As long as random mating continues, without selection, these gene frequencies will tend to remain constant. For example, if we had a human
population consisting of people of different stature, and they chose mates
without respect for height, the population would tend to continue, gener-

ation after generation, with about the same percentage of tall, average, and short persons.

In order for organisms to evolve, there must be changes in gene frequencies. The following forces are considered to be important sources of such changes.

1. Mutation—If gene allele A changes to *a*, or *vice versa*, their frequencies as represented by p and q in the binomial $(p + q)^2$, will change.

2. Differential contribution to gene pool—Carriers of all genotypes may not contribute equally to the gene pool of the next generation, so differences in adaptive values result in changes in gene frequencies.

3. Migration—A differential migration of carriers of gene A and gene *a* into, or out of, a population will cause changes.

4. Genetic drift—Large populations must be assumed, if equilibrium is to be expected. In small populations chance variations in gene frequencies may become directionally important. Occurrence of some selfing or inbreeding may alter gene frequencies.

SOURCES OF VARIABILITY

The basic source of genetic variability is mutation. Genes are characterized by their ability to reproduce themselves exactly, but occasionally this process is not perfect. A slightly changed copy of a gene (a mutant) may occur from time to time. Many, and perhaps most, of the mutations that occur are deleterious to the organism. The mutation process is not in itself adaptive, that is, it can occur in either direction without regard to adaptive value. But, through sexual reproduction and natural selection, evolution may become adaptively directional. As Dobzhansky (1950b) has expressed it, we might consider the evolutionary process in five steps: (1) the mutation process furnishes the raw materials for evolution; (2) countless gene patterns are produced through sexual reproduction; (3) the possessors of some of these have greater fitness than others in environments available; (4) natural selection tends to increase the frequency of the adaptively superior gene patterns; and (5) groups of gene combinations of adaptive worth may become segregated into closed genetic systems. Eventually the formation of a species is accomplished.

While it may seem difficult to see just how the environment takes part in evolution, it would appear that it can do so at two levels. Certainly, at the level of mutation itself, the environment, through heat, cold, or some other physical factor, may determine at the precise moment whether or not the mutation occurs. Then at the level of natural selection, it is obvious that the environment may directly affect survival of different genotypes. At this level, changes in the environment may result in a shift of survival and reproductive opportunities among the carriers of varied genotypes.

Mutations, as we have indicated, are not purposive. They are believed to occur at random. A few may be adaptive, and many may not. If a mutation has survival value, and new hereditary forms have appeared, the survival, maturity, and reproduction of the new forms may not be random at all. They may tend to increase in the population at the expense of others which have a lower selective value.

Actually, while mutations are basic to variability, mutations as such may make up but a minor part of the total variability so universal in evolution. This can be illustrated using a chart (Table 3-1) similar to that prepared by Clausen (1951). It would appear that recombination among genes, chromosome segments, and whole chromosomes might be the most important source of variability on which the forces of natural selection can operate, although the processes of duplication and addition of chromosome segments, whole chromosomes, and genomes at times are undoubtedly very important.

TABLE 3-1.   SOURCES OF GENETIC VARIABILITY*

Building Blocks	Types of Process	Source of Variation	Evolutionary Level
Genes	*Creative*	gene mutation	
	Recombination	independent assortment and crossing over	Intraspecific
	Loss	deletion of genes	
Chromosome Segments	*Recombination*	Repatterning by inversions and translocation	
	Duplication	Duplication of segments	
	Loss	Loss of segments	Intra- or Interspecific
Chromosomes	*Recombination*	Independent assortment of unchanged chromosomes	
	Duplication	of whole chromosomes	
	Loss	of whole chromosomes	
Genomes	*Duplication*	Autoploidy duplication of genomes	
	Addition	Amphiploidy addition of different genomes	Interspecific

* After Clausen. *Stages in the Evolution of Plant Species.* Cornell Univ. Press, Ithaca, N. Y., 1951.

An illustration of the importance of recombination may be found in the report of Clausen (1949) on intercrossing ecologic races of *Potentilla glandulosa.* Of 1000 F_2 plants from one cross and 578 from another, no two plants looked alike. When propagated clonally at three different altitudinal locations, the 578 F_2 plants from the second cross showed responses more diverse than had been found in all of the wild forms of the species from the many native environments of the western United States that had been tested. A great deal of genetic diversity had been created by crossing two races of the same species. This diversity was available for natural selection, which was shown by the fact that among the F_2 plants, some were found to be highly adapted to each of the three latitudinal stations, while neither of the parent races could survive at all of the three places.

Another of the important sources of genetic variability from the viewpoint of natural selection is polyploidy. The effect of polyploidy on geographic distribution, however, is not completely clear. It was suggested by Hagerup (1932) that polyploids are more tolerant to extreme ecological conditions than their diploid relatives. This concept was illustrated with examples from Northwestern Africa in three species of *Eragrostis*. A diploid annual was confined to lake margins, a tetraploid perennial was found in drier places, and a vigorous octoploid perennial was established on the very dry sand dunes. These three were considered by Hagerup to form an autoploid series.

In Europe, four floras were studied by Tischler (cited by Stebbins, 1950) who reported that the lowest percentage of polyploidy was found in the most southerly one, with 31% of polyploids. A flora in Schleswig-Holstein, in Northern Europe, had 44% of polyploids, while two floras of still more northerly location had 49% and 55% of polyploids, respectively.

This suggestion that a greater percentage of polyploids occurred in higher latitudes has been criticized by Gustafsson (1948), Müntzing (1936), and Stebbins (1950) on the basis that results obtained by analysis of whole floras might be misleading. It is known that perennial herbs have a higher percentage of polyploids than is found in annuals and woody plants. Also, the percentage of polyploids in one family may be much higher than it is in another. It is particularly high in the grasses and in the rose family.

Stebbins (1942, 1950) searched the literature for examples on the basis of plant groups (genera, subgenera, or sections of genera) instead of whole floras. He found a total of 100 examples, including 46 from the regions covered by the Pleistocene glaciers. Of the 100, 21 were Holarctic, 56 North American, and 23 from the Old World. In 60 of the 100 examples, the polyploids were found to have a wider distribution than their diploid ancestors, in 7 the area of diploids and polyploids were equal, and in 33 the polyploids occupied the smaller area. It appears that there is some tendency for polyploids to have wider ranges of distribution than their diploid relatives, but this tendency is not universal. From the viewpoint of geographic position, 31 examples were found in which the diploids were distributed about the periphery of the range, while the polyploids occupied the central position. In 28, however, the diploids were centrally located. As to latitude, in 27 examples the diploids occupied the more southerly and the polyploids the more northerly portion of the total range of distribution.

From Stebbins' study it appears that no general rules can be formulated to govern the relation between distribution of diploids and tetraploids. It is likely that the higher percentage of polyploids in high northern latitudes may be due in part to the fact the floras in these regions contain a high percentage of perennial herbs which have efficient means of vegetative propagation. Another reason may be that, because of the drastic changes in climate in northern latitudes in recent geologic times, polyploids derived from crosses between races or subspecies are likely to have wider ranges of tolerance than are possessed by the parent races. That polyploids are likely to be well adapted to colonization of newly available habitats has been pointed out by Stebbins (1942), Anderson (1936), and Babcock and Stebbins (1938).

NATURAL SELECTION—FUNDAMENTAL TO BIOLOGY

One of the simplest examples of natural selection may be taken from bacteria. There is a phage which attacks colon bacteria, *Escherichia coli*. In the absence of this phage, the occasional resistant bacterial cells, which arise as spontaneous mutants, apparently get lost in the masses of normal cells. They may be adaptively neutral if the phage is not present. When a phage is introduced into the culture, however, with the resultant destruction of the normal cells, only the resistant cells survive and reproduce. In the presence of the phage these resistant cells definitely do have adaptive value, and eventually a resistant colony of bacteria develops (Dobzhansky, 1955).

Another example of natural selection may be taken from wheat rust fungi. The fungus *Puccinia graminis tritici* is responsible for one of the most serious wheat diseases. There are many "physiological races" of this fungus which are distinguished by their ability to infect different varieties of wheat. The normal method by which the disease is spread is by windborne spores. It has been shown clearly by Stakman *et al.* (1943)

and others that the incidence of different physiological races of rust shows striking differences from year to year. These changes are due in no small part to the introduction of new varieties of wheat which are resistant to predominant races at a given time. Soon, however, rare or unknown races develop and infect the so-called resistant wheats. This means that man's selection of new wheats is matched and often surpassed by natural selection in the rusts, creating a seemingly never-ending problem of breeding for resistance.

Other examples might be cited, including house flies resistant to DDT sprays, aphids resistant to parathione, and scale insects resistant to normal doses of HCN in fumigation. In all instances, the resistant races developed through natural selection under conditions which gave the resistant type a selective advantage, or adaptive value greater than that of the normal type.

NATURAL SELECTION IN CROP PLANTS

Examples of natural selection in field crops are found in both cross- and self-fertilized species. Sylven (1937), in studies with white clover, *Trifolium repens*, showed that certain strains imported from Germany and Denmark improved greatly in forage-yielding ability in Sweden after being grown for two generations in a new environment. One important strain, however, said to be more homozygous than the others, showed little improvement with advanced generations in Sweden.

In Maryland, Kemp (1937) showed that natural selection in Kentucky bluegrass (*Poa pratensis*), orchardgrass (*Dactylis glomerata*), and white clover had operated effectively in permanent pastures. In general, this selection resulted in the ascendancy of those types of plant which are best adapted to survive close grazing conditions. A procumbent growth, with buds close to the ground level, characterized these "pasture" types.

In Australia, natural selection in subclover, *Trifolium subterraneum*, was found to change the composition of populations rapidly. Gregor (1944) cites an experiment by C. M. Donald in which an early and a midseason variety were grown together in a dry area at Adelaide. In a few generations the population consisted mainly of early maturing genotypes. It appeared that unfavorable moisture conditions effectively reduced seed setting in the late types, resulting in a preponderance of seed produced from the early maturing plants. At Adelaide Hills, a relatively wet area, similar mixed seeding soon resulted in predominantly midseason and late strains.

Red clover, *Trifolium pratense,* has given indications, in various parts of the world, of responding rapidly to natural selection. Through many years Dr. E. A. Hollowell of the United States Department of Agriculture has coordinated research efforts in cooperation with state experiment stations to determine the response of red clover varieties to climatic conditions. Regional evaluation trials in the North Central States give a clear picture of latitudinal adaptation.

Red clover is a cross-fertilized perennial (often managed as a biennial) which shows a marked photoperiodic response. Throughout the red clover growing region, local farm strains have developed over a period of years through natural selection. These strains are well adapted to local or even regional areas, and the degree of adaptation is reflected in comparative forage yields of varieties from different origins when grown in several latitudinal regions. The data given in Table 3-2 will illustrate the importance of growing adapted strains.

TABLE 3-2. ADAPTATION OF RED CLOVER AS INDICATED BY FORAGE YIELDS IN THREE AREAS OF THE RED CLOVER BELT OF THE UNITED STATES

Region of Origin	Variety	Yield in percent of Midland variety		
		Northern Area	Central Area	Southern Area
Northern Varieties	Dollard Ottawa Wegner Wis. M.R.	101	95	82
Central Varieties	Midland Emerson Rahn Pennscott Purdue	103	99	97
Southern Varieties	Kenland Van Atta Libel	97	100	109

It is evident from the data presented that varieties of northern origin are better adapted to the northern part of the red clover area (Minnesota, Wisconsin, and Michigan), whereas those of more southerly origin are better adapted to the southern part of the red clover area, namely Kansas and Missouri. There was less difference in performance in the central area, since all varieties appeared to be fairly well adapted to this region, which includes Iowa, Illinois, Indiana, and Ohio.

The performance of English strains of red clover in the United States shows an even greater contrast according to origin. Hollowell (1955) has summarized results of testing six English varieties in eight different states over a three-year period. On the average, the English strains yielded 74% of the yield of Kenland, a well adapted variety. Two factors seem to be of particular importance: the change in latitude and the greater susceptibility to winter damage in the United States environment. Under the English climate there has been little natural selection for winter-hardiness, a characteristic essential in that part of the United States where much of the red clover crop is grown.

In Sweden, Åkerberg (1948) found that local strains of red clover having dissimilar characteristics (such as yielding ability, earliness of maturity, and varying degrees of perennialism) were distributed from north to south according to climatic conditions. In Norrland, most of the naturalized strains were earlier in maturity than those brought in from central Sweden. This he considered an adaptation to the temperature-light climate of the high northern latitude of Norrland. After repeated sowings for several generations, strains brought in from southern Sweden yielded 10% to 15% more forage than those same strains introduced directly from southern Sweden.

A study of genetic shift in red clover populations, through natural selection, has been reported in Canada by McLennan, Greenshields, and McVicar (1960). The variety Lasalle, a blend of Ottawa (having a high percentage of plants with a prominent white leaf mark) and Dollard (with a minor percentage of plants having white leaf marks) has been grown through several generations in both western and eastern Canada. In western Canada there has been a shift toward the Dollard type, whereas in eastern Canada a more even balance has been maintained.

Selection for Chemical Constituents

The presence of hydrocyanic acid in white clover has been established for many years. This has been shown to be due to the presence of cyanogenetic glucosides and a hydrolyzing enzyme (Melville and Doak, 1940). Genetic studies have indicated that the production of hydrocyanic acid glucoside is determined by one gene, Ac-ac, and the enzyme by an independent gene, Li-li. Plants bearing both dominant alleles crossed with the double recessive have shown a normal dihybrid segregation in F_2 (Corkill, 1942 and Atwood and Sullivan, 1943).

Under natural conditions, the percentage of plants bearing cyanogenetic properties varies greatly with geographical origin. Daday (1954) made a collection of seed of wild white clover (*Trifolium repens*) from most of the European countries, and from some Near Eastern countries. The progenies of these collected seed lots were grown at Aberystwyth, Wales, and were classified as to cyanogenetic properties by a picric acid test. The Hardy-Weinberg formula $(p^2 + 2pq + q^2 = 1)$ was applied to determine the genotypic frequencies of the population. On this basis, it was found that there was a continuous gradual decrease in the frequencies of the glucoside and enzyme genes as the source of the samples move from the Mediterranean region to northeastern Europe. Distribution of the frequencies of the dominant alleles was correlated with January isotherms. A decrease of 1°F in the January mean temperature resulted in a reduction of 4.23% in the frequency of the glucoside gene, and a reduction of 3.16% in the frequency of the enzyme gene. Daday concluded

FIGURE 3-1.

Phenotypic and genotypic frequencies in wild populations of Trifolium repens *from different altitudes.*

Phenotypes (left)
AcLi = *glucoside and en-*
zyme
Acli = *glucoside only*
acLi = *enzyme only*
acli = *neither. glucoside*
nor enzyme

Genotypes (right)
Black section = domi-
nant homozygotes
Lined section = hetero-
zygotes
White section = reces-
sive homozygotes

[*After Daday, Heredity* 8:377–384, 1954.]

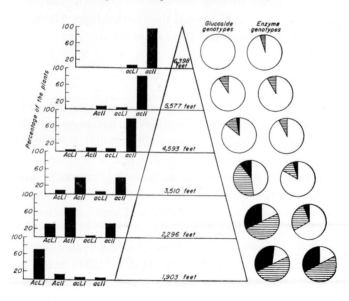

that January temperature played an important role through natural selection in the evolution of subspecies or races of white clover. Temperature effects due to differences in altitude were found to be similar to those caused by latitude, as illustrated in Figure 3-1.

Natural Selection in Alfalfa Varieties

Much alfalfa seed now being planted in the United States, especially of the newer varieties, is produced in western irrigated valleys. It is of considerable importance to know just how rapidly a variety may change, due to natural selection, when grown for seed production in an environment which differs from that prevailing where the variety originated. Present standards of seed certification are established to minimize genetic changes in varieties, particularly changes which might decrease the value of such varieties in the consuming regions.

Ranger alfalfa is a synthetic variety having a broad genetic base. It traces to three earlier varieties, Cossack, Ladak, and Turkestan. Like other winter-hardy varieties adapted to the northern states, Ranger tends to exhibit a characteristic short and somewhat spreading type of growth in the autumn, following cutting in early September. This type of growth, which is even more pronounced in the variety Ladak, is associated with fall dormancy and winter-hardiness, and has been used as a measure of trueness to type in studies of advanced generations of northern varieties in seed certification programs. Observations by Smith (1955), Canode (1958) and others have shown that natural selection exerts a marked influence on the genetic makeup of Ranger when it is grown for repeated generations in more southerly latitudes. An increasing percentage of plants which grow tall in the autumn, with an associated lower level of winter-hardiness, soon becomes apparent.

In older varieties, too, natural selection has played an important role. Grimm alfalfa was developed in Minnesota over a period of 40 or 50 years, mainly by natural selection. It is believed that the old Frankonian variety in Germany was the progenitor of Grimm. Through repeated generations of seed propagation of plants which survived Minnesota's rigorous winters and were recombined each generation by natural crossing, a high level of winter-hardiness was achieved.

Natural Selection in Barley Mixtures

It was established by Johannsen (1903) that within a pure line or a clone selection is without effect, because the selected individuals are genetically similar to the rest of the population. If a mixture of pure lines is subjected to natural selection, it would be expected that some lines would tend to increase more rapidly than others. Such a situation was created by Harlan and Martini (1938), who planted a mixture of 11 easily recognizable varieties of barley in ten different locations in the United States. Equal numbers of seeds of each variety were planted and the resulting harvest was sorted into component varieties. Planting was repeated for several generations, using the proportions of different varieties as they occurred at harvest time. The results of this study showed an early aggressiveness and dominance of one or more varieties at the expense of those less favored by the particular environment and competition which prevailed. In some instances the dominant variety was the local one, but in others it was a variety not even being grown in that area. It appeared that the changes brought about through natural selection were dependent primarily on two things: (1) the number of seeds produced, and (2) the percentage of seedlings which survived the competition. Table 3-3 gives the composition of the mixtures, on the basis of a 500-plant sample, after four to twelve generations at ten locations. Theoretical curves of natural selection compared with actual results obtained are given in Figures 3-2, 3-3, and 3-4.

TABLE 3-3.   VARIETAL COMPOSITION OF BARLEY MIXTURES AFTER SEVERAL GENERATIONS OF EXPOSURE TO EFFECTS OF NATURAL SELECTION AT DIFFERENT LOCATIONS *

Variety	Va.	N. Y.	Minn.	N. D.	Nebr.	Mont.	Idaho	Wash.	Ore.	Calif.
Coast & Trebi	446T†	57T	83T	156	224	87	210	150	6	362
Gatami	13	9	15	20	7	58	10	1	0	1
Smooth Awn	6	52	14	23	12	25	0	5	1	0
Lyon	11	3	27	14	13	37	2	3	0	8
Melvy	4	0	0	0	7	4	8	6	0	27
White Smyrna	4	0	4	17	194	241	157	276	489	65
Hannchen	4	34	305	152	13	19	90	30	4	34
Svanhols	11	2	50	80	26	8	18	23	0	2
Deficiens	0	0	0	1	3	0	2	5	0	1
Manchuria	1	343	2	37	1	21	3	1	0	0

* From Harlan and Martini. *Jour. Agr. Res.* 57:189–200. 1938.

† T = total of 2 varieties; could not be distinguished accurately.

An extension of the principles involved in the natural selection experiment with barley mixtures has been used by Suneson (1956). A thorough study of seed stocks of diverse evolutionary origins is the first step. This is followed by recombination through hybridization, the bulking of F_1 progeny, and subsequent prolonged natural selection for mass sorting of the progeny in successive natural cropping environments. Gains in yield and adaptation,

from four different hybrid populations continued in bulk
through 15 generations or more,
equaled improvement obtained
by conventional breeding methods. The essential features of this
evolution-based method are a
broadly diversified germ plasm,
and a prolonged subjection of
the mass of the progeny to competitive natural selection in the
area where the variety will be
used.

A consideration of genetic
shifts during 30 generations of
natural selection in barley composite crosses has recently been
reported by Bal, Suneson, and
Ramage (1959). From a bulk
population of 378 hybrids, known
as Composite Cross II, populations having three different selection histories were studied. In
one group (R) there was no
man-directed selection; in another group (L) from F_{11}
through F_{19} selection was practiced for large seed size; in still
another group (S) from F_{11}
through F_{19} there was selection

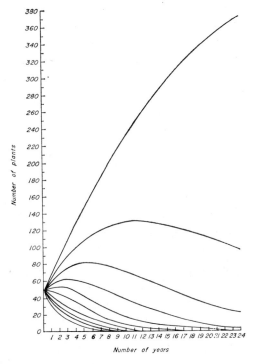

FIGURE 3-2.

Theoretical curves of natural selection in cereals. These were obtained by postulating an equal mixture of ten varieties, the poorest of which produces 45 seeds per plant, the best, 90 seeds, and the remaining 8 separated by intervals of 5 seeds each. [After Harlan and Martini, Jour. Agr. Res. 57:194, 1938.]

for small seed size. In the F_{30} generation the mean weight per 100 kernels
was 57.3 milligrams for group R, 61.5 mg for L, and 50.6 mg for S. The mean
weight per 100 kernels of all 28 parents was 48.9 mg. The effects of directed
selection persisted through 11 generations, and all had larger seed than in
earlier generations. Natural selection eliminated such characters as black,
naked, and hooded. Two-row and smooth-awned types also were practically
extinct, but in general the populations remained highly diverse and heterogeneous. Of 21 morphological characters studied, natural selection caused
a genetic shift in 15 in the R, 13 in the L and 4 in the S groups, respectively.
Relative contributions from the parental varieties were estimated and found
to be highly disproportionate.

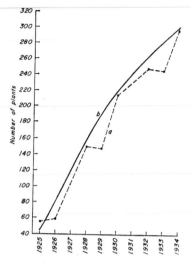

A theoretical consideration of natural selection and its measurement has been given recently by Haldane (1954). He stated that the intensity of natural selection for a given character may be defined as the logarithm of the ratio of the fitness of the optimum phenotype to that of the whole population. This, he says, can be determined from frequency distributions. Values found have ranged from near zero to approximately 12%. In all cases, according to Haldane, natural selection tends to reduce variability by weeding out extreme forms.

FIGURE 3-3.

Curve (a) of actual data of the Hannchen variety of barley at St. Paul, Minnesota, compared with theoretical curve (b) of a dominant variety. [After Harlan and Martini, Jour. Agr. Res. 57:197, 1938.]

PREADAPTATION

It is likely that plants have gained or lost certain characteristics in evolution as the result of chance. If variations resulting from mutation are neutral in survival value, they may have no more than a random chance of being saved. However, if some trait or attribute which is in itself of neutral value is associated with (linked genetically to) a feature which is essential to survival, the neutral attribute may be carried on for generations. On this basis, it has been reasoned that in warm-climate vegetation some species, subspecies, or races may possess cold-tolerance. This appears to be true, as shown in studies of White (1942), who reports that many plants have been transplanted successfully into regions having mean temperatures 10° to 30°F cooler than those of their native habitat. Similar evidence is provided by the fact that in tropical floras some species have come to require the short days of the tropics, while others are neutral as to day-length requirements. Such phenomena form the basis for the concept of preadaptation.

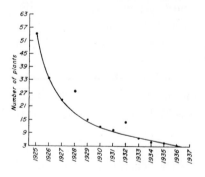

FIGURE 3-4.

Data on the Meloy variety of barley at Moccasin, Montana, showing the typical curve of a poor variety. [After Harlan and Martini, Jour. Agr. Res. 57:196, 1938.]

Daubenmire (1959) has suggested that any mutation which gives an organism some characteristic of potential value, but which at the time has no survival value, may be called a preadaptation. Disease-resistant strains of crops have been found in areas where the specific disease involved is not present. Cold-tolerant species native to warm regions, and salt tolerant plants in a species grown only in acid soils, may be considered examples of preadaptation. These phenomena help to explain how different species of the same habitat may move into rather distinctly different environments. White points out that such forest genera as *Sequoia*, *Fagus*, and *Glyptostrobus* grew in the same forest in the Miocene epoch, but later their descendants, redwood, beech, and bald cypress, came to occupy quite different climatic areas.

In considering preadaptation it is wise to view this phenomenon with caution lest we go so far that we might be accused of believing in orthogenesis and preformation.

The fate of adaptations which seem to have outlived their survival value is a puzzling problem. For example, the succulent *Sedum ternatum*, which inhabits the mesophytic deciduous forest, the semiaquatic cacti, and the xeromorphic yet hydrophytic pond pine (*Pinus rigida serotina*) are examples noted by Daubenmire. The very characteristics of these species which today seem paradoxical were at one time adaptations on which the species depended for survival. As long as these genetically fixed adaptations (although they should no longer be called adaptations) were not detrimental to the species under changed conditions of environment, the species survived. It would appear that plants have no way in which they can discard morphologic or physiologic features just because they no longer have adaptive value. Natural selection pressure tends to keep structures and functions at a high level of efficiency. Through genetic linkage, features which no longer have survival value may be so closely associated with features essential to survival that the former adaptation is carried on more or less indefinitely.

References

1. Åkerberg, Erik. 1948. Conditions of cultivation and breeding problems for cereals and herbage plants in Norrland. *Svalöf 1886–1946*. Carl Bloms, Lund, pp. 278–303.
2. Anderson, E. 1936. The species problem in Iris. *Ann. Mo. Bot. Garden*, 23: 457–509.
3. Atwood, S. S. and Sullivan, J. T. 1943. Inheritance of a cyanogenetic glucoside

and its hydrolyzing enzyme in *Trifolium repens*. *Jour. Her.* 34 (10): 311–320.

4. Babcock, E. B. and Stebbins, G. L. 1938. The American Species of Crepis: their relationships and distribution as affected by polyploidy and apomixis. Carnegie Inst. Wash. Publ. No. 504.

5. Bal, B. S., Suneson, C. A., and Ramage, R. T. 1959. Genetic shift during 30 generations of natural selection in barley. *Agron. Jour.* 51: 555–557.

6. Canode, Chester L. 1958. Natural selection within Ranger alfalfa. Univ. of Idaho, Res. Bul., 39.

7. Carter, G. S. 1958. *A Hundred Years of Evolution*. Macmillan, New York.

8. Clausen, Jens. 1949. Ecological genetics of Potentilla races. *Proc. 8th Inter. Cong. Gen.*, pp. 162–172.

9. ———. 1951. *Stages in the Evolution of Plant Species*. Cornell Univ. Press, Ithaca, N. Y.

10. Clements, F. E., Martin, E. V. and Long, F. L., 1950. *Adaptation and Origin in the Plant World*. Chronica Bot. Co., Waltham, Mass.

11. Corkill, L. 1942. Cyanogenesis in white clover (*Trifolium repens* L.). V. The inheritance of cyanogenesis. *N. Z. Jour. Sci. Tech.* 23: 178B–193B.

12. Daday, H. 1954. Gene frequency in wild populations of *Trifolium repens*. *Heredity* 8 (1): 61–78.

13. Dansereau, Pierre. 1957. *Biogeography—An Ecological Perspective*. Ronald, New York.

14. Darwin, Chas. 1859. *On the Origin of Species by Means of Natural Selection*. Reprinted by Philosophical Library, New York.

15. Daubenmire, R. F. 1959. *Plants and Environment*. 2nd ed. Wiley, New York.

16. Dobzhansky, T. 1950a. Evolution in the tropics. *Amer. Scientist* 38: 209–221.

17. ———. 1950b. Heredity, environment and evolution. *Sci.* 111: 161–166.

18. ———. 1951. *Genetics and the Origin of Species*. Columbia Univ. Press.

19. ———. 1955. *Evolution, Genetics and Man*. Wiley, New York.

20. Gregor, J. W. 1944. *Biol. Revs. Cambridge Phil. Soc.* 19: 20–30.

21. Gustafsson, A. 1948. Polyploidy, life-form and vegetative reproduction. *Hereditas* 34: 1–22.

22. Hagerup, O. 1932. Über Polyploidie in Bezichung zu Klima, Ökologie, and Phylogenie. *Hereditas* 16: 19–40.

23. Haldane, J. B. S. 1954. The measurement of natural selection. *Proc. 9th Inter. Cong. Gen.*, Bellagio, Italy, pp. 480–487.

24. Hardy, G. H. 1908. Mendelian proportions in a mixed population. *Sci.* 28: 49–50.

25. Harlan, H. V. and Martini, M. L. 1938. The effects of natural selection in a mixture of barley varieties. *Jour. Agr. Res.* 57: 189–200.

26. Hollowell, E. A. 1955. Personal communication.

27. Huxley, J. 1942. *Evolution—the modern synthesis*. Harpers, New York.

28. Johannsen, W. 1903. *Über Erblichkeit in Populationen und in Reinen Linien*. Gustav Fischer, Jena.

29. Kemp, W. B. 1937. Natural selection within plant species as exemplified in a permanent pasture. *Jour. Her.* 28: 329–333.

30. Lamarck. J. B. 1835–45. Histoire naturelle des Animaux sans Vertébres. 2nd ed. J. B. Bailliere, Paris and London.

31. Lysenko, T. D. 1946. *Heredity and its variability*. Translated by T. Dobzhansky. Kings Crown Press, New York.

32. McLennan, H. A., Greenshields, J. E. R., and McVicar, R. M. 1960. A genetic analysis of population shifts in pedigree generations of Lasalle red clover. *Can. Jour. Pl. Sci.* 40: 509–515.

33. Melville, J. and Doak, B. W. 1940. Cyanogenesis in white clover (*Trifolium*

repens L.) II. Isolation of glucosidal constituents. *N. Z. Jour. Sci. Tech.* 22: 67B–71B.

34. Müntzing, A. 1936. The evolutionary significance of autopolyploidy. *Hereditas* 21: 263–378.

35. Smith, Dale. 1955. Influence of area of seed production on the performance of Ranger alfalfa. *Agron. Jour.* 47: 301–305.

36. Stakman, E. C., Loegering, W. Q., Cassell, R. C., and Hines, L. 1943. Population trends of physiologic races of *Puccinia tritici* in the United States for the period 1930–1941. *Phytopath.* 33: 884–898.

37. Stebbins, G. L. 1942. Polyploid complexes in relation to ecology and the history of floras. *Amer. Nat.* 76: 36–45.

38. ———. 1950. *Variation and Evolution in Plants.* Columbia Univ. Press.

39. Suneson, C. A. 1956. An evolutionary plant breeding method. *Agron. Jour.* 48: 188–191.

40. Sylven, N. 1937. Imper. Bur. Plant Genetics, Herbage Plants, Bul. 21.

41. Weinberg, W. 1908. Über den Nachweis der Vererbung beim Menschen. Verein Vaterland. *Naturk. Wurtemberg Jahresh.* 64: 368–382.

42. White, O. E. 1942. Temperature reaction, mutation and geographical distribution in plant groups. *Amer. Sci. Congr., Proc. 8th Congr.* 3: 287–294.

Chapter 4

The Ecotype Concept

In the previous chapter, the effects of natural selection in establishing subspecies, varieties, or races of various crop plants were considered. Natural populations of organisms of all kinds appear to consist usually of a heterogeneous lot of genotypes, all of which are fairly well adapted to the environment which prevails.

Upon close examination of the high degree of polymorphism which exists within most species, it is found that different types do not appear to be distributed at random throughout the range of the species, but instead are grouped into ecological units showing distinct relationships to habitat differences.

In Sweden, Turesson (1922a,b) assembled collections of individual plants belonging to the same species, but native to different habitats within the species total range. These plants were propagated and studied in one experimental garden at Åcarp. Persistent differences were found among these plants, indicating that a taxonomic Linnean species is made up of numerous races which exhibit inherent differences in both morphology and physiology. Turesson found consistent differences in height of plants, growth habits, earliness of maturity, leaf characters, and reproductive habits. These differences, however, were not sufficient to warrant recognizing taxonomic distinctions. All races within a species were completely interfertile.

With several species, including Alpine bluegrass (*Poa alpina*), hawkweed (*Hieracium* spp.), and others, there were found to be genetic races especially well adapted to certain environments; some were suited to low, wet habitats, some to sunny, dry areas, some to seacoast locations, some to alpine conditions, etc. These Turesson considered truly ecologic races, or ecotypes, which represent the "genotypic response to the various environments where the species is found."

Stebbins (1942) defined an ecotype as "a group of biotypes especially adapted to a specific environmental niche." A biotype includes the members of a group having the same genetic constitution, and may be either homozygous or heterozygous. The term "niche" is used differently by different ecologists, but Odum (1959) has given it a distinction which appears logical. He suggests that if we say that a man's address corresponds to his habitat, we might say that the man's position or place in the community corresponds to the "niche" he occupies.

The importance of Turesson's work on ecotypes was recognized by Mason and Stout (1954). They noted that "with Turesson's work the concept of natural selection began to make sense and fits into the findings of the geneticist. It was a blow to Lamarckian thinking." The ecotype concept was accepted by Stapledon (1928). At Aberystwyth, Wales, Stapledon collected all of the forms of cocksfoot (*Dactylis glomerata*) that he could find in Britain for use in his grass-breeding program. The forms collected from a variety of local habitats could be grouped into six types, including: (1) lax hay, (2) dense hay, (3) tussock, (4) cups, (5) spreading pasture, and (6) dense pasture. These six ecologic races were completely interfertile and crosses among them produced remarkable variability.

The work on ecotypes was given a great stimulus by the experimental work of Clausen, Keck, and Hiesey (1940) of the Carnegie Institution, at Stanford University, California. These studies were begun by the late H. M. Hall, who devoted many years to the improvement of existing methods of plant taxonomy. He included experiments with living plants, and integrated his observations with genetic and cytogenetic analysis. In California, extremes of altitude from sea level to high alpine peaks may be found in proximity. Great contrasts in rainfall are found in going from the coastal foggy region of the redwoods, across dry valleys and wet mountain meadows, to the desert beyond. The native flora is complex, just as the climate is varied.

As the work at the Carnegie Institution laboratory progressed, studies were extended to even larger biological problems, and from investigations on relationships between plants and their environment, data became available for studies on the nature of species and of barriers separating them. Cytological and genetical studies were included, and new light was shed on basic principles regarding the nature and evolution of natural units of vegetation and their distribution.

In the studies of Clausen, Keck, and Hiesey (1940), three basic facts were recognized. First, plants are grouped by relationship into complexes of diverse content but of a common hereditary pattern. Second, such complexes are widely distributed through many environmental conditions. Third, there is a correlation between gross morphology of plants and features of their natural habitats.

Within single species it was noted that tall plants grew in the lowlands and dwarf plants in the alpine regions. Plants with coarse leaves were found in hot, sunny situations and those with broad, thin leaves were found in the shade. The Stanford group set out to determine whether such variations were heritable, or nonheritable and reversible.

It was soon discovered that a dual approach was necessary in order to determine the nature of the diversity found within a species. First, uniform heredity was studied in varied environments, and second, varied heredity was studied in a uniform environment. In studying effects of varied environments the unit of importance is the individual. To obtain constant heredity, individuals were propagated as clones, so that many observations under different conditions could be made on a single genotype.

If the main objective was to study genetic diversity within a species, larger samples of natural populations were taken for comparison in uniform environment. This was accomplished through the use of the standard-environment transplant method, developed by Turesson (1922b). The California group found, however, that more information could be obtained by rather extensive clonal propagation and establishment of variant forms in several different environments. The application of this method, known as the "reciprocal transplant" technique, has resulted in great advances in our knowledge of ecotypic variability.

TRANSPLANT STATIONS IN CENTRAL CALIFORNIA

Clausen, Keck, and Hiesey (1940) used a California transect extending from the Pacific Ocean in San Mateo County, across the Santa Cruz Mountains to Stanford University in Santa Clara County, then eastward across the Inner Coast Range, the San Joaquin Valley, and the Sierra Nevada to the Great Basin in Mono County at Benton. This transect is illustrated in Figure 4-1. Climatic and altitude conditions for three stations, Stanford, Mather, and Timberline vary greatly.

The climate at Stanford University is mild, typical of the central California coastal region. The elevation is approximately 100 feet, snow is practically unknown, but frost may occur between the first of November and mid-March. The summer and autumn months are dry, the rains being con-

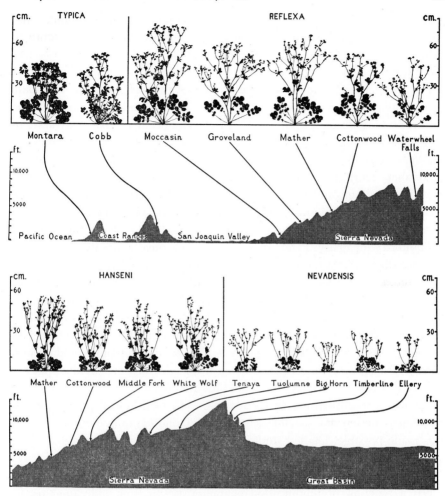

FIGURE 4-1.

Sample plants of populations of Potentilla glandulosa *grown in a uniform garden at Stanford. The populations originated in the localities shown on the profile of a transect across central California at about 38°N. The upper half of the figure shows the western half of the transect; the lower half shows the eastern half extending to the Great Basin plateau.* [*From Clausen and Hiesey, Carnegie Inst. of Wash. Publ. 615, 1958.*]

fined almost entirely to the winter and spring months. Annual rainfall ranges from 25 to 40 cm.

The Mather station is located at an elevation of 4600 feet in the Stanislaus National Forest, Tuolumme County. The summers are mild, with warm days and cool nights, and little or no rain. Autumn is usually cool and dry. Snows begin in October or November and may accumulate to a depth of two or three feet. Spring weather begins early in April, although frosts may occur until June 1.

The Timberline station is located at an elevation of 10,000 feet in Slate Creek Valley in Mono County. This valley is surrounded by peaks of the Sierras ranging up to 12,000 feet. Small glaciers occur on the shady sides of some of the crests, and snow banks persist well into July. Winter snows are not gone until June 20 or later, and the first snowfall usually arrives in September. During the entire year there are from three to six weeks of frost-free weather, and at no time is there any surety that frosts will not occur. Midwinter snows accumulate to depths of 15 or 20 feet. The rigorous climate of the Timberline station is in sharp contrast with the mild climate at Stanford University. Plants of this area are typically alpine.

In handling plants for altitudinal study, the reciprocal transplant method was used. At the time of transfer, herbarium specimens, notes, and often photographs were taken. Transplants were labeled with stakes, contamination prevented by weeding, and the whole experimental area fenced to keep out animals. In transplanting clonal material, plants were divided into as many parts as required, or as many as the size of the plant would permit. Usually, transplants dug in the summer of one season were divided, potted, and were ready for transfer to the field the following spring.

Following transplanting, yearly records were made of all plants, including annual herbarium specimens, notes, and photographs. Permanent records made possible detailed studies of the variability and adaptation of the species investigated.

The three environmental complexes of the three transplant stations produced a reaction or modification characteristic to each individual or, as stated by the Carnegie Institution group, a Stanford, a Mather, and a Timberline modification. These three responses made up a reaction or response pattern of the individual. It was found that related plants from the same or similar environments had similar reactions, while plants from widely different environments showed quite different patterns of response. This made possible a grouping of plants according to their response, or according to their adaptation to given environments.

Cytogenetic investigations were made in an effort to clarify certain relationships. Ordinarily, chromosome numbers are constant within a species, but when relationships between species are studied, differences in chromosome number may indicate barriers of great significance. In studies of polyploidy as related to adaptation, cytogenetic studies were invaluable.

One of the plant groups studied extensively by the Carnegie Institution group was *Potentilla glandulosa*, a species of the rose family commonly known as cinquefoil. The California collections were found to include four major ecotypes: (1) a Coast Range ecotype; (2) a Sierran foothill to mid-altitude ecotype; (3) a subalpine ecotype in the Sierra Nevada from 1500 to 2500 meters; and (4) an alpine ecotype, in the Sierras at 2400 to 3500 meters. These ecotypes differ in many characteristics, especially in their seasonal rhythms and in their response to different environments. The typical forms of three of these are shown in Figure 4-2.

It happens that these four ecotypes belong to three subspecies. The distinction is that a subspecies represents a morphological, geographical, and historical concept based on recognizable differences, while an ecotype represents an ecological concept based on reactions to differences in environment. There may or may not be recognizable morphological differences between ecotypes.

The Coast-Range or maritime ecotype is in active growth throughout the year at the Stanford station. Flowering is early, but is delayed at the higher elevations. The foliage is somewhat frost resistant, which permits it to grow in the cool rainy winters. When transplanted to Mather (4600 feet) there was a reduction in size, but the Coast ecotype tended to survive indefinitely. At the Timberline station (10,000 feet) the Coast ecotype was usually killed during the first winter. If it survived, the growing period was too short for seed ripening, although plants sometimes flowered before frost. Its seasonal rhythm was slower than that of the alpine ecotype.

The Sierran foothill ecotype occurs between 250 and 2200 meters elevation, and plants from the higher elevation tend to be shorter. When transplanted to the station at Stanford, this ecotype had coarser, wider, and darker green leaves, with fewer, stouter, and shorter flowering stems than when grown at Mather. At the Timberline station there was a marked reduction in size and number of herbaceous parts. Plants seldom survived the first winter at this elevation. Seasonal development was modified at the three stations. At Stanford the plants were active most of the year, although activity started later than for plants of the Coast ecotype. At Mather, there was a natural dormancy for about six months, and at Timberline active growth was limited to ten or twelve weeks. The late seasonal rhythm pattern of this ecotype did not permit reproduction at Timberline.

In the region near Mather is a midaltitude ecotype adapted to meadows between 1200 and 1800 meters elevation. Like the foothill ecotype, this meadow race grew best at Mather, but in contrast to the foothill type, it survived at Timberline rather well. At Stanford the meadow ecotype was less vigorous than at Mather, but responded well to irrigation. Its seasonal reaction at Timberline was similar to that of the foothill ecotype, but at

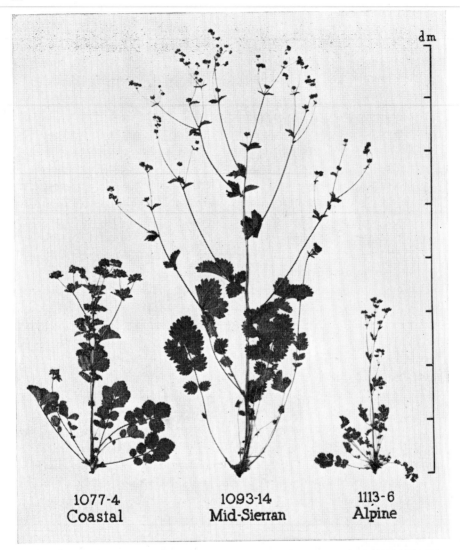

FIGURE 4-2.

Coastal, mid-Sierran, and alpine ecotypes of Potentilla glandulosa *grown in a uniform garden at 4600 feet elevation. [From Clausen and Hiesey, Carnegie Inst. of Wash. Publ. 520, 1940.]*

all stations it flowered later, although the period between flowering and ripening of seed was shorter.

Two distinct altitudinal ecotypes were distinguished in the subalpine and alpine groups. Plants from the higher elevations, 3500 meters or above, were early and small and were classified as alpines. Those from the lower elevations, 2100 to 3000 meters, were considered of the subalpine group. The subalpine ecotype showed many modifications at the different transplant stations, and survived at all three. The alpine form also may survive at all stations, but was rather weak at Stanford. When grown at Timberline many plants of the subalpine ecotype could easily be thought to belong to the same group as the alpines, but when grown at the three transplant stations, it became obvious that the alpine and subalpine groups were different.

Seasonal development is of interest. Alpine plants remained green for nine months or longer at Stanford, and then became dormant from mid-November to mid-February. At Mather, plants remained in active growth for six months and then became dormant. Seed may mature at all stations, but at Timberline the subalpine ecotype often did not mature.

With respect to vigor, it was observed that both alpine and subalpine ecotypes showed a higher index of vigor at Mather than in their native habitat. This would indicate that these plants are better adapted to intermediate than to high elevations. Their absence in the midaltitude areas may be due to their inability to compete with other races. These races in turn are not adapted to the colder climate of the higher altitudes and therefore the alpine forms are able to exist in these habitats because of less competition.

Throughout these studies, two kinds of variation were noticeable, one caused by genetic diversity, the other by environmental modifications. Whenever members of a clone were grown at the three transplant stations, modifications were evident. These might be interpreted on the basis of physiology, that is, the appearance of the plant is the result of the action of environment upon physiological processes, within the genotypic limits of the race, subspecies, or species. Clausen, Keck, and Hiesey (1940) believed that ecotypes as a rule are unable to succeed in environments which are very unlike those of their native habitats.

The character of the plants which occupy a given environment would appear to be determined by natural selection. Differences in temperature, moisture, and light no doubt profoundly influence physiological processes in plants. Success therefore requires that plants be rather well adjusted to their environment. If they are brought into a new environment, their physiological processes will act at a rate determined by the physical conditions of the new environment and by their heredity. If the genetic diversity is such that through natural selection the race or species can become adapted to the new conditions, it may be a success in the new area.

It would appear that cultivated plants are subject to the same physical forces as are wild plants, and that natural selection has resulted in ecotypes

or ecologic races here too, just as it has in wild species. There is one element of considerable difference, however: that of competition. For the most
part, competition has been altered for crop plants, often reduced, and in
some instances nearly eliminated. This means that many varieties developed by man may not have the characteristics essential to survival under
natural conditions.

From the results of the transplant studies, it may be concluded that yield
or vigor is largely dependent on the adjustment between the plant's heredity
and its environment. It is highly important for the plant breeder to develop
new strains fitted to specific environments and levels of management. Thus,
we recognize the importance of testing segregating material in the environments where the new varieties will be grown.

Within an ecotype of *Potentilla glandulosa* (Clausen, Keck, and Hiesey,
1940) considerable variation was observed. This variation included small
differences in growth habit, length of stems, pubescence, leaf size and shape,
petal size and shape, and other characters. These variations were hereditary, indicating genetic diversity within the ecotype. When compared with
differences between ecotypes, these intrapopulation differences were probably of less ecologic significance, but over the long-term evolution within
the species, they may have played an important part.

HYBRIDIZATION OF ECOLOGIC RACES

In a later publication, Clausen and Hiesey (1958) considered in detail the
genetics of ecological races of *Potentilla glandulosa*. Several crosses among
ecologic races were made in the greenhouse, and the resulting F_1 and F_2
progenies observed later under field conditions. One of these, a cross of
Upper Monarch (alpine) × Santa Barbara (coastal) combined the most
strikingly different ecological races found in central California. The parental
races differed in more than 20 describable characters relating to growth
habit, leaf, stem, flower, and fruit characters. Forty-one F_1 plants and 1015
F_2 plants were studied. In most characters the F_1 was intermediate between
the parents, and exhibited a remarkable degree of hybrid vigor when grown
at Stanford (Figure 4-3). A detailed study of segregation of 14 pairs of
characters in the F_2 was made. A typical sample of F_2 progeny grown at
Stanford is shown in Figure 4-4. Judged on the basis of these characters,
neither of the parental types was recovered in the F_2. In a rating of index
values based on 14 characters, the F_2 fell below the index value of the F_1.
When segregation of individual characters was considered, it was found
that transgressive segregation occurred in many instances. The number of

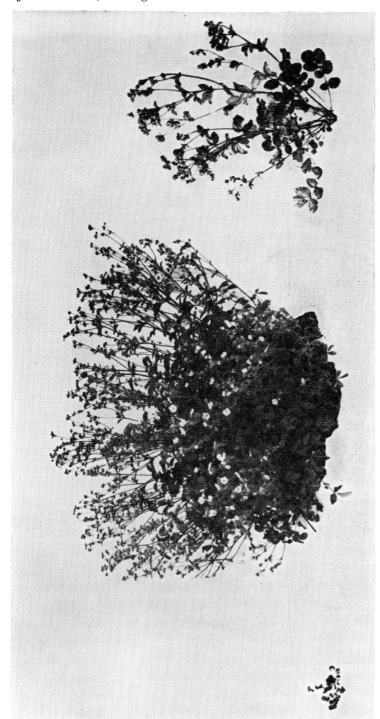

FIGURE 4-3.

Parents Upper Monarch Lake (left) and Santa Barbara (right), and their F₁ hybrid (center) grown at Stanford. [From Clausen and Hiesey—Carnegie Inst. of Wash. Publ. 615, 1958.]

FIGURE 4-4.

> *Modifications in growth of the Timberline ecotype, 1113–6, and Oak Grove ecotype, 1127–1, in three environments at Stanford, Mather, and Timberline. [From Clausen and Hiesey, Carnegie Inst. of Wash. Publ. 615, 1958.]*

genes involved was estimated to be at least 5 pairs, for seed weight, stem length, pubescence, leaf length, anthocyanin, sepal length, petal width, and petal color. This gives some indication of the tremendous genetic diversity obtained by crossing two ecotypes.

One of the most important phases of this work was the observation of response patterns at contrasting altitudes. Another cross involved a subalpine form of *Potentilla glandulosa* from 3050 meters altitude (called Timberline) and a foothills type from 700 meters elevation (known as Oak

Grove). F_1, F_2, and F_3 progeny from Timberline × Oak Grove were grown and studied at Stanford. Also, 578 F_2 plants were established by clonal propagation simultaneously at each of three transplant stations, Stanford, Mather, and Timberline, and their performance in these different environments was studied over a 5- to 9-year period. Modifications in growth of the parents, F_1, and F_2 individuals grown at three elevations are shown in Figures 4-5, 4-6, and 4-7.

Segregation for stem length (as well as for many other characters) showed striking results. Frequency distributions for stem length of 517 cloned plants are shown in Figure 4-7. The F_1 of this cross, Timberline × Oak Grove, was tall but only at the Timberline station (3050 m) did it exceed the tall parent. At Mather and at Stanford the F_1 was intermediate between the parents. It is of interest to note that the Oak Grove parent was short at the two lower elevations, but was the taller of the two parents at the Timberline station.

There was some evidence of transgressive segregation in the F_2 at Timberline, especially in the direction of taller stems. At Mather there was a high degree of transgressive segregation, stem length exceeding the parents in both directions. The relative stem lengths of the parents, F_1, and F_2 of this cross were strikingly different in the different environments. Greatest variability was found at Mather, the intermediate elevation. At the Timberline station, nearly 100 F_2 plants were taller than either parent of the F_1. The foothill parent was unable to develop normally at Timberline, but when crossed with the Timberline strain it transmitted considerable vigor to the hybrid.

Although there was some degree of correlation between stem length of the clones at the three stations, it appears obvious that selection within the F_2 generation would offer quite different possibilities, depending on the elevation at which selection was practiced.

As a result of crossing contrasting ecotypes, several conclusions may be drawn. In some instances, F_1 plants showed a wider range of tolerance than either parent. The F_2 often showed transgressive segregation, with a total range of variability far in excess of that of the parents. Phenotypic modifications due to environmental differences were great. Characters such as stem length, leaf length, seed weight, and general vigor showed a wide range of expression at all altitudes but in general varied greatly with differences in altitude.

It was concluded by Clausen and Hiesey (1958) that the present races of *Potentilla glandulosa* are the products of long-time natural selection and have attained an equilibrium with their environments. As long as the environment remains the same, natural selection will tend to favor maintenance of the present races. If major changes in the environment occur, caus-

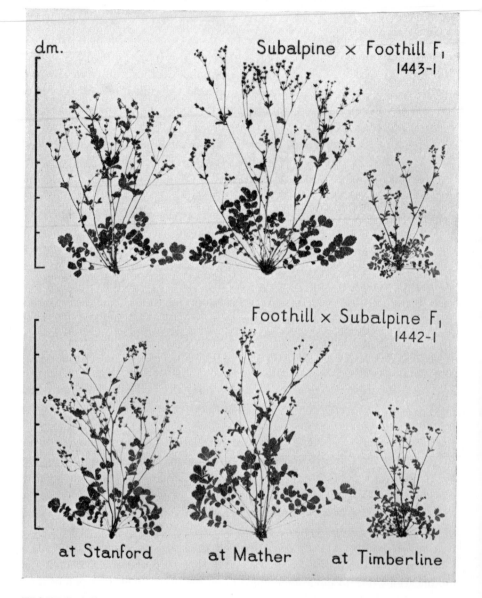

FIGURE 4-5.

Modifications in growth of the F_1 hybrid, Timberline × Oak Grove, and its reciprocal, at Stanford, Mather, and Timberline. Plants are clone members grown at the three transplant stations. [From Clausen and Hiesey, Carnegie Inst. of Wash. Publ. 615, 1958.]

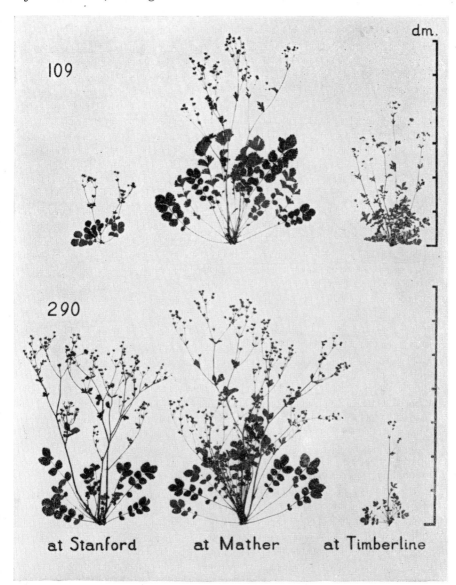

FIGURE 4-6.

Modifications of two F_2 individuals of the cross Timberline $\times$ Oak Grove.
Propagules of each plant were set at the three transplant stations in 1938,
and typical specimens were taken in 1941 and 1942. [From Clausen and
Hiesey, Carnegie Inst. of Wash. Publ. 615, 1958.]

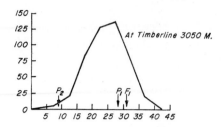

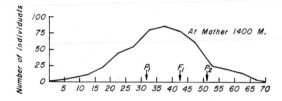

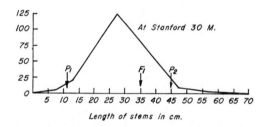

FIGURE 4-7.

Frequency distribution curves showing length of stems of 517 cloned F₂ progeny of Timberline × Oak Grove at the Stanford, Mather, and Timberline transplant stations. [After Clausen and Hiesey, Carnegie Inst. of Wash., Publ. 615, 1958.]

ing changes in selection pressure, the opportunity for intercrossing between ecotypes may increase. This will lead to an increased genetic diversity and new ecological races may arise.

LATITUDINAL RACES

A study of ecologic races of side-oats grama, *Bouteloua curtipendula*, was made by Olmsted (1943, 1944, 1945). This perennial grass species is found scattered over much of the United States, excepting the Pacific Coastal region, from southern Saskatchewan on the north to Mexico on the south. Throughout the western Great Plains states, side-oats grama is a valuable forage grass.

Seeds of 12 strains were obtained from localities between San Antonio, Texas and Cannonball, North Dakota, a range of 17° latitude. All strains were grown at the University of Chicago, and Olmsted found that those from widely differing latitudes were morphologically and physiologically distinct when grown under uniform conditions. This diversity appeared to have a genetic basis, and even within strains there was considerable genetic diversity.

Three strains from southern Texas and southern Arizona showed approximately normal vegetative and flowering behavior when grown under a 13-hour photoperiod similar to that found in their native habitat. Most of the plants in these strains failed to flower normally under 14-hour days (or longer). Some of these bloomed in the autumn under the shorter days prevailing at that time, if frost did not kill them.

A race of side-oats grama from North Dakota showed normal vegetative and flowering behavior only in photoperiods of 14 hours or longer. In shorter days, tillering and vegetative growth were satisfactory. Rhizomes developed and forage yields were fair, but lower than in the North Dakota environment.

Races from Oklahoma and New Mexico, from approximately the center (north and south) of their range of adaptation, showed considerable variation, but the photoperiodic response was correlated with latitude. Individual plants, however, showed an intermediate response to day length, some flowering normally under long days. Olmsted believes that these strains from the latitudinal center of the range have a greater genetic diversity with respect to photoperiod, and may offer greater possibilities of selection for use in different latitudes than do those strains from either the northern or southern parts of the total range. Within their own range, these strains showed response to selection for early and late maturity types.

It is believed that side-oats grama originated in Mexico or southwestern United States, and spread northward as occasional day-neutral plants appeared and survived after enforced migration took populations out of the areas of best adaptation. The typical short-day response of the three southern latitudinal ecotypes represents the original adaptation to short photoperiods characteristic of the low latitudes. Within these ecotypes, however, a few individuals may have been day neutral. This characteristic would be of no importance in their adjustment to their original environment, but may have made possible the migration to higher latitudes in which flowering must occur in longer days.

In the Midwest, ecotypes are found in bromegrass, *Bromus inermis*. Two groups of varieties are most commonly found in the bromegrass region, known popularly as the "Northern" and "Southern" types. Typical of the Southern type are the varieties Achenbach (Kansas), Lincoln (Nebraska) and Fischer (Iowa). The Northern type includes Canadian Commercial, Mandan 404 (North Dakota) and Manchar (Washington). Unpublished data at the Iowa Agricultural Experiment Station indicate that the Southern type can withstand more heat and drought than the Northern type. Data by Evans and Wilsie (1946) suggest that relatively high temperatures and high levels of fertility are essential to obtain satisfactory growth and seed setting of the Southern type, but less essential to obtain satisfactory performance of the Northern type.

Although the origin of these two ecological races, or climatypes, is obscure, it is believed by Zherebina (1931) that both came from Russia. He describes two groups of varieties which appeared to have ecological preferences, (1) a meadow group, and (2) a steppe group. The meadow ecotype was located principally in areas of good moisture conditions from Archangel to the Ukraine and possibly the Caucasus. It was characterized by having ascending culms, soft, drooping leaves, large open panicles, and rhizomes close to the surface of the ground. The steppe ecotype was described as having deeper rhizomes, ascending to erect culms, shorter, narrower, and more rigid leaves, and more compact panicles. There is enough similarity between these basic ecotypes and the American Northern and Southern types to suggest the possibility that the meadow ecotype corresponds with our Northern type and the steppe ecotype corresponds with our Southern type. Natural selection, of course, has had much opportunity to modify these climatypes in North America during the past 60 to 80 years since their introduction.

Yield trials of these varieties, conducted over a latitudinal range from 37° to 49° North, have been reported by Thomas, Hanson and Jacobs (1958). In general the southern varieties outyielded the northern, but the differential was much greater in the southern latitudes than it was at the experimental locations near the northern limits of the range involved. The southern ecotype is apparently more widely adapted within the latitudes of these experiments than is the northern ecotype. In ability to produce seed, the northern ecotype is considerably superior to the southern when grown in Canada, while in Iowa, Kansas, or Nebraska the southern ecotype shows its superiority.

Another example of latitudinal ecological races has been reported by

Vaartaja (1954). Two races of *Pinus sylvestris* and of *Alnus incana* were collected in Finland at 60° 30' and 66° 45' North Latitude, respectively. These trees were grown under two photoperiods in a uniform environment. Under continuous light, the northern ecotype grew better than the more southern one, whereas under a short photoperiod, the reverse was true. The morphological appearance of the northern and southern ecotypes was similar in each species, but the response to photoperiod was a heritable adaptation resulting from generations of natural selection.

Pauley and Perry (1954) have reported on ecotypic variation in response of *Populus* species to photoperiod. The date of height growth cessation appears to be influenced by photoperiod. When grown at the same day length, clonal lines showed marked differences in date of cessation of growth in height. There was a direct correlation between length of frost-free season prevailing in the native home of a clone and the date of its cessation in height growth.

Examples of edaphic ecotypes may be cited. Bradshaw (1960) found marked differences between races of Colonial bentgrass (*Agrostis tenuis*) from contrasting habitats in Wales. Sixty tillers were taken from each of a number of natural populations and transplanted into plots in contrasting environmental sites. A lowland ecotype suffered winter damage under upland conditions. Upland populations suffered from salt spray when transplanted to a lowland coastal habitat. An ecologic race collected from a lead mine area could tolerate lead-contaminated soils, but populations from normal pastures could not. Bradshaw concluded that natural selection had resulted in development of races having differential physiological responses, just as it had resulted in morphological differences.

On certain serpentine soils in California, Kruckberg (1951) found that a unique flora had developed. These soils are high in magnesium, chromium, and nickel, but are especially low in calcium, as well as being deficient in nitrogen, phosphorus, and molybdenum. Certain species of herbaceous plants, *Streptanthus glandulosus, Gilia capitata,* and *Achillea borealis* have developed edaphic ecotypes adapted to serpentine and nonserpentine soils.

In summary of the ecotype concept, it has been shown that natural populations of a species occur in habitats favorable for survival. Among the many genetic variations, certain individuals and even groups appear to possess survival value in specific environments. Over many generations, if different environments are present, a species may become differentiated according to ecological preferences. Variations which appear to have no survival value may be carried on more or less indefinitely providing they do not interfere with the requirements of the species for existence and reproduction.

Genetic differences occur within an ecologic race, if it is a cross-fertilizing species. Still greater differences are likely to occur between two ecotypes. Members of an ecologic race are not homogeneous, and certain biotypes within a race may be better adapted than others. Just as two individual biotypes may differ in their tolerance toward environmental change, so also do different ecotypes vary in their potential response. When two ecotypes are crossed, many new recombinations arise. This may permit survival in new and diverse environments not occupied previously, and may allow the development of new ecologic races.

In any consideration of the distribution of ecological races it is logical to inquire, as did Stebbins (1950), into the nature of the ecotype variability. Is there evidence that different biotypes are grouped into discrete wholly or partially discontinuous groups which may be recognized as ecotypes, or does the observed variability appear to be of a continuous nature? Huxley (1938) has suggested that ecotypic variability may exist in the form of a cline, or character gradient. In the Scotch pine, Stebbins (1950) has cited work of Langlet, Engler, and Burger which indicates clinal variation for chlorophyll content, length of leaves, hardiness, and rapidity of spring growth. Similar continuous variation as related to habitat was found in the sea plantains, *Plantago maritima*, by Gregor, Davey, and Lang (1936). The variability in side-oats grama studied by Olmsted would seem to show clinal variation in photoperiod response.

Both continuous and discontinuous variability would appear to be possible and in fact have been demonstrated in the ecotypic variation in *Potentilla glandulosa* (Clausen and Hiesey, 1958). In species which are widely adapted, and in which pollen is spread long distances by the wind, clinal variation is likely to develop. If pollen dissemination is restricted, and certain types of geographic barriers are important, distinct ecologic races may develop. This would seem to be especially likely in self-fertilizing species. Intraspecific variability of an ecotypic nature is characteristic of most widely distributed species, but the recognition of distinct ecologic races can be expected to vary with the nature of the genetic variability and the nature of the environmental variability.

In introducing a new species into a region where it is not growing, the greatest chances for success will be possible if all known ecotypes can be introduced at the same time. If none of the presently known races is well adapted, hybridization of ecotypes may make possible the selection of new races suited to the new environment. The fact that, when crossed, contrasting ecotypes may produce many new forms emphasizes the existence of a backlog of unused evolutionary resources in the gene pool from which new races capable of fitting into new environmental niches may be developed.

With asexually propagated plants, such as sugarcane, hybrids themselves may have wide adaptation, and sugarcane breeders may take advantage of this directly.

References

1. Bradshaw, A. D. 1960. Population differentiation in *Agrostis tenuis*. III. Populations in varied environments. New Phyt. 59: 92–103.
2. Clausen, J., Keck, D. D., and Hiesey, W. M. 1940. Experimental studies on the nature of species. I. Effect of varied environments on western North American plants. Carnegie Inst. Wash. Publ. No. 520.
3. Clausen, J., and Hiesey, W. M. 1958. Experimental studies on the nature of species. IV. Genetic structure of ecological races. Carnegie Inst. Wash. Publ. No. 615.
4. Evans, Marshall and Wilsie, C. P., 1946. Flowering of bromegrass. *Bromus inermis*, in the greenhouse as influenced by length of day, temperature and level of fertility. *Jour. Amer. Soc. Agron.* 38: 923–932.
5. Gregor, J. W., Davey, V. McM., and Lang, J. M. S. 1936. Experimental taxonomy. I. Experimental garden technique in relation to the recognition of small taxonomic differences. *New Phyt.* 35: 323–350.
6. Huxley, J. S. 1938. Clines: an auxiliary taxonomic principle. *Nature, London,* 142: 219.
7. Kruckberg, A. R. 1951. Intraspecific variation in the response of certain native plant species to serpentine soils. *Amer. Jour. Bot.* 38: 404–419.
8. Mason, H. L., and Stout, P. R. 1954. The role of plant physiology in plant geography. *Ann. Rev. Pl. Phys.* 5: 249–270.
9. Odum, E. P. 1959. *Fundamentals of Ecology.* 2nd ed., Saunders, Philadelphia and London.
10. Olmsted, C. E. 1943. Photoperiodic response in the genus *Boutelouâ. Bot. Gaz.* 105: 165–187.
11. ———. 1944. Photoperiodic responses of 12 geographic strains of side-oats grama. *Bot. Gaz.* 106: 46–74.
12. ———. 1945. Photoperiodic response of clonal divisions of three late strains of side-oats grama. *Bot. Gaz.* 107: 382–401.
13. Pauley, S. S. and Perry, T. O. 1954. Ecotypic variation of the photoperiodic response in *Populus. Jour. Arnold Arbor.* 35: 167–188.
14. Stapledon, R. G. 1928. Ecotypes in relation to the biotic factor. *Jour. Ecol.* 16: 71–104.
15. Stebbins, G. L. 1942. Genetic approach to problems of race and endemic species. *Madrono* 6: 241–258.
16. ———. 1950. *Variation and evolution in plants.* Columbia Univ. Press, New York.
17. Thomas, H. L., Hanson, E. W., and Jacobs, J. A. 1958. Variety trials of smooth bromegrass in the North Central Region. N. C. Regional Publ. No. 93. Minn. Agr. Expt. Sta.
18. Turesson, G. 1922a. The species and variety as ecological units. *Hereditas* 3: 100–113.

19. ———. 1922b. The gentotypical response of the plant species to the habitat. *Hereditas* 3: 211–350.

20. Vaartaja, Olli. 1954. Photoperiodic ecotypes of trees. *Can. Jour. Bot.* 32: 392–399.

21. Zherebina, Z. N. 1931. Botanical-agronomical studies of awnless bromegrass, (*Bromus inermis* Leyss.) *Bul. Appl. Bot. Gen. and Pl. Breed.* 25: 201–352.

Chapter 5

Origin of Cultivated Plants

Many of the crops grown in the United States today were introduced from some other part of the world. This suggests that, in order to utilize the full potential of crop plants, we should know where they came from and something of the range of heritable forms found in each important species. Many of our crops may be varieties which were selected from a minor part of the total genetic diversity available in the species. Through plant introduction, this situation is being given considerable attention.

Some of the ideas on the origin of cultivated plants have been reviewed by Darlington (1956). One of the old beliefs was that cultivated plants came to man as a gift from the gods. Also, there was the belief that the process of cultivation itself improved the heredity of plants taken from the wild. Linnaeus (1787) was concerned with this problem, but did not have sufficient information on which to base a sound theory. In 1807, Alexander von Humboldt (Translation reprinted 1869) said "we know nothing of the original sources of our most useful plants, their origin is an impenetrable secret."

Of the more modern concepts of origin, de Candolle's deserves some attention. In his *Origin of Cultivated Plants*, de Candolle (1882) attempted to make use of earlier information, taking evidence from archaeology, paleontology, history, and philology. He noted three steps between the food gathering stage and the cultivation stage, as follows:

1. The plants must be available.
2. The environment must be favorable.
3. There must be pressure for more food.

De Candolle studied 247 species, including 199 from the old world, 45 from the new world, and 3 about which he was uncertain. He attempted to trace these species back to their wild ancestors, through what he called the "botanical method." Two criteria were used: (1) occurrence of a given cultivated plant in a locality where it also grows wild, or where wild relatives were found; (2) added information from archaeological, historical, and linguistic sources.

This method was, obviously, an oversimplification of the problem of origin. De Candolle considered, for example, that all wheats belonged to two or, at most, not more than four species. He believed that all of the cultivated races of *Brassica* were still to be found in the wild state in Europe or Siberia. He was inclined also to the belief that species changes arose directly through cultivation.

Darwin (1859) showed that connections between the present forms of cultivated plants and their wild forms were in many instances impossible to trace. Ancestral wild plants appeared to him to be exceedingly rare and Darwin suggested that primitive man must have been forced to try to eat "almost anything that he could chew and swallow."

Contributions toward a solution of the problem of origin of cultivated plants were made by Mendel (1865). He believed that studies of variation in cultivated plants could tell us what we need to know about the nature of variability in wild plants. He recognized that plants in nature were subject to the same laws of evolution and genetics which operated in his garden cultures, and that changes in type could take place through natural selection, if the environment changed. Further, Mendel believed that cultivated plants are members of various hybrid series, whose further development is varied and interrupted by frequent intercrossing. He attributed the origin of cultivated plants to their special conditions of hybridization and selection. The close spacing of crop plants tends to facilitate intercrossing among the plants themselves, and with their parental species.

From Darwin's time until about 1920 relatively little progress was made in determining, on an extensive scale, the possible origin of our crop plants. Under the direction of Nikolai Vavilov, one of the greatest investigators in crop geography and genetics of all times, extensive and tremendously diverse collections of crop plants were brought into the U.S.S.R. from various parts of the world. As President of the Lenin Academy of Agricultural Science, and Director of the Institute of Applied Botany, Vavilov had almost unlimited resources at his disposal for the huge task of plant introduction.

Early in this work Vavilov criticized de Candolle's method on the basis that (1) many cultivated species do not occur outside of cultivation, and (2) wild relatives or "progenitors" may represent narrow groups of forms with but a small number of varieties, which are often isolated and which cannot explain the whole diversity by which a cultivated plant is represented.

The first principle established by Vavilov (1951) was that in modern times *"the distribution of plant species on the earth is not uniform."* A number of regions possessed large numbers of varieties. Southeastern China, Indo-China, Malaya, India, Southwestern Asia, Ethiopia, Central America, the Andean region of South America, and southern Mexico have an extraordinary number of plant varieties. Other areas, mostly northern, including Siberia, central and northern Europe, and North America, have very few varieties. A peak of concentration was believed to have been reached in the Caucasus and in the mountains and foothills of Afghanistan and northwest India.

In making a study of the collections of plants, emphasis was placed on the intraspecific composition of plants and on a careful botanical analysis of the varietal composition of certain species. The concept of species was modified somewhat as compared with older views. Vavilov concluded that "the species represents a definite heterogeneous and variable morphological-physiological system, the origin of which is associated with a particular environment and area." Monotypic species were not found; all species were made up of large or small numbers of hereditary forms.

The degree of success attained by Vavilov in locating the principal geographic centers of origin of cultivated plants probably can be attributed to the extensiveness of his plant collections and the thoroughness with which these collections were studied. His "differential phytogeographic method" involved several logical steps and procedures, some of which will be considered.

1. The collections of plants were classified into Linnean species by the use of accepted taxonomic methods. Then they were arranged into genetic groups based on morphological features, fertility relationships, cytological similarities, and reaction to diseases. This step involved the growing of much plant material, and included extensive investigations in breeding, genetics, cytology, and pathology.

2. A detailed determination was made of the nature and degree of variation in morphological and physiological characters in each species, botanical variety, and race.

3. With this botanical information at hand, and the geographical, eco-logical, and climatological data having been obtained from the areas where the plant collections had been made, attempts were made to locate the original areas occupied by these species in the past, before natural migra-tion or transport by man had resulted in a wide geographical distribution. A concentration and great diversity of heritable forms, certain endemic varietal characters, and presence of closely related wild or cultivated forms were considered confirming evidence of probable centers of origin.

Genetically dominant characters were believed to be indicative of origi-nal centers, while recessive forms were thought more likely to occur at the periphery of basic areas.

Any additional bits of information from archaeology, history, or linguistic studies were used as further evidence of origin, but were considered too general to be of much usefulness in themselves.

Based on these principles and the detailed studies of the thousands of forms of plants collected, Vavilov (1926, 1951) recognized six and later eight primary centers of probable origin of cultivated plants. These centers seem to exist. It is not known, however, whether they are truly centers of origin or just centers of great diversity. Harlan (1951a) has suggested that, at least in some instances, they are centers of origination. Vavilov pointed out that in some regions, especially Transcaucasia and adjacent portions of northwest Iran and northeast Turkey, the process of species formation in such plants as wheat, alfalfa, pear, almond, and pomegranate is taking place at the present time. He emphasized also that it is essential to differentiate between primary and secondary centers. In Spain an exceptionally large number of varieties and species was found, but the number of subspecies within the limits of separate species was small compared to the number found in the real centers of initial formation of these species. Another ex-ample might be taken from the cucurbits which have developed a great diversity in Asia Minor. It is not certain whether this diversity is indicative of a primary center of origin or, as Harlan (1951b) concluded, definitely of a secondary center of much later development.

Vavilov believed that he had located rather accurately the basic areas of origin of the primary species of wheat, barley, corn, and cotton, crops grown widely on all continents. He emphasized, however, that the task of deter-mining origin of cultivated plants had only begun. Had he been permitted to continue in this work, he planned more expeditions into Southeast Asia, China, Indo-China, and India in order to locate primary centers of origin with greater accuracy. Figure 5-1 shows the approximate location of Vavi-lov's eight primary centers of origin, and lists of many of the important crop plants from each center are given in the following outline.

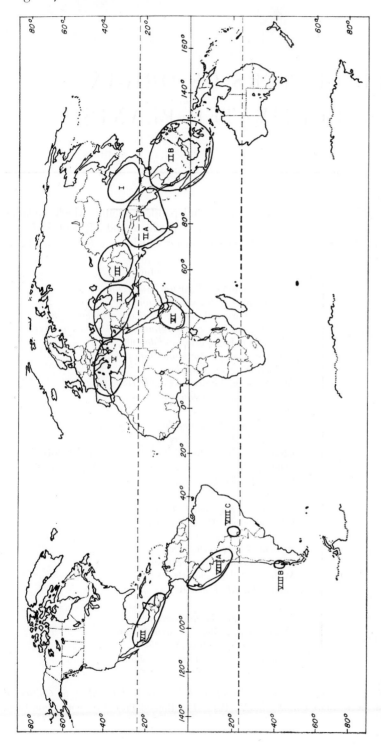

FIGURE 5-1.

Chief world centers of origin of cultivated plants. [*Source: Vavilov, Origin, Variation, Immunity and Breeding of Cultivated Plants. N. Y.: Ronald Press, 1951.*]

WORLD CENTERS OF ORIGIN
OF CULTIVATED PLANTS*

I. CHINESE CENTER: The largest independent center which includes the mountainous regions of central and western China, and adjacent lowlands. A total of 136 endemic plants are listed, among which are a few known to us as important crops.

CEREALS AND LEGUMES	1. Broomcorn millet, *Panicum miliaceum*
	2. Italian millet, *Panicum italicum*
	3. Japanese barnyard millet, *Panicum frumentaceum*
	4. Kaoliang, *Andropogon sorghum*
	5. Buckwheat, *Fagopyrum esculentum*
	6. Hull-less barley, *Hordeum hexastichum*
	7. Soybean, *Glycine hispida*
	8. Adzuki bean, *Phaseolus angularis*
	9. Velvet bean, *Stizolobium hassjoo*
ROOTS, TUBERS, AND VEGETABLES	1. Chinese yam, *Dioscorea batatas*
	2. Radish, *Raphanus sativus*
	3. Chinese cabbage, *Brassica chinensis, B. pekinensis*
	4. Onion, *Allium chinense, A. fistulosum, A. pekinense*
	5. Cucumber, *Cucumis sativus*
FRUITS AND NUTS	1. Pear, *Pyrus serotina, P. ussuriensis*
	2. Chinese apple, *Malus asiatica*
	3. Peach, *Prunus persica*
	4. Apricot, *Prunus armeniaca*
	5. Cherry, *Prunus pseudocerasus*
	6. Walnut, *Juglans sinensis*
	7. Litchi, *Litchi chinensis*
SUGAR, DRUG, AND FIBER PLANTS	1. Sugarcane, *Saccharum sinense*
	2. Opium poppy, *Papaver somniferum*
	3. Ginseng, *Panax ginseng*
	4. Camphor, *Cinnamomum camphora*
	5. Hemp, *Cannabis sativa*

* From N. I. Vavilov, *The Origin, Variation, Immunity and Breeding of Cultivated Plants,* transl. by K. Starr Chester, N. Y., 1951. The Ronald Press Co., with permission.

II. INDIAN CENTER:

A. **Main Center:** Includes Assam and Burma, but not Northwest India, Punjab, nor Northwest Frontier Provinces. In this area, 117 plants were considered to be endemic.

CEREALS AND LEGUMES	1. Rice, *Oryza sativa* 2. Chickpea or gram, *Cicer arietinum* 3. Pigeon pea, *Cajanus indicus* 4. Urd bean, *Phaseolus mungo* 5. Mung bean, *Phaseolus aureus* 6. Rice bean, *Phaseolus calcaratus* 7. Cowpea, *Vigna sinensis*
VEGETABLES AND TUBERS	1. Eggplant, *Solanum melongena* 2. Cucumber, *Cucumis sativus* 3. Radish, *Raphanus caudatus* (pods eaten) 4. Taro, *Colocasia antiquorum* 5. Yam, *Dioscorea alata*
FRUITS	1. Mango, *Mangifera indica* 2. Orange, *Citrus sinensis* 3. Tangerine, *Citrus nobilis* 4. Citron, *Citrus medica* 5. Tamarind, *Tamarindus indica*
SUGAR, OIL, AND FIBER PLANTS	1. Sugar cane, *Saccharum officinarum* 2. Cocoanut palm, *Cocos nucifera* 3. Sesame, *Sesamum indicum* 4. Safflower, *Carthamus tinctorius* 5. Tree cotton, *Gossypium arboreum* 6. Oriental cotton, *Gossypium nanking* 7. Jute, *Corchorus capsularis* 8. Crotalaria, *Crotalaria juncea* 9. Kenaf, *Hibiscus cannabinus*
SPICES, STIMULANTS, DYES, AND MISCELLANEOUS	1. Hemp, *Cannabis indica* 2. Black pepper, *Piper nigrum* 3. Gum arabic, *Acacia arabica* 4. Sandalwood, *Santalum album* 5. Indigo, *Indigofera tinctoria* 6. Cinnamon tree, *Cinnamomum zeylanticum* 7. Croton, *Croton tiglium* 8. Bamboo, *Bambusa tulda*

B. **Indo-Malayan Center:** Includes Indo-China and the Malay Archipelago. Fifty-five plants were listed, including the following:

CEREALS AND LEGUMES	1. Job's tears, *Coix lacryma* 2. Velvet bean, *Mucuna utilis*

FRUITS	1. Pummelo, *Citrus grandis* 2. Banana, *Musa cavendishii, M. paradisiaca, H. sapientum* 3. Breadfruit, *Artocarpus communis* 4. Mangosteen, *Garcinia mangostana*
OIL, SUGAR, SPICE, AND FIBER PLANTS	1. Candlenut, *Aleurites moluccana* 2. Cocoanut palm, *Cocos nucifera* 3. Sugarcane, *Saccharum officinarum* 4. Clove, *Caryophyllus aromaticus* 5. Nutmeg, *Myristica fragrans* 6. Black pepper, *Piper nigrum* 7. Manila hemp or abaca, *Musa textilis*

III. CENTRAL ASIATIC CENTER:

Includes Northwest India (Punjab, Northwest Frontier Provinces and Kashmir), Afghanistan, Tadjikistan, Uzbekistan, and western Tian-Shan. Forty-three plants are listed for this center, including many wheats.

GRAINS AND LEGUMES	1. Common wheat, *Triticum vulgare* 2. Club wheat, *Triticum compactum* 3. Shot wheat, *Triticum sphaerocoecum* 4. Pea, *Pisum sativum* 5. Lentil, *Lens esculenta* 6. Horse bean, *Vicia faba* 7. Chickpea, *Cicer arietinum* 8. Mung bean, *Phaseolus aureus* 9. Mustard, *Brassica juncea* 10. Flax, *Linum usitatissimum* (one of the centers) 11. Sesame, *Sesamum indicum*
FIBER PLANTS	1. Hemp, *Cannabis indica* 2. Cotton, *Gossypium herbaceum*
VEGETABLES	1. Onion, *Allium cepa* 2. Garlic, *Allium sativum* 3. Spinach, *Spinacia oleracea* 4. Carrot, *Daucus carota*
FRUITS	1. Pistacia, *Pistacia vera* 2. Pear, *Pyrus communis* 3. Almond, *Amygdalus communis* 4. Grape, *Vitis vinifera* 5. Apple, *Malus pumila*

IV. NEAR-EASTERN CENTER: Includes interior of Asia Minor, all of Transcaucasia, Iran, and the highlands of Turkmenistan. Eighty-three species were located in this region.

GRAINS AND LEGUMES	1. Einkorn wheat, *Triticum monococcum* (14 chromosomes) 2. Durum wheat, *Triticum durum* (28 chromosomes) 3. Poulard wheat, *Triticum turgidum* (28 chromosomes) 4. Common wheat, *Triticum vulgare* (42 chromosomes) 5. Oriental wheat, *Triticum orientale* 6. Persian wheat, *Triticum persicum* (28 chromosomes) 7. *Triticum timopheevi* (28 chromosomes) 8. *Triticum macha* (42 chromosomes) 9. *Triticum vavilovianum*, branched (42 chromosomes) 10. Two-row barleys, *Hordeum distichum, H. nutans* 11. Rye, *Secale cereale* 12. Mediterranean oats, *Avena byzantina* 13. Common oats, *Avena sativa* 14. Lentil, *Lens esculenta* 15. Lupine, *Lupinus pilosus, L. albus*
FORAGE PLANTS	1. Alfalfa, *Medicago sativa* 2. Persian clover, *Trifolium resupinatum* 3. Fenugreek, *Trigonella foenum graecum* 4. Vetch, *Vicia sativa* 5. Hairy vetch, *Vicia villosa*
FRUITS	1. Fig, *Ficus carica* 2. Pomegranate, *Punica granatum* 3. Apple, *Malus pumilo* (one of the centers) 4. Pear, *Pyrus communis* and others 5. Quince, *Cydonia oblonga* 6. Cherry, *Prunus cerasus* 7. Hawthorn, *Crataegus azarolus*

V. MEDITERRANEAN CENTER: Includes the borders of the Mediterranean Sea. Eighty-four plants are listed for this region.

CEREALS AND LEGUMES	1. Durum wheat, *Triticum durum expansum* 2. Emmer, *Triticum dicoccum* (one of the centers) 3. Polish wheat, *Triticum polonicum* 4. Spelt, *Triticum spelta* 5. Mediterranean oats, *Avena byzantina* 6. Sand oats, *Avena brevis* 7. Canarygrass, *Phalaris canariensis* 8. Grass pea, *Lathyrus sativus* 9. Pea, *Pisum sativum* (large seeded varieties) 10. Lupine, *Lupinus albus*, and others

FORAGE PLANTS	1. Egyptian clover, *Trifolium alexandrinum* 2. White Clover, *Trifolium repens* 3. Crimson clover, *Trifolium incarnatum* 4. Serradella, *Ornithopus sativus*
OIL AND FIBER PLANTS	1. Flax, *Linum usitatissimum,* and wild *L. angustifolium* 2. Rape, *Brassica napus* 3. Black mustard, *Brassica nigra* 4. Olive, *Olea europaea*
VEGETABLES	1. Garden beet, *Beta vulgaris* 2. Cabbage, *Brassica oleracea* 3. Turnip, *Brassica campestris, B. napus* 4. Lettuce, *Lactuca sativa* 5. Asparagus, *Asparagus officinalis* 6. Celery, *Apium graveolens* 7. Chicory, *Cichorium intybus* 8. Parsnip, *Pastinaca sativa* 9. Rhubarb, *Rheum officinale*
ETHEREAL OIL AND SPICE PLANTS	1. Caraway, *Carum carvi* 2. Anise, *Pimpinella anisum* 3. Thyme, *Thymus vulgaris* 4. Peppermint, *Mentha piperita* 5. Sage, *Salvia officinalis* 6. Hop, *Humulus lupulus*

VI. ABYSSINIAN CENTER: Includes Abyssinia, Eritrea, and part of Somaliland. In this center were listed 38 species.

GRAINS AND LEGUMES	1. Abyssinian hard wheat, *Triticum durum abyssinicum* 2. Poulard wheat, *Triticum turgidum abyssinicum* 3. Emmer, *Triticum dicoccum abyssinicum* 4. Polish wheat, *Triticum polonicum abyssinicum* 5. Barley, *Hordeum sativum* (great diversity of forms) 6. Grain sorghum, *Andropogon sorghum* 7. Pearl millet, *Pennisetum spicatum* 8. African millet, *Eleusine coracana* 9. Cowpea, *Vigna sinensis* 10. Flax, *Linum usitatissimum*
MISCELLANEOUS	1. Sesame, *Sesamum indicum* (basic center) 2. Castor bean, *Ricinus communis* (a center) 3. Garden cress, *Lepidium sativum* 4. Coffee, *Coffea arabica* 5. Okra, *Hibiscus esculentus* 6. Myrrh, *Commiphora abyssinicia* 7. Indigo, *Indigofera argente*

VII. SOUTH MEXICAN AND CENTRAL
AMERICAN CENTER: Includes southern sections of Mexico, Guatemala, Honduras and Costa Rica.

GRAINS AND LEGUMES	1. Maize, *Zea mays* 2. Common bean, *Phaseolus vulgaris* 3. Lima bean, *Phaseolus lunatus* 4. Tepary bean, *Phaseolus acutifolius* 5. Jack bean, *Canavalia ensiformis* 6. Grain amaranth, *Amaranthus paniculatus leucocarpus*
MELON PLANTS	1. Malabar gourd, *Cucurbita ficifolia* 2. Winter pumpkin, *Cucurbita moshata* 3. Chayote, *Sechium edule*
FIBER PLANTS	1. Upland cotton, *Gossypium hirsutum* 2. Bourbon cotton, *Gossypium purpurascens* 3. Henequen or sisal, *Agave sisalana*
MISCELLANEOUS	1. Sweetpotato, *Ipomea batatas* 2. Arrowroot, *Maranta arundinacea* 3. Pepper, *Capsicum annuum, C. frutescens* 4. Papaya, *Carica papaya* 5. Guava, *Psidium guayava* 6. Cashew, *Anacardium occidentale* 7. Wild black cherry, *Prunus serotina* 8. Cochenial, *Nopalea coccinellifera* 9. Cherry tomato, *Lycopersicum cerasiforme* 10. Cacao, *Theobroma cacao* 11. *Nicotiana rustica*

VIII. SOUTH AMERICAN CENTER: (62 plants listed)

A. Peruvian, Ecuadorean, Bolivian Center: Comprised mainly of the high mountainous areas, formerly the center of the Megalithic or Pre-Inca civilization.

Endemic plants of the Puna and Sierra high elevation districts included:

ROOT TUBERS	1. Andean potato, *Solanum andigenum* (96 chromosomes) 2. Other endemic cultivated potato species. Fourteen or more species with chromosome numbers varying from 24 to 60. 3. Edible nasturtium, *Tropaeolum tuberosum* Coastal regions of Peru and non-irrigated subtropical and tropical regions of Ecuador, Peru and Bolivia included:
GRAINS AND LEGUMES	1. Starchy maize, *Zea mays amylacea* 2. Lima bean, *Phaseolus lunatus* (secondary center) 3. Common bean, *Phaseolus vulgaris* (secondary center)

| ROOT TUBERS | 1. Edible canna, *Canna edulis* |
| | 2. Potato, *Solanum phureja* (24 chromosomes) |

VEGETABLE CROPS	1. Pepino, *Solanum muricatum*
	2. Tomato, *Lycopersicum esculentum*
	3. Ground cherry, *Physalis peruviana*
	4. Pumpkin, *Cucurbita maxima*
	5. Pepper, *Capsicum frutescens*

| FIBER PLANTS | 1. Egyptian cotton, *Gossypium barbadense* |

FRUIT AND MISCELLANEOUS	1. Passion flower, *Passiflora ligularis*
	2. Guava, *Psidium guajava*
	3. Heilborn, *Carica candamarcensis*
	4. Quinine tree, *Cinchona calisaya*
	5. Tobacco, *Nicotiana tabacum*

B. Chiloe Center (Island near the coast of southern Chile)

1. Common potato, *Solanum tuberosum* (48 chromosomes)
2. Wild strawberry, *Fragaria chiloensis*

C. Brazilian-Paraguayan Center

1. Manioc, *Manihot utilissima*
2. Peanut, *Arachis hypogaea*
3. Rubber tree, *Hevea brasiliensis*
4. Pineapple, *Ananas comosa*
5. Brazil nut, *Bertholletia excelsa*
6. Cashew, *Anacardium occidentale*
7. Purple granadilla, *Passiflora edulis*

From Vavilov's lists, it is apparent that a majority of the cultivated plants appear to have originated in Asia. Of more than 600 plants, approximately 100 originated in the Americas, whereas more than 400 originated in Southern Asia, mainly between 20° and 45° north latitude. It was suggested by Vavilov that these eight primary centers of origin developed independently, although there is a noticeable overlapping of two centers in the Iraq-Iran region.

Within a center of origin there would seem to be smaller centers, which Vavilov spoke of as agro-ecological groups. This idea was extended by Harlan (1951a), who believes that in addition to dividing the area into rather distinct geobotanical areas, even further refinement in variation patterns may be drawn. In Turkish Thrace, a wheat field may contain many forms, including several species, many botanical varieties, and dozens to hundreds of agronomic varieties. Species represented may include *Triticum vulgare, T. durum, T. compactum, T. monococcum, T. spelta,* and others. Wild relatives may be found around the borders, in weed rows, roadsides, and waste spaces. Also, borders may have forms of *Aegilops, Haynaldia,* and wild forms of *Secale.*

This Thracian wheat population appears to be interbreeding, even though many fields are known to be made up of mechanical mixtures. These places, where interbreeding populations are located, Harlan calls gene microcenters. The basic characteristic of such a microcenter is that evolution is proceeding at a rapid rate right now. Gene microcenters are in evidence in Turkey for a number of cultivated plants in addition to wheat, including maize, vetches, lupines, peas, clovers, and several cucurbits. Such evidence, along with that presented by Vavilov in the Caucasus region, suggests active centers of evolution, which over a few centuries could easily be confused with true centers of origin.

LAW OF HOMOLOGOUS SERIES

The general concept of species, as introduced by Linnaeus, has varied greatly in its interpretation by different investigators. The objective in systematics is to arrange in some convenient system all of the morphological and physiological characteristics in an attempt to establish relationships. Species have been divided into subspecies, varieties, and races. Genetic studies have shown the possibility of further divisibility within morphophysiological units.

In considering this problem of classification Lotsy (1916) felt that the Linnean species was collective and heterogeneous in nature, and he preferred designating species, *Linneons.* Then, the next subdivision he proposed was *Jordanons,* in honor of the systematist Jordan. Lotsy reserved the term *species* for genotypes making up genetically homogeneous groups of individuals. Vavilov (1951) noted that this last proposal is contrary to established usage, but he did make full use of the terms Linneons and Jordanons. In the 19th Century, species were considered as ultimate units, whereas in the 20th Century they have been subdivided into a great number of Jordanons, which may be distinguished both morphologically and physiologically.

In studies of the extensive collections of crop plants, Vavilov found that all Linnean species were made up of subspecies, varieties, and races. There were no monotypic species in all of the collections made. In soft wheat, he estimated that there were 3000 Jordanons, distinguishable morphologically and physiologically. Also, there were more than 400 heritable characters determined, which in most cases can combine freely, making possible millions of recombinations.

Thousands of forms were found in barley and oats, and hundreds of forms in rye, corn, beans, peas, flax, cotton, and hemp. Wild species were found to vary no less than tame ones, and there was an amazing similarity of polymorphism in both cross-pollinated and self-pollinated plants.

Vavilov realized that, following the detailed differentiation based on morphology, physiology, and genetics, an integration of this information was essential. Early in his work he recognized that there were certain regularities in the diversity of varieties and races within a species. This concept was not entirely original for, as Vavilov pointed out, the philosophical idea of uniformity in inheritance of organic matter was expressed earlier by Goethe, St. Hilaire, Walsh, Darwin, and others.

The first regularity observed was the similarity in characters which distinguish different varieties and races which make up Linnean species. For example, the parallelism in phenotypic variation among species of the genus *Triticum* may be noted. Wheat species may be grouped into three genetic and geographic types, distinguished on the basis of chromosome number ($2x = 14, 28, 42$).

Group I (42 chromosomes) Basic area: S.W. Asia	*Triticum vulgare*	Vill.
	Triticum compactum	Host.
	Triticum spelta	L.
	Triticum sphaerococcum	Perc.
	Triticum macha	Decap.
	Triticum vavilovianum	Jakub.
Group II (28 chromosomes) Basic area: Abyssinia, Transcaucasus and Mediterranean region	*Triticum durum*	Desf.
	Triticum turgidum	L.
	Triticum polonicum	L.
	Triticum dicoccum	Schr.
	Triticum persicum	Vav.
	Triticum timopheevi	Zhuk.
Group III (14 chromosomes) Basic area: Asia Minor and Transcaucasia	*Triticum monococcum*	L.

For a single species, *Triticum vulgare,* the many varieties and races may be divided into several groups: (1) awned, awnless, and semi-awned forms with bent awns and inflated glumes; (2) white-, grey-, red-, and black-headed forms; (3) forms with hairy glumes and smooth glumes; (4) forms with white or red grains; and (5) winter and spring forms. The species closely related to *T. vulgare*, namely *T. compactum*, *T. spelta*, *T. sphaerococcum*, and *T. macha*, all have exactly the same kind of variations.

In the second group, characterized by 28 chromosomes, the series of characters found in the first group may be repeated. Here too are forms with red, white, or black heads, forms with red or white grains, and winter or spring types. Likewise, a similar pattern of variability exists in the 14-chromosome group, excepting that there are no awnless forms.

In a similar manner Vavilov (1951) showed that among genera such as wheat and rye many examples of parallel variation may be found. In fact, he showed how this kind of homology exists in whole systematic families, such as the grasses or the legumes. On such a basis, then, the Law of Homologous Series was developed (Vavilov, 1922). It may be stated as follows:

(1) Species and genera that are genetically closely related are characterized by similar series of heritable variations with such regularity that knowing the series of forms within the limits of one species, we can predict the occurrence of parallel forms in other species and genera. The more closely related the species and Linneons in the general system, the more resemblance will there be in the series of variations.

(2) Whole families of plants in general are characterized by definite cycles of variability occurring through all genera and species making up the family.

It would be difficult indeed to evaluate the importance of Vavilov's work in determining world centers of origin of cultivated plants. Some investigators have criticized his conclusions on the basis that insufficient information made it impossible to distinguish basic centers from secondary centers. This is suggested with reference to many of the cucurbits, considered by Vavilov to have originated in Asia Minor. In the view of Harlan (1951b) these plants came from the Americas and would represent only a rather late secondary center in Asia Minor. Schiemann (1951) has suggested that evidence points to the Caucasus as the center of origin of hexaploid wheats, Helbaek (1959) and Whyte (1959) favored the foothill areas of the Near East, whereas Vavilov and Kihara (1959) leaned toward the Hindu Kush region as the basic center. These discrepancies are to be expected where gaps in evidence are so great. No one else has yet suggested a classification of origin of such a large number of crops with anything like the degree of completeness attained by Vavilov. He would have been the first to agree that the task was not finished, and his writings show that he expected to add to and modify his conclusions as more information became available.

PROBABLE DATES OF DOMESTICATION

A growing body of evidence indicates that we may some day be able to estimate rather accurately the time when man first began to cultivate plants instead of just gathering the harvest wherever it happened to grow. With the development of radiocarbon dating (Libby, 1955), some rather realistic estimates have become possible.

The Near East is of special interest in any consideration of domestication of food plants. This region includes, roughly, the area extending from the Libyan-Egyptian border on the west to the Baluchi Hills above the Indus Valley on the east. Sometimes the Indus Valley, Transcaucasia, and Greece are included. The central core of the region, however, is the drainage basin

FIGURE 5-2.

Map of the "fertile crescent" of the Near East showing positions of sites for which radiocarbon determinations have been made. Modern cities are underlined. The "hilly flanks" natural habitat zone follows an arc from Kurdistan to north of the city of Diyarbekir, to Cilicia, and down the Syro-Palestinian littoral. [After Braidwood, Science 127:1421, 1958.]

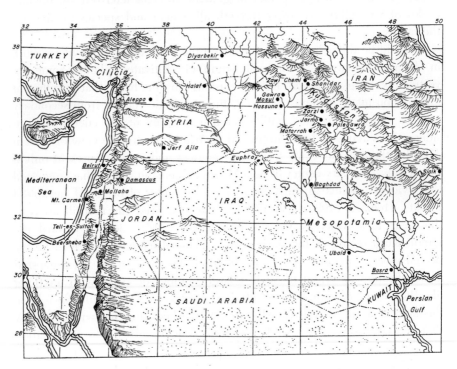

of the Tigris and Euphrates rivers, and the highlands and plateaus immediately adjacent to this basin (Figure 5-2).

According to Braidwood (1958), three great cultural-historical events occurred in the Near East which were of profound importance to the development of man: (1) The earliest appearance of the blade-tool tradition, about 40,000 years ago; (2) the earliest appearance of the settled village farming community based on small grain and animal domestication, about 10,000 years ago; and (3) the appearance of urban civilization in Mesopotamia about 5500 years ago, and just slightly later in Egypt.

During the course of field diggings conducted by the archeological-botanical scientists at Jarmo, Iraq, in a project sponsored by the Oriental Institute of the University of Chicago, certain materials were found which aid greatly in dating early plant culture. Jarmo is located in the Kurdish foothills, between Mosul and Sulimaniya. Remains of a number of settled village sites were found, the most ancient of which was believed to be one of the earliest settled village-farming communities in that part of the world.

The material recovered at Jarmo, discussed by Braidwood (1958) and Helbaek (1959), consisted of imprints of grains and spikelets in baked clay and adobe, as well as carbonized grains and seeds and spikelets. The estimated date of Jarmo, as determined by the radiocarbon method, is about 7000 B.C. Evidence of three cereal grains was found:

1. Two-row barley—similar to the wild *Hordeum spontaneum* but showing some evidence of advance toward modern two-row barley.

2. Diploid wheat—similar to the wild wheat *Triticum aegilopoides* or possibly intermediate between that species and einkorn, *T. monococcum*.

3. Tetraploid wheat—similar to the wild form *T. dicoccoides* and somewhat like emmer, *T. dicoccum*.

The barley kernels were hulled, straight, and unwrinkled, with spikes of the two-row type. Lateral florets were not sessile as in modern two-row barley, but had short pedicels. In general the Jarmo barley resembled the wild, two-row *Hordeum spontaneum*, which is naturally distributed widely over the Near East. Some evidence of domestication was found, however, because the spike was not as brittle as in the wild form, but had attained a degree of toughness with less susceptibility to shatter when ripe. There was no evidence of six-row barley, and Helbaek believes that this form may have arisen in cultivation when barley was moved from the mountainous habitat to the irrigated plains at lower elevations. Mutation from the two-row to six-row form has been demonstrated in recent years as a response to radiation (Nybom, 1954).

Of the two wheats found at Jarmo, the tetraploid type, similar in appearance to *T. dicoccoides,* probably was of greatest interest. Some of the large grain specimens appeared to be a more advanced type, similar to domesticated emmer, *T. dicoccum.* Here were wild species which still occur in the Kurdish foothills today, but which showed significant advance toward the modern domesticated type as early as 9000 years ago. Helbaek emphasizes the fact that the appearance of wild cereals at Jarmo was the earliest in any known cultural context. Grains and fragments of glumes of the related genus *Aegilops* also were recovered from the Jarmo deposits.

At another site in the Kurdish uplands, but at lower elevation, evidences of cultivated emmer only (dated 6000 B.C.) were found. In the upper Tigris-Euphrates region a sprinkling of einkorn, *T. monococcum,* derived from *T. aegilopoides,* was believed to be present. In the fifth millennium B.C. the alluvial plain of Iraq was colonized. Emmer apparently adjusted itself to the new ecology of irrigated land, but einkorn did not. At this time there was no evidence that hexaploid wheats were known.

Helbaek has emphasized the principle that the locus for domestication of the wild plant must necessarily be its area of natural distribution. In the primary Old World agrarian cultures, both barley and wheat were grown extensively. Thus, Helbaek believes that the center of emergence of the wheat-barley cultures must be the common area of distribution of the two plant species. The wild species *Hordeum spontaneum,* the probable progenitor of cultivated barley, is distributed widely from Turkestan to Morocco. The large-grained wild wheat, *Triticum dicoccoides,* however, grows only in small natural areas within this great territory. Accordingly to Helbaek, therefore, the cradle of Old World plant husbandry probably lies within the general area of the arc (or fertile crescent) constituted by the western foothills of the Zagros Mountains (Iraq-Iran), the Taurus (southern Turkey), and the Galilean uplands (Northern Palestine). Levels or eras of food-getting practices in this region and a possible time scale for these events are shown in Figure 5-3.

In order to domesticate wheat, Helbaek suggests that it had to be moved from its natural habitat on mountain slopes between 2000 and 4300 feet above sea level, to more level areas at lower altitudes. This forced movement by man probably resulted in the emergence of mutations, hybridization, and changes in the genetic composition of the cultivated forms. Natural selection in cultivation probably favored individuals which had little chance of survival in the original habitat. Thus, it became possible for the domesticated type of wild *Triticum dicoccoides* named *T. dicoccum* to develop. From this species other species of wheat are derived, excepting einkorn, *T. monococcum,* which appear to be the progeny of the wild wheat, *T. aegilopoides.* Neither emmer nor einkorn was able to survive in

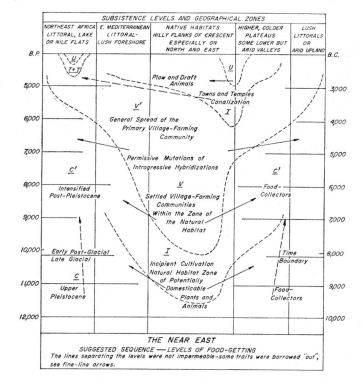

FIGURE 5-3.

Levels or eras of food-getting practices in the Near East with respect to geographical regions and times as determined by radioactive carbon dates for the range from circa 5000 to 12000 years ago. [After Braidwood, Science *127:1425, 1958.]*

the wild, probably because of the loss of competitive ability caused by loss of their ability to disperse.

The spread of these early-known grains to Europe began very early, probably by the end of the fifth millennium B.C. By the third millennium B.C., emmer and einkorn had spread to Switzerland, France, Italy, Spain, Britain, Central Europe north of the loess belt, and Scandinavia, as well as to the west coast lands of the Black Sea and into southern Russia.

The hexaploid wheats including *T. spelta,* club wheat (*T. compactum*), and the common bread wheat (*T. vulgare*) probably originated from a cross of emmer and the wild grass *Aegilops squarrosa.* Evidence of club wheat was found in Egypt late in the fifth millennium B.C., and in Switzerland during the third millennium B.C. In Iraq, evidence was found for the cultivation of *T. vulgare* about 3000 B.C. and club wheat about 2000 B.C. Helbaek believes that club wheat may have arisen as a hybrid in Asia Minor, but because of unfavorable surroundings it may have disappeared, only to reappear again at a somewhat later time.

In the Fayum A deposits of lower Egypt, emmer and barley were found, but this was somewhat later than the Jarmo dates (Braidwood, 1952). Also, evidence of cultivation in central Iran and the Indus Valley, at a date perhaps 1000 years later than at Jarmo, has been found. In the fifth millennium B.C. it is believed that flax was grown in the Kurdish foothills and on the plains of Mesopotamia and Egypt. Much later, probably about 1000 B.C., oats came into cultivation, and rye is considered to be of considerably later origin.

EARLY CULTIVATION IN THE AMERICAS

The big-game hunting pattern, prevalent in North America during the later stages of Wisconsin glaciation, is believed to have become widely disseminated through Central America and South America during the period of 9000 to 5000 B.C. (Willey, 1960). Following the glacial retreat and the climatic shift to increased warmth and dryness, modified hunting patterns developed. Populations in some areas were forced into new subsistence patterns of food collecting. The change from food collecting to plant cultivation apparently required a long time, possibly 5000 years. In the Americas, according to Willey, there were four distinct traditions of incipient farming. Two of these are Nuclear American.[*] The northern one, the probable propagator of maize, was located in Middle America (Mexico-Guatemala) and in the adjacent deserts of Northern Mexico and Southwestern United States; the southern one had its center on the Peruvian coast. A third incipient-cultivation tradition centered in the tropical forests of the Amazon or Orinoco. A fourth, and distinctly lesser tradition developed in eastern North America in the Mississippi Valley system. A schematic chart indicating subsistence and settlement type levels in native America is presented in Figure 5-4.

One of the oldest evidences of cultivation in Middle America is that of the Infiernillo phase, dating from 7000 to 5000 B.C. In the semiarid hill country of Tamaulipas, deposits in dry caves have revealed traces of domesticated squash and of possible domesticates of peppers, gourds, and

[*] Nuclear America includes the southern two-thirds of Mexico, all of Central America, and Andean and coastal Colombia, Ecuador, and Peru, with adjacent portions of Bolivia.

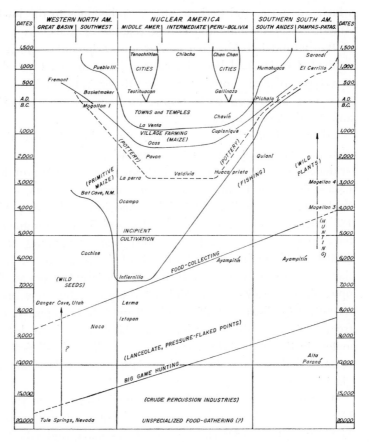

FIGURE 5-4.

Subsistence and settlement type levels in native America: a cross section for western North America, Nuclear America, and southern South America. [After Willey, Science 131:74, 1960.]

small beans. According to Kaplan and MacNeish (1960), runner beans, *Phaseolus coccineus*, were known, but probably not domesticated 7500 to 9000 years ago. The common bean *P. vulgaris* is believed to have been cultivated 4300 to 6000 years ago in that region of Mexico.

The origin and history of the development of maize is of great interest to agricultural science. Two places of possible origin have been suggested, the Mexico-Guatemala region and the Peru-Bolivia-Ecuador region. Mangelsdorf and Reeves (1938, 1939) and Mangelsdorf (1947) proposed a theory of origin known as the "tripartite hypothesis" which may be stated as follows: (1) cultivated maize originated from a wild form of pod corn which was once, and perhaps still is, indigenous to the lowlands of South America; (2) teosinte, the closest relative of maize, is a recent product of the natural hybridization of *Zea* and *Tripsacum*, which occurred after cultivated maize had been introduced by man into Central America; (3) new types of maize originating directly or indirectly from this cross and exhibiting admixture with *Tripsacum* comprise the majority of Central and North American varieties.

Other evidence has accumulated since the tripartite theory of origin of maize was published. In the explorations of Bat Cave in New Mexico, evidences of maize were found to an average depth of five or six feet (Mangelsdorf and Smith, 1949). Six successive layers, each one foot in thickness, were studied. Materials found included 766 specimens of cobs, 125 kernels, 8 husks, 10 leaf sheaths, and 5 tassel fragments. These materials represented a period of 3000 years, beginning approximately in 3600 B.C. Through a careful analysis of the successive strata, it was found that there was a progressive increase in variability from stratum to stratum upward. The ancient types did not disappear, but new ones arose. More recently, Barghoorn, Wolfe, and Clisby (1954) reported on cores taken from borings at different depths at Mexico City. At levels from 69–70 meters in the Belle Artes core, there were large fossil pollen grains which resembled those of maize. Carbon dating places these in early Wisconsin glacial time.

Weatherwax (1954) noted that in much more recent times (pre-Columbian days) there were three principal centers of cultivation of corn: (1) Mexican plateau, (2) Yucatan and Guatemala, and (3) Peru. These appear to correspond to the three great civilizations of early America:

1. The Aztec, which reached its greatest height in the highlands of Mexico in the 15th century A.D.

2. The Mayan, which flourished from 600 B.C. to 600 A.D., declined and moved to northern Yucatan, then rose again from 964 to 1191 A.D.

3. The Incaic, which developed in Peru during the period 0 to 1000 A.D.

Weatherwax and Randolph (1955) favored the view of Vavilov that maize probably originated in Mexico or Central America. They pointed out that the fossil pollen of *Zea, Euchlaena,* and *Tripsacum* found in the Belle Artes core in Mexico City was well preserved and easily identified. *Zea* and *Tripsacum* pollens were found at the lowest depth, about 200 feet, but teosinte pollen was not found below 10 or 12 feet. Large pollen grains similar to those of modern corn were found at 200 feet. This would appear to be proof that maize was indigenous to the Mexican region. The present center of diversity also seems to be in the Mexican area. Weatherwax and Randolph believe that evidence favors an independent origin of the three genera, *Zea, Euchlaena,* and *Tripsacum.* They have noted further that while natural hybrids of maize and teosinte have been found in Mexico and Guatemala, there is no evidence of natural hybridization between maize and *Tripsacum,* nor between teosinte and *Tripsacum.*

In a recent recapitulation of evidence of time and place of origin of maize, Mangelsdorf and Reeves (1959) noted that there is substantial proof of origin in the Americas, especially through identification of fossil pollen in the Valley of Mexico by Barghoorn, *et al.* (1954). It is suggested further that the place of origin may be Middle America, instead of South America as previously proposed, and that the date of origin of cultivated maize may be somewhere in the vicinity of 5000 to 6000 years ago.

Additional information bearing on the origin and diversity of maize has been presented by many workers, including Anderson and Cutler (1942), Carter and Anderson (1945), Brown and Anderson (1948), and Wellhausen, Roberts and Hernandes (1952).

In addition to the common crops of American origin, Sauer (1950) calls attention to the extensive use of the grain amaranths. There were many species of New World origin which spread throughout the world. One of these, *Amaranthus leucocarpus,* was especially desirable as a food crop. Seeds were fairly small, but yield was good. Seeds were parched or popped for eating. They were made into balls with syrup, ground into meal, made into cakes, and mixed into drinks. The large compound heads had many seeds, and the total yield often surpassed that of maize. Grain amaranths were of great importance as a food crop at the time of the conquest of Mexico.

THEORY OF PLANT INTRODUCTION

As emphasized by Vavilov (1951), crop plants originally were not distributed uniformly throughout the world. Many of the agricultural achievements of the United States and Canada, for example, have been made possible through the introduction and development of crops which originated in Asia, Europe, Africa, and South America. In a similar way it can be said that the economy of practically every country has been influenced markedly by plant introduction. Even in areas well supplied with a wide genetic diversity of a given crop, great benefits have been obtained through exchange of breeding materials with research workers in other countries.

Man's role in plant migration has indeed been so great that, as

Darlington (1956) has suggested, centers of diversity have changed from time to time. Heaviest production of important crop species may be found in areas quite removed from centers of origin. For example, the United States produces a higher percentage of the world's corn crop, but this tropical species originated in Middle America (Mexico-Guatemala) or in Northern South America. Much of the world's rubber is produced in the Malayan region, but the rubber tree, *Hevea braziliensis,* is a South American native. Similarly, coffee has become a most important crop in the New World, but is presumably of African origin.

Plant exploration and introduction in the United States is an important function of the New Crops Research Branch, Agricultural Research Service, U. S. Department of Agriculture. Four federal introduction stations are maintained, at Glenn Dale, Maryland, Savannah, Georgia, Miami, Florida, and Chico, California. The station at Glenn Dale serves as the plant quarantine station.

In addition to the federal stations, there are four regional plant introduction stations located at Geneva, New York, Experiment, Georgia, Ames, Iowa, and Pullman, Washington. These stations are operated in cooperation with the State Agricultural Experiment Stations and serve as centers for the introduction, increase, preliminary evaluation, and distribution of introduced plant materials. After preliminary screening, introductions are made available to plant breeders and other interested workers for further evaluation and possible use as breeding materials or as potential new crops.

The work of Vavilov has been invaluable to plant introduction work. Plant breeders, for example, look to early centers of diversity for possible resistance to disease and other environmental hazards. It appears likely that even now, with all of the introduction work that has taken place, we have still sampled but a small part of the total genetic diversity available in most of our crop plants.

Climatic and edaphic conditions have been given increasing attention in plant introduction work. Shortly after the close of World War II, the importance of this aspect of introduction was brought to sharp focus. To aid in rehabilitation of war-devastated areas, great quantities of seed and other plant materials were shipped from the United States. While mistakes probably were made, a strong effort was exerted to send materials to areas having similar climatic conditions. For example, California wheats were rather successful in Greece and certain small grain and corn varieties from the Midwest were well adapted to areas in Yugoslavia.

To further this agro-ecological approach, a series of publications was prepared by Nuttonson (1947–1950) on ecological crop geography and agroclimatic analogues. Climatic analogues were defined as "areas suf-

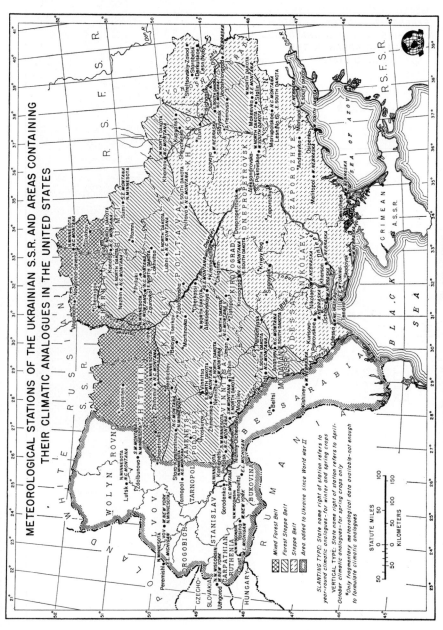

FIGURE 5-5. *Climatic and vegetational areas of the Ukraine, together with approximate climatic analogues in the United States.* [From Nuttonson, Amer. Inst. Crop Ecol., Study No. 1, 1947.]

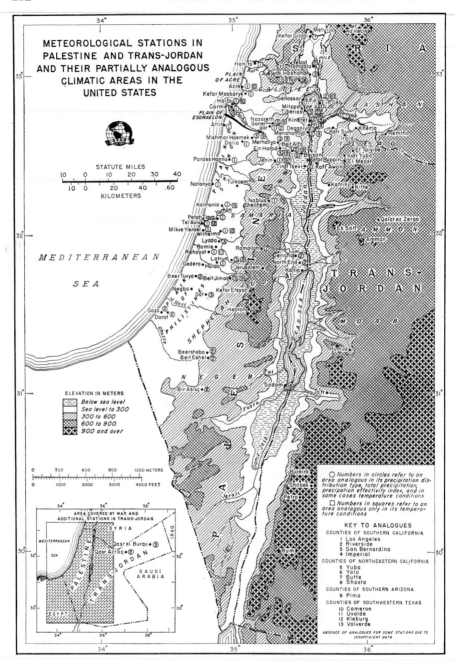

FIGURE 5-6.

Meteorological stations in Palestine and Trans-Jordan, and their partially analogous climatic areas in the United States. [Courtesy of American Institute of Crop Ecology and U. S. Dept. of Agriculture, Foreign Agricultural Service.]

ficiently alike with respect to major weather characteristics affecting crop production, to offer a fair chance for success of plant material transplanted from one area to its climatic counterpart." Figure 5-5 shows approximate United States climatic analogues for the Ukraine and Figure 5-6 for Palestine and Trans Jordan.

In many instances climatic analogues for "winter" and "spring" crops were given because of the fact that in general the climate of Europe is cooler in summer and milder in winter than in much of the United States.

This effort by Nuttonson and others, under the auspices of the American Institute of Crop Ecology, has given considerable stimulation to a fuller recognition of the importance of learning as much as possible about the climatic and soil conditions of areas where exchanges of plant materials are contemplated.

A consideration of some of the important aspects of plant introduction has been presented by Whyte (1959). He proposes a well-coordinated international approach as the only way in which plant introduction can be made effective for all countries interested without swamping introduction laboratories with vast collections of plant material. Better cooperation between the country receiving collections and the country where collections are being made is urgently needed. This involves close collaboration of specialists in the various aspects of crop science during collection, and as thorough an understanding as is possible of the diversity of the species collected, related wild species, and primitive forms which may still be in existence.

References

1. Anderson, E. and Cutler, H. C. 1942. Races of *Zea Mays:* 1. Their recognition and classification. *Ann. Mo. Bot. Gard.* 29: 69–89.
2. Barghoorn, E. S., Wolfe, M. K. and Clisby, K. H. 1954. Fossil maize from the Valley of Mexico. *Bot. Mus. Leaf.*, Harvard University 16: 229–240.
3. Braidwood, R. J. 1952. *The Near East and the Foundation for Civilization.* Univ. Ore. Press, Eugene, Oregon.
4. ———. 1958. Near East prehistory. *Sci.* 127: 1419–1430.
5. Brown, W. L. and Anderson, E. 1948. The southern dent corns. *Ann. Mo. Bot. Gard.* 35: 255–268.
6. Carter, G. F. and Anderson, E. 1945. A preliminary survey of maize in southwestern United States. *Ann. Mo. Bot. Gard.* 32: 297–322.
7. Darlington, C. D. 1956. *Chromosome Botany.* Geo. Allen and Unwin, Ltd., London.
8. Darwin, Chas. 1859. *Origin of Species by Means of Natural Selection.* Reprinted by Philosophical Library, New York.

9. de Candolle, Alphonse. 1882. *Origin of Cultivated Plants*. Appleton, New York.

10. Harlan, Jack. 1951a. Anatomy of gene centers. *Amer. Nat.* 85: 97–103.

11. ———. 1951b. New World crop plants in Asia Minor. *The Sci. Mo.* 72: 87–89.

12. Helbaek, H. 1959. Domestication of food plants in the Old World. *Sci.* 130: 365–371.

13. Humboldt, Alexander von. 1869. *Views of Nature*. Transl. by Otté and Bohn. Bell and Daldy, London.

14. Kaplan, L. and MacNeish, R. S. 1960. Prehistoric bean remains from caves in the Ocampo region of Tamaulipas, Mexico. *Bot. Mus. Leaf.*, Harvard University 19 (2): 33–56.

15. Kihara, H. 1959. *Japanese* expeditions to the Hindu Kush. *Proc. 1st Inter. Wheat Gen. Symp.*, Aug. 11–15, 1958. Winnipeg.

16. Libby, W. F. 1955. *Radiocarbon Dating*. University of Chicago Press, Chicago.

17. Linnaeus (Linné), Carl von. 1787. *The Families of Plants*. Transl. from *Genera Plantarum* by a Botanical Society of Lichfield. Pr. by J. Jackson, Lichfield.

18. Lotsy, L. P. 1916. *Evolution by Means of Hybridization*. M. Nijhoff, The Hague, Netherlands.

19. Mangelsdorf, P. C. 1947. The origin and evolution of maize. *Adv. Gen.* 1: 161–207.

20. ——— and Recves, R. G. 1938. The origin of maize. *Proc. Nat. Acad. Sci.* 24: 203–312.

21. ———. 1939. The origin of Indian corn and its relatives. Texas Agr. Exp. Sta. Bul. 574.

22. Mangelsdorf, Paul and Smith, C. E. 1949. New archaeological evidence on evolution of maize. *Bot. Mus. Leaf.*, Harvard University 13: 213–247.

23. Mangelsdorf, P. C. and Reeves, R. E. 1959a. The origin of corn. 1. Pod corn the ancestral form. *Bot. Mus. Leaf.*, Harvard University 18 (7): 329–356.

24. ———. 1959b. The origin of corn. 3. Modern races, the production of teosinte introgressing. *Bot. Mus. Leaf.*, Harvard University 18 (9): 389–411.

25. ———. 1959c. The origin of corn. 4. Place and time of origin. *Bot. Mus. Leaf.*, Harvard University 18 (10): 413–440.

26. Mendel, Gregor. 1865. *Experiments in Plant Hybridization*. Verh. naturf. Ver. in Brunn. Abhandlungen IV. English translation by Harvard University Press, Cambridge, 1925.

27. Nuttonson, M. Y. 1947–50. Ecological Crop Geography of the Ukraine (and others). Inter. Agro. Clim. Series. Studies 1–13. Amer. Inst. Crop Ecol., Washington, D. C.

28. Nybom, Nils. 1954. Mutation types in barley, *Acta Agr. Scand.* 4: 430–442.

29. Reeves, R. E. and Mangelsdorf, P. C. 1959. The origin of corn. 2. Teosinte. A hybrid of corn and *Tripsacum*. *Bot. Mus. Leaf.*, Harvard University 18 (8): 357–387.

30. Sauer, Jonathan. 1950. The grain amaranths: A survey of their history and classification. *Ann. Mo. Bot. Gard.* 37: 561–632.

31. Schiemann, Elizabeth. 1951. New results on the history of cultivated cereals. *Heredity* 5: 305–320.

32. Vavilov, N. I. 1922. The law of homologous series in variation. *Jour. Gen.* 12: 47–89.

33. ———. 1926. Studies on the origin of cultivated plants. *Inst. Appl. Bot. and Pl. Breed.*, Leningrad.

34. ———. 1951. *The Origin, Variation, Immunity and Breeding of Cultivated Plants*. Ronald, New York.

35. Weatherwax, Paul. 1954. *Indian Corn in old America*. Macmillan, New York.

36. —— and Randolph, L. F. 1955. History and origin of corn. In *Corn and Corn Improvement,* G. F. Sprague, ed. Academic, New York.
37. Wellhausen, E. J., Roberts, L. M., and Hernandes, X. E. 1952. Races of maize in Mexico. *Bussey Inst.* Harvard University.
38. Willey, Gordon R. 1960. New World prehistory. *Sci.* 131: 73–86.
39. Whyte, R. O. 1959. International approach to plant exploration and introduction. *Euphytica* 8: 196–208.

Ecosystems

Plants, like animals and other organisms, ordinarily do not live alone in nature. Instead, they are associated together in biotic communities. The biotic community has been described by Odum (1959) as a functional unit, held together by the interdependence of its members. It is composed of smaller groups or populations whose members are more intimately associated with each other. Populations are usually considered to be composed of individuals of the same species, but other groups such as races, ecotypes, and varieties also may be considered as having ecological unity.

The ecology of populations and communities is often spoken of as **synecology,** in contrast to **autecology** which deals with relationships between the individual, or species, and its environment. The physical conditions of the habitat must also be taken into consideration in population and community ecology. The dynamic whole, formed by the habitat and the associated living organisms that occupy it, is known as the **ecosystem.** In the ecosystem, the living organisms and their nonliving environment are inseparably related and are constantly interacting with each other. Odum (1959) has suggested that any area of nature that includes living organisms and nonliving substances interacting to produce an exchange of materials between the living and nonliving parts constitutes an ecosystem. Thus a forest, a lake, a field, or a pond may be considered an ecosystem.

The complexity of the environment has been emphasized. Its factors act singly, together, and, above all, in a holocoenotic manner upon plants and animals. At the same time, it is recognized that the living organisms, in turn, react upon their environment, often producing marked modifications.

From the functional viewpoint, the ecosystem has two components: (1) an **autotrophic,** or self-nourishing component, in which light energy is fixed, simple organic substances used, and complex substances built up; and (2) a **heterotrophic** component, in which utilization, rearrangement, and decomposition of complex materials predominate.

Every ecosystem is comprised of four elements (Odum, 1959): (1) *abiotic substances,* basic inorganic and organic compounds of the environment; (2) *producers,* autotrophic organisms, mainly green plants, which manufacture food from simple inorganic substances; (3) *consumers,* heterotrophic organisms, chiefly animals, which ingest other organisms or parts; (4) *decomposers,* heterotrophic organisms, mainly bacteria and fungi, which break down the complex compounds of dead protoplasms, absorb some of the products of decomposition, and release simple substances usable by the producers.

The ecosystem appears to be the basic functional ecological unit. Villar (1929) has classified ecosystems into 25 categories, based upon the nature of the substratum, first order of response, harmony of controls, nature and quantity of control, and the ultimate order of response. On geophysical substrata, examples of different kinds of ecosystems include lakes, ponds, marshes; sea, salt lakes; tropical rainforest, deciduous forest, Mediterranean forest; desert, savanna, tundra; seashore, bogs, dunes, crevices, yards, railways, and bird cliffs. Those on organic substrata include logs under water, rotting logs, bark of trees, living wood, and intestines of animals.

Odum (1959) suggested that in a small pond the basic components of the ecosystem might be:

1. *Abiotic substances:* water, carbon dioxide, calcium, nitrogen, phosphorus, salts, etc. Some of the nutrients are in solutions, but a large portion is held in solid form, especially in bottom sediments, as well as in the organisms themselves. The rate of release of nutrients is important in regulating the rate of function of the whole ecosystem.

2. *Producer organisms:* rooted or large floating plants, growing in shallow water, and minute floating plants, the phytoplankton algae. In lakes and large ponds, phytoplankton may be more important than rooted vegetation in producing food for the ecosystem.

3. *Consumer organisms:* animals, such as fish, crustacea, and insect larvae. Primary consumers (herbivores) feed directly on living plants or plant remains, usually zooplankton and bottom forms. Secondary consumers (carnivores) feed on the primary consumers.

4. *Decomposer organisms:* aquatic bacteria and fungi, distributed throughout the pond, but especially abundant in the mud-water interface along the bottom where bodies of plants and animals accumulate, and in the photosynthetic zone where plankton and rooted vegetation are concentrated. Figure 6-1 is a representation of a pond ecosystem.

The ecological importance of decomposers in the ecosystem can easily be overlooked. Decomposition results from the processes by which bacteria and fungi obtain their food. It is absolutely essential, because if it did not occur, all nutrients would soon be tied up in dead organic matter and new life would not be possible. Decomposition is effected through enzymatic action; some of the products are used as food by the bacteria or fungi, and other products remain in the environment or are excreted from the cells. Fats, sugars, and proteins are decomposed readily, but cellulose, lignin, hair, and bones are broken down slowly. A study of the decomposition of marsh grass by Burkholder and Bornside (1957) showed that under the most favorable conditions, decomposition was rapid for about 10 days, and then proceeded at a much reduced rate for the next

FIGURE 6-1.

Diagram of a pond ecosystem. Basic units include: I, abiotic substances—basic inorganic and organic compounds; II A, producers—rooted vegetation; II B, producers—phytoplankton; III-IA, primary consumers (herbivores)—bottom forms; III-IB, primary consumers (herbivores)—zooplankton; III-2, secondary consumers (carnivores); III-3, teritary consumers (secondary carnivores); IV, decomposers—bacteria and fungi of decay. [After Odum, Fundamentals of Ecology *2nd Ed., Philadelphia: Saunders, 1959.]*

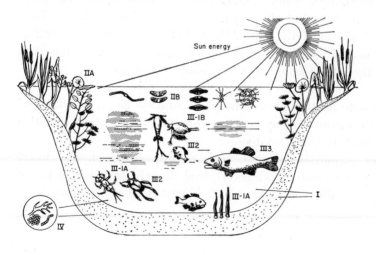

two weeks. The decomposition of grass left submerged in water was influenced greatly by temperature, being more rapid in summer than in winter. After a year, 10% of the grass was still not decomposed. Cellulose decomposition has been considered a bottleneck in the functioning of ecosystems (Siu and Reese, 1953).

In addition to obtaining their own food, the functions of decomposer organisms in the ecosystem appear to be: (1) mineralization of dead organic matter, (2) production of food for other organisms, and (3) production of ectocrine substances. Some of these ectocrine substances released into the environment, such as penicillin, have inhibiting effects; some, such as Vitamin B_{12}, histidine, and biotin, have stimulating effects (Huxley, 1935; Lucas, 1947; Daisley, 1957; Droop, 1957; Williams and Spicer, eds., 1957).

Man's power to change or redirect the normal functioning of ecosystems should not be minimized. Odum (1959) has suggested the dangers of tinkering with basic ecosystems: it is conceivable that profound changes by man could result either in a glorious future or complete destruction. Although natural ecosystems have built-in homeostatic mechanisms, these buffer limits can easily be exceeded by man. For example, wanton destruction of forests and indiscriminate road building have drastically changed the characteristics of important watersheds. Plowing of vast areas of subhumid and semiarid grasslands in order to grow more grain crops has greatly disturbed stable natural ecosystems. Even lands left in grass have been ruined by overgrazing and other forms of mismanagement. Where moisture is limiting, these practices have resulted in a replacement of palatable grasses by mesquite, cactus, sagebrush, and weedy grasses. It took centuries for forests and natural grasslands to evolve, but they can be destroyed in a short time. Man's influence can quickly change the direction of certain forces and effects in the balance of a natural ecosystem. Wisely directed, it can lead to the conservation and perpetuation of an abundance of natural resources.

An important aspect of ecosystems is the pattern of circulation of the essential elements in the system. This may be illustrated by the many organic-inorganic cycles which exist in nature. The nitrogen cycle, for example (Figure 6-2), represents a very complex but rather complete cycle in which organic matter is broken down to inorganic form by decomposer bacteria. Some of this nitrogen goes directly back into the air, while some of it ends up as nitrate, to be used in the nutrition of green plants. Nitrogen is constantly being returned to the air through the action of denitrifying bacteria. Through nitrogen fixation by bacteria or blue-green algae, and by the action of lightning, nitrogen returns to the cycle

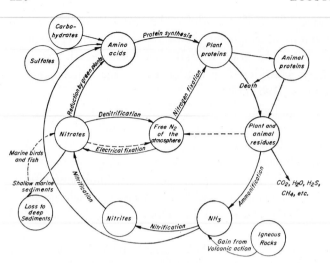

FIGURE 6-2.

The nitrogen cycle. [Modified after Meyer, Anderson, and Böhning, Plant Physiology. *N. Y.: D. Van Nostrand Co., 1960.]*

where it is again built into protoplasm in plants through protein synthesis.

In the nitrogen cycle, which is considered a relatively perfect self-regulating cycle, there is little over-all change in available nitrogen in large ecosystems or in the biosphere as a whole, even though there often is a rapid circulation of materials.

A small loss of nitrogen from the air to sediments appears to be balanced by the gain from volcanic action. According to Hutchinson (1944), the amount of nitrogen fixed from the air (noncyclic) for the biosphere as a whole is estimated at 140 to 700 mg per square meter (one and six pounds per acre) per year. Most of this is biological fixation, which in fertile areas may be much greater than the biosphere average, up to 200 or more pounds per acre (Lyon and Bizzell, 1934). Environmental factors affecting the nitrogen cycle, especially as related to sources of nitrogen for seed plants, have been studied by Shields (1953). This subject is discussed in greater detail under "Symbiosis-Nitrogen Fixation" in Chapter 12.

Other biogeochemical cycles, such as those of phosphorus, calcium, carbon, oxygen, and carbon dioxide, are highly important. The phosphorus cycle (Figure 6-3) is of particular interest, since phosphorus is a necessary constituent of protoplasm (Hutchinson and Bowen, 1948). Organic phosphorus compounds are broken down to inorganic forms, which are again available for plant growth. The reserve of phosphorus is found in rocks and other deposits formed in past ages. Erosion has released phosphate to ecosystems, but has also caused great losses into the seas. Whether phosphorus can be returned to its cycle fast enough to compensate for losses is often questioned. In some parts of the world, such as the Pacific Coast of Peru, sea birds have been responsible for returning much phosphorus to the cycle, but in other areas the phosphorus return is quite inadequate.

Radiophosphorus has been exceedingly useful in quantitative measurement of the phosphorus exchange rates in various components of the ecosystem (Hutchinson, 1957). Here, two concepts are essential, the turnover rate and the turnover time (Robertson, 1957). Turnover rate is the fraction of the total amount of a substance in a component which is released (or enters) in a given length of time. Turnover time is the reciprocal of this, the time required to replace a quantity of substance equal to the amount in the component. Smaller lakes, for example, have a shorter turnover time for phosphorus than large lakes because the ratio of the bottom mud surface to the volume of water is greater. Turnover time for a small or shallow lake may be one week and for a large lake two or more months.

Phosphorus cycling in land ecosystems has shown similar patterns. The recovery of fertilizer phosphorus by the crop planted immediately following the fertilizer application often amounts to only 10–30% of the quantity added to the soil. Much of the remainder is rendered insoluble or "fixed" in the soil. In acid soils, fixation of phosphorus is primarily due to the formation of highly insoluble compounds of iron and aluminum (Hemwall, 1957).

FIGURE 6-3.

The phosphorus cycle. [After Odum, Funda-mentals of Ecology. *2nd Ed., Philadelphia: Saunders, 1959.]*

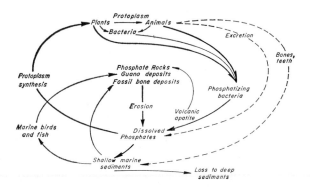

Burd (1948) has shown that in calcareous and alkaline soils the concentration of calcium in the soil solution is the dominant factor in phosphorus fixation.

Organic phosphorus too may be fixed as was demonstrated by Bower (1949). Certain phosphorus-containing compounds, namely phytin and its derivatives, may form insoluble aluminum, iron and calcium compounds under soil conditions similar to those favorable for inorganic phosphorus fixation.

One practical result of these studies of nutrient cycles is the recognition that balanced fertilization is the important objective and that over-fertilization may be bad ecological practice just the same as under-fertilization. Ryther (1954) has reported a study of the effects of heavy fertilization of portions of Long Island Sound, New York. Extensive development of large duck farms on Long Island resulted in a great increase in the fertilizer constituents of duck manure washed into the bay by streams. The organic form of nutrients added, and particularly the low nitrogen-phosphorus ratio, resulted in a complete change in the major producers, the phytoplankton of the area. It appears that the famous "blue point" oysters which had been harvested for years in the area had thrived on the normal phytoplankton but were unable to utilize the new food supply. The oysters gradually disappeared because of the disturbance of the formerly balanced ecosystem.

The cycling of carbon and oxygen may be considered together (Woodbury 1954). Carbon must be in the gaseous form (CO_2) to be used by plants. It is completely useless to plants when fixed as a solid in the soil or in rocks. When they can take it from the air as a gas, or from water in solution, plants transform carbon into organic compounds which may be used by animals and nongreen plants as their carbon supply. Carbon is returned to the atmosphere or to the water as a gas (CO_2) through the metabolic processes of organic life.

Solid carbon stored in bodies of organisms where they die may be unavailable unless it is released through decomposition or fire. Organic matter preserved from decay may be stored underground in the form of peat bogs, coal beds, or petroleum. When kept under water for long periods at warm temperatures, the end product is limestone ($CaCO_3$), which forms huge deposits in the warmer regions of the earth.

Oxygen is essential to the metabolism of all living organisms. It is so prevalent in the atmosphere that there is unlikely to be a shortage for most air-breathing organisms. It is made available both directly as a gas (O_2) and indirectly in chemical compounds. It is, of course, much less readily available in water or in soil, and may be so scarce in stagnant

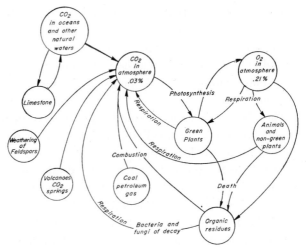

FIGURE 6-4.

The carbon and oxygen cycles. [Modified after Meyer and Anderson, Plant Physiology, *N. Y.: D. Van Nostrand Co., 1952, and Woodbury,* Principles of General Ecology, *N. Y.: Blakiston Co., 1954.]*

water and mud that anaerobic bacteria and other organisms thrive which could not exist if oxygen were freely available. Oxygen is consumed by green plants at all times, is consumed by animals, and during the daytime is released by green plants. The carbon and oxygen cycles are shown in Figure 6-4.

The cycling of nonessential elements in the ecosystem has been treated by Odum (1959). Normally, many of these elements are present in non-toxic quantities but, through atomic blasts and nuclear power operations, radioactive isotopes of some of these elements may accumulate at un-desirable levels. The cycling of radioactive strontium, iodine, cesium, ruthenium, and other elements may likely become a grave concern for the ecologist of this atomic age.

ENERGY IN ECOSYSTEMS*

Energy can be transformed from one type to another, but it is never created nor destroyed. This is the first law of thermodynamics. The second law

* The material in this section has been taken mainly from H. T. Odum and E. P. Odum. Principles and concepts pertaining to energy in ecological systems, by Odum, E. P., *Fundamentals of Ecology*, Saunders, New York. 1959.

states (essentially) that energy transformation will not occur spontaneously in a process unless there is a degradation of the energy from a concentrated form into a dispersed form. Some energy is always dispersed into unavailable heat energy so that no spontaneous transformation of light energy, for example, into potential energy in the form of protoplasm is completely efficient.

The second law of thermodynamics thus deals with the transfer of energy toward a less available and a more dispersed state. For the solar system as a whole, a dispersed state would be one in which all the energy is in the form of heat energy. While the earth is far from being in a state of stability with respect to energy, it would appear to be in the process of going toward the stable state.

Of the light energy absorbed by green plants, only a small portion is transformed into potential energy; most of it goes into heat energy. An animal takes in chemical potential energy (food) and converts a large part of it into heat to enable a small part of the energy to be reestablished as the chemical potential energy of new protoplasm. Step by step, the transfer of energy from one organism to another results in a large part of the energy being degraded into heat.

The stability principle concept is that any natural enclosed system with energy flowing through it tends to change until a stable adjustment, with self-regulating mechanisms, is developed.

With these basic principles of energy transfer in mind, the ecological problems of food chains and productivity concept will be considered.

The Food Chain

Odum and Odum (1959) have defined the food chain as the transfer of food energy from the source in green plants through a series of organisms, with repeated eating and being eaten. The number of links, or steps, in the chain is usually limited to four or five because of the losses in heat energy. In principle, the shorter the food chain, the greater the available energy which can be converted into living weight (**biomass**) and/or dissipated by respiration.

Three kinds of food chains are recognized: (1) the **predator chain,** which goes from smaller to larger animals; (2) the **parasite chain,** which goes from larger to smaller organisms; and (3) the **saprophytic chain,** which goes from dead matter into microorganisms. Organisms whose food is obtained from plants by the same number of steps are said to belong to the same **trophic level.** Green plants occupy the first trophic level;

herbivores, or planteaters, the second level; carnivores, which eat the herbivores, the third level; and secondary carnivores, the fourth level. A given species population may occupy one or more than one trophic level, depending on the source of energy actually assimilated. The energy flow through a trophic level equals the total assimilation at that level, which in turn equals the production of biomass plus respiration.

The workings of the two laws of thermodynamics in ecological communities may be illustrated by the diagram of energy flow in Figure 6-5.

The inflow of energy is balanced by the outflow as required by the first law; each energy transfer is accompanied by the dispersion of energy into an unavailable form (dispersed heat) as required by the second law.

Food chains are more or less familiar, as man himself occupies an important position near the end of several. However, it is not always emphasized sufficiently that only a small percentage of the solar energy received on the earth's surface is fixed by green plants, and that at each food transfer potential energy is lost.

FIGURE 6-5.

Energy-flow diagram of a community, showing successive fixation and transfer by components, and the large respiratory losses at each transfer. P = gross primary production, P_N = net primary production, and P_2, P_3, P_4 and P_5 = secondary production at the indicated levels. [After Odum, Fundamentals of Ecology. 2nd Ed., 1959. Philadelphia. Saunders.]

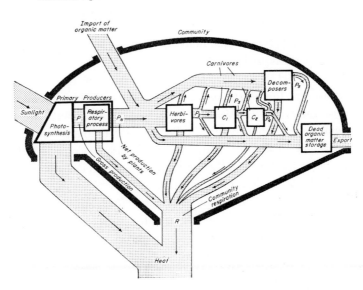

In ecology, total assimilation of a trophic level is known as the *energy flow* through that level. This flow is always less at each trophic level than it was at the preceding level. Respiration accounts for much of the energy loss in the whole ecosystem, but other losses occur because some available food is not utilized, and not all potential energy ingested by heterotrophic organisms is actually assimilated. Farm animals are known to differ in the "efficiency" with which they convert gross energy from plants into utilizable meat, milk, or other product. The pig, for example, can convert about 20% of the gross energy available in its feed into products eaten by man. Much of the 80% loss is due to respiration, some to food the pig ate but did not assimilate, and some to food converted into bone, hair, etc. which man cannot use (Maynard, 1954).

The trophic level of organisms is one of function and not necessarily of species. A species may actually occupy more than one trophic level. If a population of animals, for example, obtains 80% of its energy from eating plants and 20% from eating animals, 80% of its energy flow is at the herbivore level and 20% at the carnivore level.

A well-managed fish pond furnishes excellent examples of food chains. The object of the fish pond is to furnish a maximum number of fish of a particular species and size, so management is provided to channel as much energy as possible into the final product. Often this is done by reducing the number of "side food chains" or niches. The producers may be restricted mainly to one type, floating algae or phytoplankton. Other green plants are discouraged. Zooplankton feed upon the phytoplankton and both of these groups are eaten by certain invertebrates such as blood worms and chironomids. These invertebrates are preferred food of bluegills and other small fishes, which are in turn consumed by bass. The balance maintained between the bluegills and bass is very important if a good fishing pond is to be maintained.

Elton (1927) has pointed out that size of food is one of the basic reasons for the existence of food chains. There are definite upper and lower limits to the size of food that can support many animals. This limitation may hardly be applied rigidly to man, but it is still of some importance. Esthetics and economics also become highly important in supplying food efficiently for man. The shorter the food chain, the more people that can live on a given land area. Thus, where population pressure is great, rice and other vegetable foods furnish the main portion of the diet. With fewer people greater inefficiencies may be permitted: animal products—meat, milk, butter, and cheese—replace vegetable sources, and a more varied diet is possible.

Ecological Efficiency

To determine "ecological efficiencies" expressed as percentages, ratios between energy flow at different points along the food chain are used (Lindeman, 1942). These ratios may have useful meaning in reference to the component populations in the biological community.

As noted in Chapter 9 on light, Rabinowitch (1951) estimated that of the total insolation reaching plants, only about 1% of the energy is fixed. In water the efficiency of light energy is still less, Riley (1944) having estimated it for the ocean as a whole at 0.18% of the total radiation energy reaching the ocean surface.

Experimental efforts to produce large quantities of food through mass cultures of algae have shown that somewhat higher efficiencies can be attained. In diffuse light, efficiencies of mass cultures of *Chlorella* and *Scenedesmus* have reached 20% to 50%, but when large tanks are used under full daylight, efficiency drops to from 2% to 6% (Tamiya, 1957). On a large scale, it was estimated that 100 acres of land would be needed for a plant site. Evidence has been obtained that a production of 32 tons per acre per year can be achieved at a cost of 17 to 25 cents per pound of dry *Chlorella*. If population pressure requires it, food production by mass algal culture appears to be feasible.

Communities may be considered to have a definite **trophic structure** because of the interaction of food chain phenomena (energy loss at each transfer) and size-metabolism relationships. This structure may be defined in terms of standing crop per unit area, or in terms of energy fixed per unit area per unit time at successive trophic levels. Also, trophic structure and function may be shown by means of **ecological pyramids,** in which the producer level forms the base and successive levels the tiers to make up the apex. These pyramids may be shown in terms of numbers, or biomass, or of energy.

It was shown by Odum and Odum (1959) that the number and weight of organisms which can be supported at any level in any situation depends on the *rate* at which food is being produced. The energy pyramid gives the best over-all picture of the functional nature of a community, or what goes on in the living part of the ecosystem.

An example of an energy pyramid may be taken from an imaginary alfalfa-calf-boy food chain as indicated in Figure 6-6 (respiration is omitted).

While cows do not usually eat only alfalfa, nor boys exist entirely on

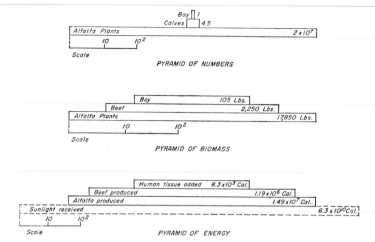

FIGURE 6-6.

Three types of ecological pyramids illustrating a hypothetical alfalfa-calf-boy food chain computed on a basis of 10 acres and one year and plotted on a log scale. [Compiled from: Sunlight, Haurwitz and Austin (1944), Climatology. Alfalfa: U.S.D.A. Statistics, 1951; U.S.D.A. Yearbook, 1948; Morrison (1947), Feeds and Feeding. Beef Calf: Brody (1945), Bioenergetics and Growth. Growing boy: Fulton (1950), Physiology; Dearborn and Rothney (1941), Predicting the Child's Development. Odum, Fundamentals of Ecology. 2nd Ed., Philadelphia: Saunders, (1959).]

meat, this diagram does represent a realistic model of an ecosystem in which man plays an important role. Most domestic animals are herbivores, and man could subsist mainly on meat, if necessary. Or, man could consume vegetable foods only, in which instance more people could be supported with the same primary fixation of solar energy. In principle, it is believed that man-controlled ecosystems are basically no different from natural systems as far as the general energy relationships are concerned. However, one may well question what factors determine the relative efficiencies at the different trophic levels, and to what extent man can increase the primary energy fixation or the rate of transfer to any of the higher trophic levels.

From this discussion of energy relationships in ecosystems we go logically to another important concept in ecology, that of **primary productivity**. Because this subject forms an interesting aspect of one of the most important considerations in crop ecology, it will be discussed in some detail in Chapter 18 as a part of the concept of ecological optimum.

References

1. Bower, C. A. 1949. Studies on the forms and availability of soil organic phosphorus. Iowa Agr. Exp. Sta. Res. Bul. 362.
2. Burd, J. S. 1948. Chemistry of the phosphate ion in soil systems. *Soil Sci.* 65: 227–247.
3. Burkholder, P. R. and Bornside, G. H. 1957. Decomposition of marsh grass by aerobic marine bacteria. *Bull. Torrey Bot. Club* 84: 366–383.
4. Daisley, K. W. 1957. Vitamin B_{12} in marine ecology. *Nature* 180: 142–143.
5. Dansereau, P. 1957. *Biogeography.* Ronald, New York.
6. Droop, M. R. 1957. Vitamin B_{12} in marine ecology. *Nature* 180: 1041–1042.
7. Elton, Charles. 1927. *Animal Ecology.* Macmillan, New York.
8. Hemwall, J. B. 1957. The fixation of phosphorus by soils. *Adv. in Agron.* 9: 95–112.
9. Hutchinson, G. E. 1944. Nitrogen in biogeochemistry of the atmosphere. *Amer. Sci.* 32: 178–195.
10. ———. 1957. *A Treatise in Limnology.* Wiley, New York.
11. ——— and Bowen, V. T. 1948. A direct demonstration of phosphorus cycle in a small lake. *Proc. Nat'l Acad. Sci.* 33: 148–153.
12. Huxley, Julian. 1935. Chemical regulation and the hormone concept. *Biol. Rev.* 10: 427.
13. Lindeman, R. L. 1942. The trophic-dynamic aspect of ecology. *Ecol.* 23: 399–418.
14. Lucas, C. E. 1947. The ecological effects of external metabolites. *Biol. Rev. Cambr. Phil. Soc.* 22: 270–295.
15. Lyon, T. L. and Bizzell, J. A. 1934. A comparison of several legumes with respect to nitrogen accretion. *Jour. Amer. Soc. Agron.* 26: 651–656.
16. Maynard, L. A. 1954. Animal species that feed mankind: the role of nutrition. *Sci.* 120: 164–166.
17. Odum, Eugene P. 1959. *Fundamentals of Ecology.* Saunders, New York.
18. Odum, H. T. and Odum, E. P. 1959. Principles and concepts pertaining to energy in ecological systems. In Odum, E. P. *Fundamentals of Ecology.* Saunders, New York, pp. 43–87.
19. Rabinowitch, E. I. 1951. *Photosynthesis and Related Processes.* Vol. II (1): 603–1208. Interscience, New York.
20. Riley, G. A. 1944. The carbon metabolism and photosynthetic efficiency of the earth. *Amer. Sci.* 32: 132–134.
21. Robertson, J. S. 1957. Theory and use of tracers in determining transfer rates in biological systems. *Physiol. Rev.* 37: 133–154.
22. Ryther, John H. 1954. The ecology of phytoplankton blooms in Moriches Bay and Great South Bay, Long Island, New York. *Biol. Bul.* 106: 198–209.
23. Shields, Lora M. 1953. Nitrogen sources of seed plants and environmental influences affecting the nitrogen cycle. *Bot. Rev.* 19: 321–376.
24. Siu, R. G. H. and Reese, E. T. 1953. Decomposition of cellulose by microorganisms. *Bot. Rev.* 19: 377–416.
25. Tamiya, H. 1957. Mass culture of algae. *Ann. Rev. Pl. Phys.* 8: 309–334.
26. Villar, E. H. 1929. *Geobotanica.* Editorial Labor, Barcelona–Buenos Aires.
27. Williams, R. E. O. and Spicer, C. C. (editors) 1957. *Microbial Ecology.* 7th Symp. of Soc. Gen. Microbial. Cambridge Univ., Cambridge.
28. Woodbury, A. M. 1954. *Principles of General Ecology.* Blakiston, New York.

ENVIRONMENTAL
FACTORS

The Moisture Factor

INTRODUCTION

The ecological importance of moisture to plants can hardly be overemphasized. Within large areas having similar temperature conditions the relative scarcity or abundance of moisture probably has a greater influence than any other environmental factor in determining the kind of vegetation present. An abundance of moisture results in a rich natural flora and makes possible a wide choice of crops. Deficiency of moisture, on the other hand, permits only a narrow range of potential crops, and is accompanied by hazards to efficient production.

The importance of water is realized when we consider the more important functions for which it is essential. These have been included in four groups by Kramer (1959):

1. Water is a constituent part of protoplasm. Usually it forms 85% to 90% of the green weight of actively growing tissues.

2. Water is a reagent, essential in photosynthesis and in hydrolytic processes such as digestion of starch to sugar.

3. Water is a solvent in which salts, gases, and other materials move into the plant and through the cell walls and xylem tissues to create a more or less continuous solvent system throughout the plant.

4. Water is essential for turgidity, cell growth, maintenance of leaf form, operation of stomata, and structural movement of the plant.

In order to gain a fuller understanding of the universal importance of water in crop ecology, we must give consideration to some of the over-all aspects of moisture as related to plant growth. These include atmospheric moisture, precipitation and its effectiveness, adaptation to moisture conditions, transpiration and water use, drought resistance, response to increasing moisture stress, and effects of too much moisture.

ATMOSPHERIC MOISTURE

The moisture in the atmosphere may be expressed either as *absolute humidity* or as *relative humidity*. Absolute humidity is the amount of water vapor present in a unit volume of air. Relative humidity expresses the amount of water vapor in the atmosphere as a percentage of that which could be held at saturation at a particular temperature and pressure. At saturation the number of molecules of water vapor escaping from the surface of liquid water is the same as the number returning to the liquid, and the actual concentration depends upon the temperature. At 0°C water is in equilibrium with a water vapor pressure of 4.58 mm of mercury, while water at 100°C is in equilibrium with a water vapor pressure of 1 atmosphere, or 760 mm of Hg. This effect of temperature may be expressed in another way. For example, the atmosphere over one square foot of the earth's surface at the equator will contain approximately 50 pounds of water vapor, at 50° north latitude it will contain 18 pounds, and at 70° north, only 4 or 5 pounds. Zonal distribution of the water vapor content of the atmosphere, as it varies through the seasons, is indicated in Figure 7-1.

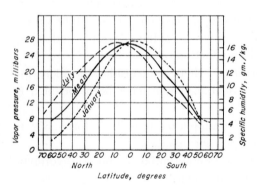

FIGURE 7-1.

Zonal distribution of the water-vapor content of the air. Specific humidity is highest near the equator and decreases toward the poles. There is a northward displacement in July and a southward displacement in January owing to a similar distribution of temperature. [After Haurwitz and Austin, Climatology. N. Y.: McGraw-Hill, 1954.]

The use of the term relative humidity as an expression of moisture conditions is not always satisfactory in ecological studies because identical relative humidities do not indicate similar conditions unless the temperatures are the same. It is better to express humidity values in terms of water vapor pressure (Oosting, 1956). The difference between the actual water vapor pressure and that needed to saturate the air at the same temperature is called the **vapor-pressure deficit.** The vapor pressure of saturated air at 20°C is 17.54 mm of mercury, and at a relative humidity of 60% is 10.52 mm. The vapor-pressure gradient (or diffusion-pressure gradient) between the water vapor of air at 20°C and 60% relative humidity, and saturated air at the same temperature, is 17.54 − 10.52, or 7.02 mm. At 30°C with similar relative humidity, the vapor-pressure gradient would be 31.82 − 19.09, or 12.73 mm. Thus, we realize the marked effect of temperature on the processes of evaporation and transpiration. The general relationships between relative humidity, vapor pressure, and vapor-pressure deficit at different temperatures are given in Table 7-1.

TABLE 7-1. RELATIONSHIPS BETWEEN RELATIVE HUMIDITY, VAPOR-PRESSURE DEFICIT, AND VAPOR PRESSURE AT DIFFERENT TEMPERATURES

Temperature °C	°F	0	Actual Vapor Pressure (mm Hg) at Indicated Relative Humidity (read down)									
			10%	20%	30%	40%	50%	60%	70%	80%	90%	100%
0	32	0	0.46	0.92	1.37	1.83	2.29	2.75	3.21	3.66	4.12	4.58
5	41	0	0.65	1.31	1.96	2.62	3.27	3.92	4.58	5.23	5.89	6.54
10	50	0	0.92	1.84	2.76	3.68	4.60	5.53	6.45	7.37	8.29	9.21
15	59	0	1.28	2.56	3.84	5.12	6.40	7.67	8.95	10.23	11.51	12.79
20	68	0	1.75	3.51	5.26	7.02	8.77	10.52	12.28	14.03	15.79	17.54
25	77	0	2.38	4.75	7.13	9.50	11.88	14.26	16.63	19.01	21.38	23.76
30	86	0	3.18	6.36	9.55	12.73	15.91	19.09	22.27	25.46	28.64	31.82
35	95	0	4.22	8.44	12.65	16.87	21.09	25.31	29.53	33.74	37.96	42.18
40	104	0	5.53	11.06	16.60	22.13	27.66	33.19	38.72	44.25	49.79	55.32
45	113	0	7.19	14.38	21.56	28.75	35.94	43.13	50.32	57.50	64.69	71.88
50	122	0	9.25	18.50	27.75	37.00	46.26	55.51	64.76	74.01	83.26	92.51
		100%	90%	80%	70%	60%	50%	40%	30%	20%	10%	0%

Vapor-pressure Deficit (mm Hg) at Indicated Relative Humidity (read up)

Atmospheric moisture is measured with the psychrometer and the hygrometer. The psychrometer consists of two thermometers, one of which has the bulb covered with wet cloth. Both are subjected to air in motion. The "wet bulb" is cooled by evaporation of the moisture (present in the wet cloth) into the atmosphere. The difference in temperature between the wet and dry bulb readings is used to determine relative humidity, using standard tables.

The hygrograph is a recording hygrometer which gives a continuous record of relative humidity on a sheet attached to a rotating drum. In principle, this instrument depends on the contraction and expansion of some material (usually hair) to denote changes in relative humidity. The instrument is convenient, but subject to inaccuracies unless handled with extreme care.

Dew

The effect of temperature on vapor-pressure deficit in the atmosphere has been indicated. In clear weather, with little or no wind, cooling of the surface layers of atmosphere at night may result in the formation of dew or white frost. As a result of rapid radiation from the earth's surface, the adjacent layer of air may be cooled to the point of saturation (dew point) and condensation takes place. If the dew point is above 32°F, the condensed water vapor will be in the form of dew; if it is below 32°F, white frost will form.

The value of dew to plants is a subject of considerable controversy. Many early experiments, which reported direct absorption of dew through the leaves, were lacking in convincing evidence. Fowells and Kirk (1945) showed that Ponderosa pine seedlings depleted soil moisture considerably below the permanent wilting percentage and still survived. Stone, Went, and Young (1950) found that seedlings of *Pinus coulteri* survived in dry soil below the wilting point in an atmosphere of high humidity. They suggested that survival may have been made possible through a "negative transpiration," with water moving into the plant through the leaves and down through the plant into the soil. It was emphasized, however, that it was not known whether the inverse flow of moisture was of real significance as a survival factor, or just a physical phenomenon made possible when plant tissues were rigid enough to resist collapse when desiccated.

Further experiments, particularly with Ponderosa pine seedlings exposed to mists after their roots were sealed into empty flasks or cans of soil, showed that under fluctuating temperatures some backward movement of water took place into the empty flasks. However, there was no measurable reverse flow into the roots of the trees sealed in the cans of soil (Stone, Shachori, and Stanley, 1956, and Stone, 1957). It was concluded that prolonged survival of pine seedlings growing in soil at low moisture content, close to or at the wilting percentage, probably was made possible by the resaturation of needle tissues with the concomitant reduction in the amount of water removed from the soil.

The work of Slatyer (1956) with seedlings of *Pinus echinata* lent support to the idea that dew can be absorbed by the plant in all but very wet soils. If the atmosphere was saturated, or nearly so, dew absorption appeared to take place as long as a diffusion-pressure gradient existed from the atmosphere to the leaves.

On the other hand, the importance of dew has been questioned by Angus (1959). He estimated that the maximum condensation of dew on an extensive area is probably not more than 10% of the water transpired during the day. He gave two reasons for this low estimate: (1) the upper limit of energy that can be released from the latent heat of dew condensation, and (2) the relatively small vapor-pressure gradient from the atmosphere to the leaf surfaces.

In arid regions, such as Palestine, a much greater importance has been given to dew by Ashbel (1949), who estimated that moisture added by dew amounts to as much as 10 to 15 cm per year.

Dew may play two possible roles of benefit to plants (Angus, 1959). The first of these is a passive role in which dew delays the rise in temperature and onset of transpiration stress the following day. The second role is a possible active role in which dew is taken up by the plant and enters the dynamic liquid cycle (Stone, Went, and Young, 1950; Stone, Shachori, and Stanley, 1956; Slatyer, 1956).

Fog

Minute hygroscopic particles are effective as condensation nuclei about which water droplets form. Salt and smoke are among the most important of these fine particles. When air masses of high moisture content close to the surface are cooled, fog may form. In low latitudes, cool ocean currents tend to be concentrated along the eastern sides of oceans making adjacent coastal regions subject to fogs (Trewartha, 1954). Fog also develops over middle-latitude oceans as a result of warm air moving poleward in the warm sector of cyclonic storms. In the United States, regions of maximum fog are found along the North Atlantic Coast, the Pacific Coast, and the Appalachian Highlands. Other areas subject to fog include the Great Lakes states, bottom lands of the principal rivers, and the Gulf and Atlantic coastal regions. Western Europe and the British Isles are subject to many winter fogs.

THE PRECIPITATION CYCLE

The cycle of precipitation may be divided into four principal steps:

1. *Evaporation.* The primary source of water vapor in the atmosphere is

moisture evaporated from the oceans. Continental precipitation finds its way back to the sea indirectly through evaporation and transpiration, and directly through ground water return (Holzman, 1937).

2. *Transportation.* Humid, tropical air masses which become cooled as they travel poleward carry huge quantities of water vapor. Also, in the reverse direction, much water vapor is transported by the polar continental air masses which pass equatorward over land areas, absorbing moisture evaporated from the land, and eventually being transformed into moist, tropical air masses over the oceans (Trewartha, 1954).

3. *Condensation.* Water vapor is converted to the liquid state when the air temperature is reduced to or below the dew point. Hygroscopic nuclei aid greatly in facilitating this process. Warm air rises and will continue to rise until it reaches layers having its own temperature. The process of cooling by the expansion associated with rising air is the only one capable of producing condensation on such a scale that abundant precipitation results (Trewartha, 1954).

4. *Precipitation.* Condensed water vapor floats through the air in the form of clouds. Through the process of adiabatic cooling, extensive air masses fall below the dew point. Water particles increase in size until they

FIGURE 7-2.

The hydrologic cycle correlated with the air-mass cycle. [*After Holtzman, U. S. Dept. of Agric., Tech. Bul. 589, 1937.*]

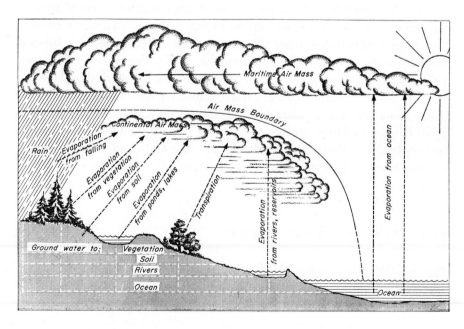

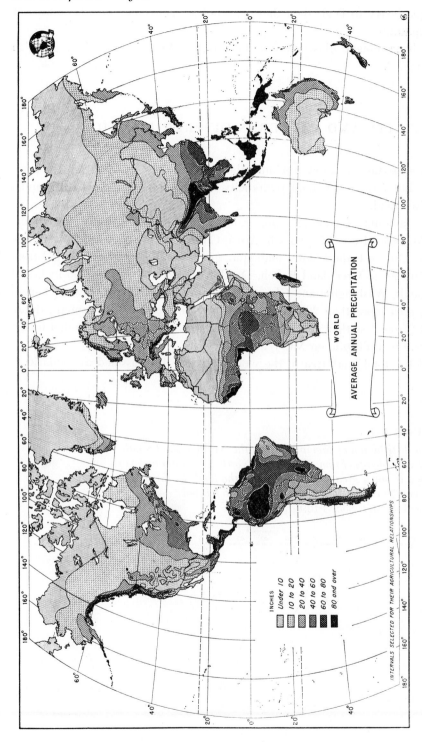

FIGURE 7-3. *World average annual precipitation.* [*Courtesy U. S. Dept. Agr., Foreign Agr. Service.*]

are too heavy to float; then they may fall as rain, snow, or other forms of precipitation.

A diagrammatic illustration of the complete hydrologic cycle is given in Figure 7-2.

QUANTITY AND PATTERNS OF PRECIPITATION

It is important to know not only the total average precipitation for a region, but also its seasonal periodicity and its dependability, both annual and seasonal.

The amount of average annual rainfall, measured in various parts of the world, varies from .02 inches in Arica, Chile, to 905 inches in Cherrapunjii, India. On the United States mainland, annual precipitation has varied from 1.45 inches at Greenland Ranch, Death Valley, California, to 130 inches at Quinault, Washington and Glenora, Oregon. In the State of Hawaii, a small land area more than 2000 miles from any large continent, annual rainfall varies from less than two inches in windward-sea-level areas to 460 inches at 4500 feet altitude on Mt. Waialeale, Kauai.

Of the total land area in the world 55% may be classified as semiarid to

FIGURE 7-4.

Zonal distribution of precipitation in the Northern and Southern Hemispheres. From 40° to 60° North, precipitation over the sea is much greater than it is over the land. In this graph the average condition is represented. [After Brooks and Hunt, Mem. Roy. Met. Soc. 3:139–157, 1930.]

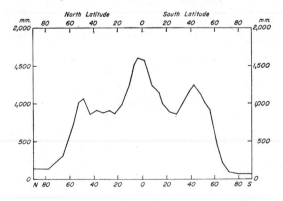

arid, with less than 20 inches of precipitation per year; 20% subhumid, with 20 to 40 inches; 11% humid, with 40 to 60 inches; and 14% wet, with 60 inches or more annually. The average annual precipitation in inches throughout the world is given in Figure 7-3.

Trewartha (1954) defined three primary controls affecting the distributional pattern of rainfall: (1) the great latitudinal zones of horizontal atmospheric convergence and divergence, (2) the distribution of land and water, and (3) highlands.

A simplified profile of zonal distribution of precipitation is shown in Figure 7-4. A strong primary maximum (70 to 80 in.) of precipitation occurs in a belt about 10° in width near the equator. Belts of much lower rainfall are found in latitudes of 20° to 30° N and S. Then poleward from the subtropics secondary maxima (40 to 50 in.) are indicated for latitudes 40° to 55°. In this zonal belt, rainfall is less in the Northern than in the Southern Hemisphere. Poleward from 55° rainfall decreases sharply.

Distribution patterns based on average monthly precipitation in various regions of the United States are of much interest. Examples of two of these, highly contrasting in pattern, are shown in Figure 7-5.

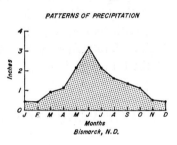

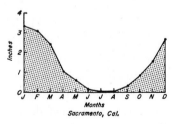

The Bismarck, North Dakota, pattern is typical of the continental dry-winter–moist-summer type, suitable for the production of short season cereal grains and hardy perennial grasses. The Sacramento, California, pattern is just the reverse, with dry summers and moist winters. Without irrigation, winter annuals and drought-resistant perennials can be grown. With irrigation, a wide variety of cropping possibilities may be realized.

The nature of the precipitation is also important. It may consist of rain and snow, and the amount and distribution of snowfall may greatly influence winter survival of crop plants. It may consist of rain only, which may come in thunderstorms, with heavy showers during the hottest part of the day. or in cyclonic type, in which rainfall comes irrespective of the time of day. The intensity pattern will greatly influence the runoff to be expected.

FIGURE 7-5.

Contrasting patterns of precipitation distribution. Bismarck, North Dakota, has a typical continental dry-winter, wet-summer pattern, whereas Sacramento, California, has a wet-winter, dry-summer pattern.

Patterns and classes of rainfall in Michigan were analyzed by Smith and Crabb (1956). Of a total of 957 rainstorms during a 10-year period, 295 produced more than .25 inch and contributed 77.4% of the total. Storms with great intensity, that is those with 85% of the total amount occurring in intensities of more than .50 inch per hour, were predominant in June, July, and August. Under cultivated conditions, total storm rainfall was of more significance than intensity in producing runoff. However, because of the complex interrelations between intensity, total amount, soil moisture, and vegetative cover, all of these factors must be evaluated as causes of runoff.

Klages (1942) called attention to the difference between equal and equivalent rainfalls in the United States as one goes from Canada to the Gulf of Mexico. For example, we might consider the 20-inch annual rainfall line at the Canadian border. Going southward this line passes through the eastern third of North Dakota and South Dakota, western Nebraska and Kansas, and through western Texas. From the standpoint of crop production, the line of equivalent rainfall is considerably farther east as one goes south from the Canadian border, primarily because of the higher mean temperature with its corresponding increased rates of evaporation. Thirty or more inches of rainfall may be required in Texas to be equivalent to 20 inches at the Canadian border.

EFFECTIVENESS OF PRECIPITATION

In addition to the total amount and seasonal distribution of precipitation, it is highly important to have some measurement of its effectiveness. This has been considered under the somewhat broader term "water economy" by Thornthwaite and Mather (1955). It is in this area particularly that man can exercise considerable influence. While it is true that there are regions where precipitation is continually excessive and, likewise, areas where it is continually deficient, there are also large areas where precipitation is excessive during one season and deficient in another. In such locations man can often do a great deal to improve the water economy for crop production.

Measures of precipitation effectiveness have been sought for a long time. One of the early methods suggested was that proposed by Transeau (1905), who developed a formula based on the ratio of total precipitation to total evaporation: $R = (P/E) \times 10,000$. The resulting P-E ratios were used in a study of climatic conditions as related to the distribution of forest vegetation in the United States.

Evaporation data are obtained by measuring water loss from a standardized open tank. It is now recognized that the accuracy of evaporation measurements is affected by the size of the tank, the height of the rim of the tank above the water level, the color of the tank, and possibly other factors. Furthermore, the P-E ratio, based on annual data, gives little information on seasonal aspects of the precipitation-evaporation relationship, which may be highly important as applied to crop adaptation and production.

The weakness of using annual data in computing a P-E ratio was recognized by Thornthwaite (1931, 1933), who developed a precipitation effectiveness index based on monthly data as follows:

$$\text{P-E index} = \sum_{}^{12} 10\left(\frac{P}{E}\right)n,$$

where $n = 1$.

This index was computed by summing the 12 values of precipitation divided by evaporation and multiplying by 10 to eliminate fractions. This formula was found to have only limited use because of the scarcity of evaporation data. Later, reasoning that temperature was the principal factor in determining evaporation, Thornthwaite suggested a substitute formula based upon mean monthly temperature and precipitation values:

$$\text{P-E index} = \sum_{}^{12} 115\left(\frac{P}{T\text{-}10}\right)^{10/9}n,$$

where $n = 1$.

On the basis of this formula Thornthwaite mapped "humidity provinces" for the United States.

Further studies by Thornthwaite (1948) resulted in a more accurate method for characterizing precipitation effectiveness through the use of the evapotranspiration concept. Potential evapotranspiration was defined as the combination of evaporation and transpiration when the surface is completely covered with vegetation and there is an abundance of moisture. The water lost to the precipitation cycle under these conditions was called the water need for the particular location.

The potential evapotranspiration, or P.E.T., was computed by means of an empirical formula involving primarily the mean monthly temperatures and length of day. Wind, humidity, solar radiation, and temperature appeared to vary together. To obtain P.E.T. the water supplied was compared with the water need for the same period. Through the use of his empirical formula, Thornthwaite determined that the approximate P.E.T. for the United States ranged from 60 inches annually at the southern tip of Texas and Florida to approximately 20 inches at the Canadian border.

Efforts were made also to develop instruments for measuring P.E.T. An experimental evapotranspirometer was set up in 1945, and many have been used in various parts of the world since that time. Three essential parts are:

1. A field tank (soil tank with vegetation).
2. A water supply with overflow apparatus.
3. A mechanism for controlling water level in the field tank.

The difference between the water added to the field tank by precipitation (or irrigation) and that lost from it to the overflow tank is the potential evapotranspiration. Tanks should be within a field of the same vegetation and the field should receive the same watering treatment. The size of this buffer area depends on the climate; in a moist climate such as that of Ireland, a square 50 meters on a side is enough, but in a desert climate a square 400 meters on a side would not be too large.

Further study and experience with installations for measuring evapotranspiration have brought many refinements to Thornthwaite's earlier concept of potential evapotranspiration. In a publication entitled "The Water Balance," Thornthwaite and Mather (1955) discuss results obtained from 20 experimental evapotranspirometers, and draw certain conclusions. Evapotranspiration depends on: (1) the external supply of energy to the evaporating surface, principally by solar radiation; (2) the capacity of the air to remove water vapor, that is, wind speed, turbulent structure, and decrease of vapor concentration with height; (3) the nature of the vegetation, especially the capacity to reflect incident radiation, the extent to which it fully occupies the soil, and the depth of the root system; (4) the nature of the soil, especially the amount of water in the root zone.

Thornthwaite and Mather note further that solar radiation is the master factor, is related to the second factor, and that factors 3 and 4 are much less important than 1 and 2. Soil moisture is important, however, especially where it falls far below field capacity. In very dry soils the proportion of net radiation that is used for evaporation falls drastically, the greatest share of it going into convection.

The amount of solar radiation reflected back into the atmosphere (called *albedo*) may be a sizable amount, which has been estimated for a grass surface at 0.26%; an oak woodland, 0.175%; a pine forest, 0.14%; and bare moist sand, 0.09%.

Estimates of maximum evapotranspiration from different surfaces have been computed for Riverside, California, and Miami, Florida, for a day in summer when total solar and sky radiation is at maximum. A monthly value computed at the same daily rate also is included in Table 7-2.

These values may be too high, as indicated by Thornthwaite and Mather, but in general they are of the correct order of magnitude. Finally they point out that the albedo of an evaporating surface must be standard, the rate

**TABLE 7-2. MAXIMUM DAILY AND MONTHLY EVAPOTRANSPIRA-
TION FROM DIFFERENT SURFACES** (in millimeters)

	Grass		Oak		Pine		Moist sand	
	Day	Month	Day	Month	Day	Month	Day	Month
Riverside, Calif.	4.8	144	5.6	168	5.8	174	6.3	189
Miami, Florida	4.6	138	5.1	153	5.3	159	5.6	168

of evapotranspiration must not be influenced by advection of moist or dry air, and the ratio of the energy used in evaporation to that of heating the air must remain constant if accurate values for evapotranspiration are to be obtained.

The relationship between precipitation and water need throughout the year for two contrasting climates, in Berkeley, California and Seabrook, New Jersey, is shown in Figure 7-6.

Penman (1948) has developed a formula for evapotranspiration which is somewhat more elaborate than the one suggested by Thornthwaite. He computes evapotranspiration on the basis of the estimated energy received by a surface and the distribution of this energy to (1) the heating of the air, and (2) evaporation. Included in Penman's formula are solar radiation, reflection coefficient, percentage of sunshine, temperature, vapor pressure, and wind speed.

Van Bavel and Verlinden (1956) applied the Penman formula to a study of agricultural drought in North Carolina. The moisture-holding capacity of the crop root zone was estimated to range from one to five inches in different soils, but as a general base value for a crop like tobacco, two inches of soil moisture storage was considered a good average value.

April 1 was chosen as the date to begin the study, since soil moisture is usually at field capacity on that date and the crop

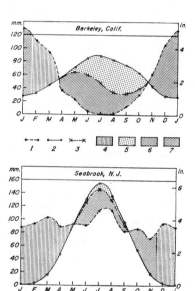

FIGURE 7-6.

Average march of (1) precipitation, (2) potential evapotranspiration, and (3) actual evapotranspiration through the year at Berkeley, California, and Seabrook, New Jersey. Diagram also shows (4) periods of water surplus and (5) water deficit, (6) soil moisture utilization, and (7) soil water recharge. [After Thornthwaite and Mather, Drexel Inst. Tech., Publ. in Climat. 8:25, 1955.]

season is just beginning. A daily balance was then recorded by adding any precipitation which fell and subtracting the estimated evapotranspiration. Days in which the water balance fell to zero (computed from the base amount) were called drought days. In the Piedmont and Coastal Plain of North Carolina estimates of evapotranspiration in inches per day were as follows:

April	.11	July	.16
May	.14	August	.14
June	.17	September	.11

On the basis of average monthly precipitation and evapotranspiration values, the probable frequency of drought days was computed for several weather stations in North Carolina.

At Raleigh, for example, Van Bavel and Verlinden showed that with a two-inch soil-moisture base, 20 drought days may be expected in 75% of the years, and in half of the years approximately 40 drought days may be expected. It should be emphasized that for a deep-rooted crop such as alfalfa, a different soil moisture base would have to be used even in the same location, and the number of drought days would likely be considerably fewer.

A limitation of Penman's method is its complexity and the fact that some of the climatological data needed are not generally available except at first-order weather observation stations.

Drought hazard in the production of corn and soybeans in Iowa has been studied by Barger and Thom (1949) and Schwab, *et al.* (1958).

A criterion of drought intensity was developed, based on the association of certain minimum required total rainfall amounts with time intervals of varying duration, that is, the amount of rainfall which will just permit normal plant development during a period of n consecutive weeks is the minimum required total rainfall for that duration. These minimum amounts were found to increase parabolically with duration and to differ considerably among weather stations in different locations in Iowa.

On the basis of this drought criterion, estimations were made of the minimum amount of rainfall needed during a given number of consecutive weeks in a particular area, and of the probability of getting less than this amount (the drought base) during the period in question.

Effects of supplemental irrigation in central and southeastern Iowa also were determined. While additional water, added to overcome water deficits, was responsible for somewhat higher yields of corn and soybeans in years when water deficits were frequent, high temperatures (above 90°F) appeared to prevent maximum yields. Correlations between maximum rainfall deficits and deviations in corn yields from normal showed that, in years when drought conditions occurred, from 25% to 60% of the total variation in yield was explained by this drought criterion.

MOISTURE INDEXES

A moisture index, obtained by comparing the water need at a given place with the moisture surplus and deficit, is essential to a satisfactory classification of climates (Thornthwaite, 1948). Where precipitation is the same as potential evapotranspiration all the time and water is available as needed, there is neither a water surplus nor deficiency and the climate is neither moist nor dry. As water deficiency becomes larger, the climate becomes more arid; as water surplus becomes larger, the climate becomes more humid. Where a water surplus exists, and no deficiency, an index of humidity can be computed; where there is a water deficiency, and no surplus, an index of aridity can be computed. But in many places water surpluses and deficiencies occur at different times of the year, so both must be used in a moisture index for that location. The generalized moisture index is computed using the following formula:

$$I_m = \frac{100s - 60d}{n},$$

where n = water need, s = surplus, and d = deficiency.

Periods of moisture deficiency are weighted less than periods of moisture surplus because of stored moisture in the soil (considered to be about four inches). Moist climates have positive values, whereas dry climates have negative values. Moisture provinces in the United States, as delineated by Thornthwaite's moisture index, and seasonal variations in effective moisture are shown in Figures 7-7 and 7-8.

The zero line, extending from northwestern Minnesota down through eastern Nebraska and Kansas, central Oklahoma, and finally eastern Texas, separates the humid from the dry climates. This would appear to be a very important division in any climatic classification. It is really not a fine, definite line, however, but over the years a broad variable strip extending several hundred miles in width as based on extreme annual values which vary greatly from year to year.

Perhumid climates are not extensive in the United States, but occur along the Pacific Coast of northern California, Oregon, and Washington. Small areas are found also at high elevations in the Rockies and Appalachians. Another narrow perhumid belt exists along the Maine coast. Subhumid

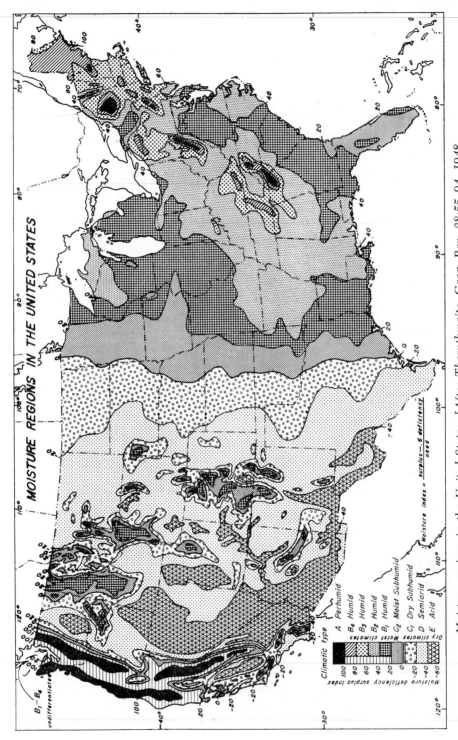

FIGURE 7-7. Moisture regions in the United States. [After Thornthwaite, Geog. Rev. 38:55–94, 1948. Courtesy of the American Geographical Society.]

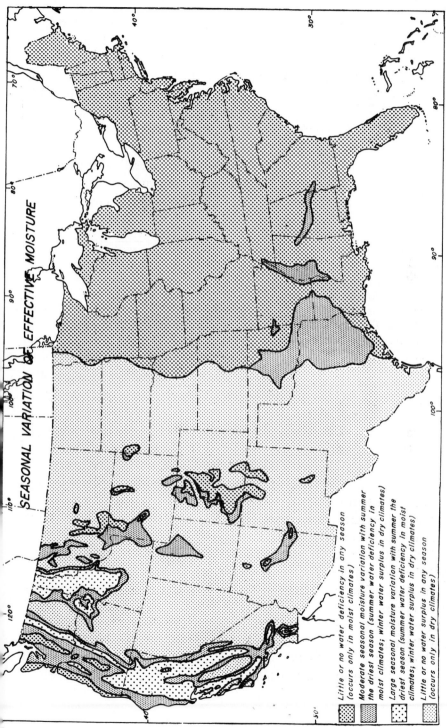

FIGURE 7-8. *Seasonal variation of effective moisture in the United States.* [After Thornthwaite, Geog. Rev. 38:55–94, 1948. Courtesy of the American Geographical Society.].

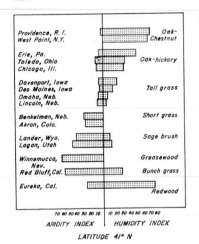

ARIDITY INDEX | HUMIDITY INDEX

LATITUDE 41° N

FIGURE 7-9.

Relationship between moisture index and distribution of natural vegation across the United States. [After Thornthwaite and Mather, Drexel Inst. Tech., Publ. in Clim. 8:72, 1955.]

climates are extensive in the midwest from the Canadian border to the Gulf of Mexico. Much of Florida is subhumid moist, as are also some western belts along lower mountain slopes. Much of the Great Plains area is semiarid, and arid climates are found in the Southwest and farther north between the Rockies on the east and the Sierras and Cascades on the west.

Thornthwaite's generalized moisture index is made up of two separate indexes, an index of humidity and an index of aridity:

$$I_h = \frac{100s}{n},$$

$$I_a = \frac{100d}{n},$$

where s = water surplus, d = water deficiency, and n = water need.

These two indexes, of humidity and aridity, as shown by Thornthwaite and Mather (1955) are related to the distribution of natural vegetation across the North American continent (Figure 7-9).

In the eastern states, where the humidity index is 50 or more and the aridity is close to zero, oak-chestnut forests make up much of the natural vegetation. From Ohio westward through Indiana and Illinois oak-hickory forest prevails, and in Illinois the transition between woodland and grass begins. In eastern and central Iowa tall grass prairie vegetation is dominant, changing farther west, as the aridity index increases and the humidity index declines, to short grass and eventually to desert vegetation. Then, in Red Bluff, California the pattern shows both high aridity and high humidity indexes (at different seasons) and bunch grass is dominant. Finally on the northern California coast in the moist Pacific fog belt, the redwood forest occurs.

Thornthwaite and Mather (1955) suggest that these attempts to correlate climate and vegetation are to be considered tentative, but that the soil moisture regime and the influence of soil moisture on climax vegetation is extremely important in determining plant distribution.

ADAPTATION TO MOISTURE CONDITIONS

An ecological classification of plants, on the basis of their water relations, was made by Warming (1909). Three groups were distinguished: hydrophytes, mesophytes, and xerophytes.

Hydrophytes

Two kinds of hydrophytes have been recognized: aquatic plants which normally grow in water and swamp, and bog plants which can grow in soils too wet for ordinary plants. Hydrophytes extend their roots into water or into saturated soil. Structurally, most hydrophytes are characterized by sponginess of tissues. Stomata may be numerous but are located mainly on the upper surface of the leaves. A number of ecological groups of hydrophytes have been described by Daubenmire (1959). Suspended hydrophytes, such as phytoplankton, are in contact only with water. Floating hydrophytes include such plants as duckweed (*Lemna minor*) and water hyacinth (*Eichhornia*). Some hydrophytes are submerged, yet anchored to the earth below, such as eelgrass (*Zostera*), pondweed (*Potamogeton*), and many small algae. Another group has floating leaves, but is anchored below, such as water lily (*Castalia*), spatterdock (*Nuphar*), and burrweeds (*Sparghanium*). A final group may be called anchored, emergent hydrophytes. They grow in shallow water and extend their shoots above the surface. Examples include cattail (*Typha*), bullrush (*Scirpus*), cordgrass (*Spartina*), sedges (*Carex*), bald cypress (*Taxodium*), mangrove (*Rhizophora*), and some varieties of rice (*Oryza sativa*).

Mesophytes

Most common land plants, including common crops excepting certain types of rice are mesophytes. Stomata often are confined to, or are more numerous on, the underleaf surfaces. Root hairs are abundant and root length and volume often equal or exceed the top growth. Experimental studies of forage grasses by Paltridge and Mair (1936) furnished a new basis for classification in moisture adaptation groups. Under controlled conditions the xerophytic nature of several species was determined, based on water losses as the permanent wilting percentage was approached. Species which wilted permanently after losing 25% of their total water content were considered to be true mesophytes. Xerophytic mesophytes were those which wilted after losing from 25% to 50% of their water, including *Festuca, Bromus, Lolium,* and *Themeda* species.

Xerophytes

These plants were described as being capable of enduring prolonged drought without injury. They will grow on a substrate which becomes depleted of water for growth to a depth of eight or ten inches (or more) during a normal season. In the grass experiments of Paltridge and Mair, species were classified as xerophytes if they wilted permanently only after losing from 50% to 75% of their total water content. These included species of *Eragrostis* and *Danthonia.* True xerophytes were considered those species which could be reduced to a water residium of about 25% without wilting. This group included *Agropyron, Phalaris, Oryzopsis, Stipa,* and *Erharta* species. It seems likely that many ecologists may question whether all of these last mentioned grasses are to be considered true xerophytes. However, Paltridge and Mair based their classification on actual experimental results and in any case we can accept the idea that, relatively, *Agropyron* and *Stipa* species are more drought tolerant than are *Bromus* and *Festuca* species.

TRANSPIRATION AND WATER USE

Of all materials used by plants, water is by far the greatest in quantity. Most of the water absorbed by the roots of the plant, however, is not retained but is evaporated into the air from the leaves and other aerial parts of the plant. The wet surfaces of water-filled mesophyllic cells in the leaves are in intimate contact with intercellular spaces, which lead to the outside atmosphere through the stomata. Water evaporated from the mesophyll cells goes through the intercellular spaces to the external air. Water lost from the leaves is replaced by water brought up through the vascular system of the plant from its root system (Bonner and Galston, 1952). In general, water relations of the plant as a whole involve absorption of water, ascent of sap, and loss of water through transpiration.

The process of transpiration is essentially one of a loss of water in the vapor form, through leaf stomata (and lenticels of woody plants). The opening and closing of the stomates are controlled by environmental factors: light, water content of the leaves, and temperature. In general, stomates open in the light and close in darkness, the CO_2 content of the substomatal cavity probably being critical (Bonner and Galston). When the

CO_2 content drops (because of the photosynthetic use of CO_2), the stomatal guard cells become turgid owing to an increase in diffusion pressure deficit and uptake of water, and the stomates open.

Transpiration rate is determined by the steepness of the vapor-pressure-deficit gradient. It will increase with an increase in temperature, a decrease in atmospheric vapor pressure, an increase in wind speed, and an adequate supply of moisture to the leaves. Plant factors affecting transpiration include leaf structure, orientation of leaves, curling or rolling of leaves, total leaf area, root-shoot ratio, osmotic pressure of the cell sap, and presence of fungi, sprays, and dusts (Turrell, 1936; Parker, 1949; Miller, 1916; Boon-Long, 1941; Yarwood, 1947; Horsfall and Harrison, 1939; and Shirley and Meuli, 1938).

Transpiration has been measured by enclosing a plant, a branch, or a single leaf in a transparent container through which an air stream is passed. Water vapor transpired is measured by collecting it in an absorbent such as calcium chloride, an infrared gas analyzer, or a Thermoflux, in which water vapor is measured by the heat produced upon reaction with sulfuric acid (Heinicke and Childers, 1936; Decker and Wetzel, 1957; and Huber and Miller, 1954). Another device, a humidity-sensing instrument which measured changes in humidity of air passing over plant material, was used by Went (1957). A gravimetric determination of transpiration was made by Nutman (1941) with coffee trees and by Veihmeyer (1927) with fruit trees by enclosing a large soil mass containing the tree in a container from which water could not evaporate. Soil moisture was replenished frequently to prevent water from becoming a limiting factor. Water loss through transpiration was computed at regular intervals. The container used by Veihmeyer had a capacity of 1000 pounds, and that used by Nutman a capacity of about 5000 pounds. These workers recognized that the potted trees were not under normal field conditions, and, especially because they were not subjected to the same cycle of increase and decrease in moisture as is present in the field, transpiration values were hardly considered comparable to field values.

The daily rhythm of transpiration was reported by Briggs and Shantz (1916). Their data showed conclusively that the rate of transpiration is controlled primarily by solar radiation. The daily march of transpiration for alfalfa, indicating its relation to solar radiation and air temperature is given in Figure 7-10. The daily maximum transpiration rate was usually reached between 2 and 4 p.m. The average transpiration at night was approximately 3% to 5% of that of daylight hours.

Seasonal aspects of transpiration are of great importance. Comparisons of coniferous and broad-leaved deciduous trees in autumn and in winter were

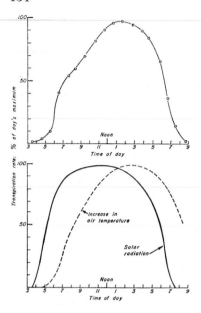

FIGURE 7-10.

The daily march of solar radiation and transpiration in an alfalfa field. [After Briggs and Shantz, Jour. Agr. Res. 5:583, 1916.]

made by Weaver and Mogensen (1919). Total transpiration from conifers in autumn was as great as it was for broad-leaved trees. Defoliation of broad-leaved trees in late autumn caused a reduction in water losses not unlike that in conifers. Winter transpiration of conifers was from 1/55 to 1/250 as great as it was in autumn and was similar to that from defoliated deciduous trees.

The magnitude of water losses through transpiration is indeed great. An acre of Iowa corn transpires enough water in a single season to make from 12 to 16 inches of rainfall. To produce a ton of alfalfa hay in the Great Plains region may require the transpiration of 700 to 1000 tons of water. It was estimated by Hoover (1944) that a hardwood forest in the southern Appalachians transpired 17 to 22 inches of water per year, and a single tree lost as much as 50 to 100 gallons of water in a single day. The ratio of the amount of water transpired to the amount of dry matter produced is an expression of the transpiration ratio.

Many studies have been made of water losses through the transpiration of various crops. The transpiration ratios obtained have varied greatly with differences in environmental factors, particularly solar radiation, soil moisture, soil fertility, atmospheric vapor-pressure deficit, and plant diseases. Following extensive studies on transpiration rates and wilting percentages by Briggs and Shantz (1912a, 1912b, 1912c), Briggs (1914), Shantz and Piemeisel (1927) listed the relative water requirements for a number of crops at Akron, Colorado (Table 7-3).

The effects of rainfall and nitrogen supply on transpiration ratios of several grasses have been reported by Burton, Prine, and Jackson (1957), and are given in Table 7-4.

Increasing nitrogen resulted in much more efficient water use (except with Pangolagrass). The two most drought-tolerant varieties, Coastal and Suwanee Burmudagrass, developed through breeding and selection, produced more dry matter per unit of water transpired under the dry conditions of 1954 than in the wet year of 1953. Common Bermudagrass, how-

TABLE 7-3. RELATIVE WATER REQUIREMENT OF SEVERAL CROPS AT AKRON, COLORADO

Crop	Relative Water Requirement
Proso millet	1.00
Common millet	1.07
Sorghum	1.14
Corn	1.31
Barley	1.94
Wheat	2.09
Oats	2.18
Rye	2.37
Legumes	2.81
Grasses	3.10

ever, was less efficient in water use under drought conditions than it was under favorable moisture.

In Australia, Williams (1935) found that increased phosphorus decreased the transpiration ratio of oats in two ways: (1) by decreasing transpiration per unit of leaf weight, and (2) by decreasing ratio of leaf weight to total plant weight during the latter part of the growth cycle.

Plant diseases may greatly affect water requirement of cereals. Johnston and Miller (1934) estimated that the water requirement of wheat may be increased by from 30% to 100% as a result of leaf-rust infection. Murphy (1935) showed that a susceptible variety of oats, inoculated with crown-rust in the seedling stage, may use up to four times as much water as a resistant variety.

TABLE 7-4. TRANSPIRATION RATIOS FOR SEVERAL GRASSES IN A DRY AND A WET SEASON, WITH DIFFERENT RATES OF NITROGEN

	Pounds of Water Used per Pound of Dry Matter Produced			
	1953 (wet year)*		1954 (dry year)†	
	Nitrogen added		Nitrogen added	
Grass	50 lbs/acre	200 lbs/acre	50 lbs/acre	200 lbs/acre
Coastal Bermudagrass	2478	803	1547	641
Suwanee Bermudagrass	1923	692	1107	452
Common Bermudagrass	6812	1546	9738	4336
Pensacola Bahiagrass	2200	870	3103	1239
Pangolagrass	2249	2240	2843	3016

* Rainfall April 1 to November 1, 39.66 inches in 1953.
† Rainfall April 1 to November 1, 13.68 inches in 1954.

It has been claimed that transpiration benefits the plant in a number of ways: (1) by cooling the leaves, (2) by preventing excessive turgidity, (3) by causing water movement to the leaves, and (4) by increasing absorption and translocation of minerals. The importance of the first three points has been discounted by Curtis (1936), Miller (1938), and Bonner and Galston (1952), but evidence that increased water absorption results in increased salt absorption has been presented (Winneberger, 1958).

On the other hand, these are certain harmful effects of transpiration. These include rapid water loss, resulting in loss of turgor and temporary wilting during the middle of the day. Growth cessation may occur, but this may not be serious if tissues recover turgor each evening. But, even with some loss of turgidity, stomates may close, photosynthesis is retarded, and dehydration disturbs the starch-sugar balance, respiration rate, and other processes. Excessive transpiration is regarded as a dangerous process for the plant and, as Bonner and Galston suggest, might be considered as "an unfortunate coincidence associated with the structural features of leaves which make them adapted to efficient photosynthesis."

PLANT RESPONSE TO MOISTURE

Cell-water Relations

Living plant cells are composed of protoplasts surrounded by more or less rigid walls which limit volume changes. The protoplast consists of a thin layer of cytoplasm in which a nucleus and sometimes plastids are embedded, with a central vacuole filled with cell sap (Kramer and Kozlowski, 1960). Cell walls are highly permeable to water and to solutes. The cytoplasmic membranes are relatively permeable to water, but less permeable than the cell walls. The cytoplasmic membranes are relatively impermeable to sugars and to most ions; therefore, solutes which have accumulated in the vacuoles tend to remain there. This produces osmotic pressures which vary from 10 to 20 atmospheres in most mesophytes (Meyer, 1956; Stocking, 1956). In xerophytes osmotic pressures up to 60 atmospheres, and in halophytes up to 100 atmospheres have been recorded (Maximov, 1929; Oppenheimer, 1951). Osmotic pressure represents the potential, or maximum, pressure that can be developed in a solution when separated from pure water by a membrane permeable only to water (Meyer and Anderson, 1952).

The accepted principle of water movement in plants is that water moves along gradients of decreasing free energy. The difference between the free energy of pure water and that of water in a solution (water in the soil or in the plant cell sap) can be measured. This difference is called the diffusion-pressure deficit by Meyer (1945) and is identical with "suction force" as used by many research workers, especially in Europe. The diffusion-pressure deficit, or DPD as it is generally called, is a measure of the net tendency of water to diffuse into the plant cell. Thus we can see how the presence of a decreasing free energy gradient, or DPD, results in movement of water from the soil to the plant to the air (Table 7-5).

TABLE 7-5. GRADIENT OF DIFFUSION-PRESSURE DEFICIT FROM SOIL TO PLANT TO AIR*

	Diffusion-pressure Deficit in Atmosphere
Soil near field capacity	0.1
Roots at zero turgor	5–6.0
Leaves at zero turgor	10–50.0
Air at 90% relative humidity	140.5

* After Kramer and Kozlowski, 1960.

The osmotic relations of water and plant cells, as indicated by Meyer, Anderson, and Böhning (1960) and Kramer and Kozlowski (1960), may be expressed as follows: Diffusion-pressure deficit (DPD) = osmotic pressure (OP) − wall pressure (WP). The wall pressure = turgor pressure.

Cells will absorb water from the soil or from adjacent cells having a lower DPD and will lose water to cells of higher DPD. As water diffuses into the cell, the cell volume increases, producing increasing wall pressure (turgor pressure). When the turgor pressure becomes equal to the osmotic pressure of the cell, the DPD becomes zero and the entrance of water ceases. Interrelationships among cell volume, turgor pressure, osmotic pressure, and diffusion-pressure deficit are shown in Figure 7-11. Slatyer (1957) noted that the DPD may increase until it is even greater than the osmotic pressure of the cell sap, resulting in a negative cell-wall pressure or tension.

Soil Moisture and Internal Water Balance

Water held in the larger pores in most soils drains away within a few days after

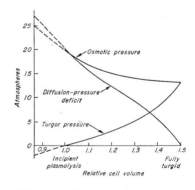

FIGURE 7-11.

Interrelationships among cell volume, turgor pressure, osmotic pressure, and diffusion pressure deficit. [After Höfler in Kramer and Kozlowski, Physiology of Trees. N. Y.: McGraw-Hill, 1960.]

a heavy rain. This leaves the soil at a moisture content known as **field capacity,** often defined as the amount of water retained in the soil after gravitational drainage of excess water. Field capacity varies with soil texture, with a range of 5% to 40% for most soils. Plants will extract water, if none is added, until they eventually wilt. The permanent wilting percentage for a soil refers to the moisture content at the time a plant permanently wilts unless moisture is added. The difference between field capacity and the permanent wilting percentage represents available water for plant use. Again, available water varies greatly with soil texture, as do the permanent wilting percentage and the field capacity.

Briggs and Shantz (1912a, 1912b, 1912c) reported that soil moisture percentage at the time of permanent wilting of plants showed little variation from plant to plant on any one soil, regardless of the species or the environmental conditions. They believed that vegetative growth practically ceased at the wilting point. This view was supported in general by Veihmeyer and Hendrickson (1927, 1928, 1929, 1934, 1945, 1948, 1949, 1950), who introduced the term "permanent wilting percentage," defined as the percentage of water remaining in the soil at the time of permanent wilting.

Hendrickson and Veihmeyer (1945) noted two methods for determining wilting point values: (1) following a systematic sampling of the soil for moisture, the moisture content at the point where the plant no longer extracts moisture at any one horizon was called the wilting point; (2) a method which involved the growing and wilting of indicator plants in the greenhouse. When wilted, plants were placed in a dark chamber at high humidity. If they recovered, they were wilted further, until they no longer recovered after 24 hours in the humid dark chamber. The moisture content of the soil was determined at this point and expressed as a percentage of dry weight of soil.

The work of Taylor, Blaney, and McLaughlin (1934) suggested that the term "wilting range" was better than wilting percentage. This range extended from the "wilting coefficient" value of Briggs and Shantz (1912a) to the ultimate wilting percentage, beyond which recovery did not take place.

It should be remembered that plant growth is controlled largely by the internal water balance of the plant (Kramer, 1959). The rates of various physiological processes are closely related to internal water balance and plant turgor, which in turn are dependent on the relative rates of water absorption and water loss.

Internal water deficits occur in plants when water loss through transpiration continues to be greater than absorption of water through the roots. The transpiration rate of normal, well-watered plants is controlled by plant factors including leaf area, internal leaf structure, thickness of cutin, and

extent of stomatal openings, and by environmental factors including solar radiation, humidity, temperature, and wind (Kramer,
1959). Water absorption by the roots is dependent on rate of transpiration, extent and
efficiency of the root system, and availability of
soil moisture. It is affected by aeration, concentration of the soil solution, and soil temperature, as well as by soil moisture tension. The
rate of water absorption tends to lag behind
the rate of transpiration because of resistance
to the movement of water into the roots, as
indicated in Figure 7-12.

On hot, sunny days severe water deficits
often develop by noon or early afternoon.
These deficits are usually eliminated by absorption of water during the night but, as soil

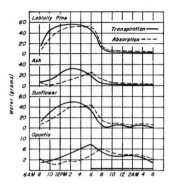

FIGURE 7-12.

*Diurnal variations in rate of
transpiration and rate of water absorption for four plant
species. [After Kramer, Amer.
Jour. Bot. 24:10–15, 1937.]*

moisture becomes depleted, water absorption becomes slower, until finally
internal deficits cannot be remedied and growth ceases. This situation is
complicated by the fact that excessive transpiration may occur during hot,
windy weather even though soil moisture is high. Also, in damp, foggy
weather, plants in dry soil may not suffer severe water deficits because of
the low rate of water loss. The internal water balance, therefore, is the important aspect of moisture as far as growth is concerned. This principle has
been recognized in sugarcane production by Clements and Kubota (1942),
who found that young leaf sheath moisture content was a good indication of
internal water balance and of the "general well-being of the plant."

The availability of soil moisture for potential absorption has been defined
in terms of total soil moisture stress. This value, TSMS, is equivalent to the
combined effects of soil moisture tension, the osmotic pressure of the soil
tension, and the osmotic pressure of the soil solution. It is comparable to
the diffusion pressure deficit previously discussed (Meyer, 1945; Richards
and Wadleigh, 1952).

With increasing soil moisture stress, turgor in the plant tissues decreases
and growth rate decreases. When DPD increases to the point where turgor
pressure is zero, growth will cease. Actually, experimental data have shown
that decreased growth has often been evident at relatively low levels of
soil moisture stress. This evidence tends to show rather clearly that growth
is retarded before the permanent wilting percentage is reached (Kenworthy,
1949; Richards and Wadleigh, 1952; Bernstein and Pearson, 1954; and
Slatyer, 1957). This is in contrast to the view that soil moisture between
field capacity and the wilting point is equally available for plant growth.

It has been suggested that the reason why growth is retarded before the permanent wilting percentage is reached is the direct effect of decreasing hydration on growth. Slatyer has noted that growth will be affected more than transpiration, with decreasing turgor, because transpiration is caused largely by the diffusion-pressure gradient from leaf to atmosphere and the rate of water supplied to the roots. Further, Slatyer has suggested that the permanent wilting percentage is basically a value determined by the osmotic characteristics of the plant, rather than by soil characteristics. The osmotic pressure of the cell sap is especially important because it is this value which determines the DPD that exists at zero turgor pressure in the cells of the leaves of the plant. For many common mesophytic plants, including the sunflower, which has been used extensively in wilting-point determinations, a TSMS of approximately 15 atmospheres corresponds roughly with the permanent wilting percentage (Richards and Weaver, 1943, 1944; Robertson and Kohnke, 1946). However, as Slatyer (1957) has shown, interpretations of wilting percentage determinations must be made with caution and must not be assumed to have universal application.

Effects of Water Deficits

The direct effects of soil moisture stress on plant growth were considered by Hagan (1957) as having definite plant factor, soil factor, and weather factor aspects. Of the plant factors, elongation of plant organs and increase in fresh or dry weight are sensitive to soil moisture stress, whereas photosynthesis and respiration are relatively insensitive. The percentage of sugar in cane and beets increases with moisture stress. In tobacco, increasing stress results in a lower sugar content but a higher content of nicotine and nitrogen. During the maturation period, moisture stress may greatly influence the value of the tobacco crop.

The stage of growth may also be an important factor in determining the effect of moisture stress. Corn is especially sensitive to stress at the time of anthesis and shortly thereafter, probably owing to the greater likelihood of a disturbance of internal water balance in the plant at that particular stage of growth (Tatum and Kehr, 1951; Zuber and Decker, 1956).

Studies by Denmead and Shaw (1960) showed that a severe soil moisture stress prior to silking reduced the grain yield of corn by 25%, moisture stress at silking reduced grain yield by 50%, and moisture stress at ear stage, 30 days after silking, reduced yield by 21%.

The nature of the root system is another plant factor markedly affecting the relation of soil moisture stress to plant growth (Hagan, 1957). Under favorable conditions, perennial crops tend to develop well-branched root systems which permeate the soil rather thoroughly, the depth depending on the nature of the species. Below this depth, roots do not occupy all of the soil area and moisture extraction must be in a variable pattern. In some annual crops a well-branched root system develops, permeating rather completely a soil volume which is continually increasing. If the soil is wet to field capacity, such an ever-expanding root system may contact new sources of water rapidly enough to replace water losses by transpiration. The watermelon plant is an example of such root development and it responds little to irrigation even when a rather high soil moisture stress is apparent. Other crops have widely spaced roots, leaving soil relatively untapped for moisture. Such crops may respond to irrigation when soil moisture stress is still low. The principle, that the sparser the roots the greater the likelihood that growth will be retarded by delayed irrigation is illustrated in Figure 7-13.

Slatyer (1955) reported on a comparison of three crops, cotton, peanut, and grain sorghum during a period of severe moisture stress. The water balance of the plants was followed using Weatherly's (1950) "relative turgidity" technique, a measurement of leaf turgor. As moisture stress increased, the sorghum plants maintained higher levels of leaf turgor and showed a slower rate of decreasing turgor. In cotton, turgor decrease was rapid. A decrease in growth rate followed the turgor decrease, occurring in cotton just as soon as soil moisture stress occurred. In sorghum, however, growth rate did not decrease until severe soil moisture stress occurred. The peanut plants were intermediate in reaction to moisture stress. Slatyer indicated that grain sorghum showed remarkable adaptation to conditions of moisture stress by having the best developed root system of the three crops, and the most effective internal control over transpiration.

The nature of the root system may be influenced considerably by soil moisture stress. In Alabama, Bennett and Doss (1960) found that rooting depths of six cool-season forage species were influenced more by differences in soil moisture than by inherent species differences.

Plants removed moisture first from the top six inches of soil, where concentration of roots was greatest. As moisture stress

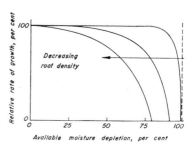

FIGURE 7-13.

Effects of spatial density of roots on relation of growth to apparent depletion of available moisture. [After Hagan, Rept. 14th Inter. Hort. Congr., Wageningen, Netherlands, pp. 82–98, 1955.]

increased, moisture was extracted from successively lower soil depths. Wilt-ing was frequent before much of the available moisture at the lower rooting depths was depleted. More than 70% of the total weight of roots was found in the top 12 inches of soil for all species at all moisture levels. Tall fescue and reed canarygrass had the most profuse rooting systems of the species tested, but Atlantic alfalfa produced the greatest total weight of roots. Orchardgrass had the smallest total root system, with roots extending only to 26 inches at high levels and to 48 inches at low levels of moisture.

In a similar study of four warm-season forage species, Doss, Ashley, and Bennett (1960) showed that the depth of soil moisture extraction increased as soil moisture decreased. Three moisture regimes were established by irrigating when 30%, 65%, and 85% of the available soil moisture had been removed in the surface 24 inches. An average for all species showed that roots extracted soil moisture to a depth of 25 inches, 29 inches, and 36 inches respectively for the three moisture regimes of increasing soil mois-ture stress. Burmudagrass had the greatest total amount of roots followed in order by Bahiagrass and Dallisgrass.

Soil factors which affect root density may influence the response of plants to decreasing moisture supply. Mechanical impedance, slow water penetra-tion, poor internal drainage, and deficient aeration may cause sparse and shallow roots (Hagan, 1957). Soil structure, texture, depth, and moisture-release characteristics all affect the rate of change in soil moisture stress. A stable water table in the lower portion of the root zone may supply a large part of the water absorbed by the roots, but a fluctuating water table may cause shallow rooting. Salinity may effectively increase soil moisture stress and decrease root development. Soil temperature is also an important factor in determining the growth rate and distribution of roots. Soil-borne diseases and nematodes may reduce root surface area and cause poor plant growth at low levels of soil moisture tension.

The effect of moisture stress on tenderness of citrus fruit to frost, fumiga-tion, spray, and storage was studied by Monselise and Turrell (1959). By sampling citrus groves in a 5000-square-mile area in California, from the desert to the coastal region, it was found that fruit grown in the drier areas had a peel of higher puncture-pressure and dry weight than did fruit grown in the coastal, more humid areas. This tougher peel, associated with higher moisture stress in the growing area, was correlated with resistance to dam-age by frost, fumigation, spray, or storage conditions.

Problems of the production of seed *versus* forage in legumes are often associated with soil moisture conditions. In the Corn Belt states, seed yields of alfalfa, red clover, and other legumes are usually low. Soils are likely to be moist, often near field capacity, sometime during the season of flowering and seed maturation. In the summer-dry climate of many of the valleys of the Pacific Coast region, irrigation is so regulated that soils are under progressively increasing moisture stress during the flowering period. While there are other very important factors involved, especially insect pollination, nevertheless soil moisture appears to be an important aspect of legume seed production.

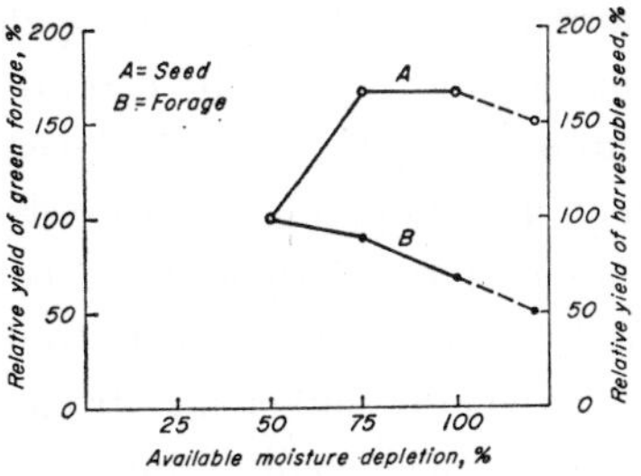

FIGURE 7-14.

Yield of forage and seed of Ladino clover in California with increasing soil-moisture depletion. [After Hagan, Calif. Agr. 11:11, 1957.]

In producing Ladino clover seed in California, Hagan (1957) has shown that a relatively high level of soil moisture is a detriment to seed production. Under a decreasing soil moisture supply, forage yield drops whereas seed yield may increase materially (Figure 7-14).

Stanhill (1957) noted that crops harvested for their vegetative parts are more likely to show deleterious effects from increased moisture stress than those harvested for their reproductive organs or seed. A possible exception may be the effect of moisture stress on fruit, reported by Magness, Degman, and Furr (1935). An increasing soil moisture stress was found to cause an early closing of the stomata, a marked reduction in fruit size, and poor coloring of the fruit.

Drought Resistance

The term "drought" usually refers to a deficiency of available soil moisture which produces water deficits in the plant sufficient to cause a reduction in growth (Kramer and Kozlowski, 1960). Associated with low soil moisture in most instances, the effects of drought are greatly enhanced by atmospheric conditions, including low humidity, high temperature, and wind. Atmospheric drought may cause wilting of plants, although this is usually temporary. Extensive areas with sparse vegetation and drying winds are subjected to atmospheric drought which often occurs even when soil moisture is not a limiting factor. Injurious results of atmospheric drought are most likely to occur in areas near the physiological limits of production (Klages, 1942). Shimper (1903) spoke of "physiological drought," a condition resulting from cold soil or high osmotic pressure of the soil solution, but data by Walter (1955) would appear to discount osmotic pressure as a cause of this condition.

The term "drought" has a relative meaning, depending on location. The normal rainfall cycle and pattern should be taken into consideration in designating a drought condition for a given area. In climates having dry summers, such as Pacific Coast valleys, the long period without rain is normal, and cropping plans are designed to correspond with the seasonal moisture patterns. Irrigation, of course, eliminates the necessity of planting so as to avoid serious effects from the long dry summer. If the moisture pattern deviates sufficiently from normal, however, to result in reduced yields of crops, we usually think of that as a drought situation.

Just as drought often must be considered in general terms, so must drought resistance. There are definable differences between species in their drought tolerance, but the concept also may have connotations of relative differences. For example, in humid areas *Bromus inermis* is often called drought resistant, but in the short-grass steppe region it is not considered drought resistant as compared with such species as *Agropyron smithii*.

The nature of drought resistance has been controversial for many years. Early ideas considered water loss the primary factor, but later studies suggested that the capacity to endure desiccation was the most important basis of true drought resistance. Russell (1959a) used the term *drought resistance* to refer to the over-all suitability of plants for cultivation under dry conditions, and *drought hardiness* to describe the capacity to endure desiccation.

The nature of drought resistance has been reviewed by Levitt (1951, 1956), Kursanov (1956), Parker (1956), Iljin (1957), and others. At present, it is believed that many factors influence drought resistance, including those which tend to delay dehydration, such as efficiency of absorbing surfaces and water conducting system, leaf area and structure, stomatal behavior, osmotic pressure, and another group of factors which enable the plant to survive dehydration, such as cell size, cell shape, and ability of the protoplasm to withstand desiccation.

Adaptations to Escape or Delay Drought Damage

In arid regions there may be a brief rainy season when conditions are favorable for germination and establishment of seedlings. Short-lived annuals which grow quickly, mature, disperse seed, and die before the soil dries out are drought-escaping rather than drought-enduring plants. The long dry season is passed while the plant is in the form of seeds which are able to avoid effects of drought.

Succulents are plants characterized by a proliferation of parenchyma cells, enlargement of vacuoles, and reduction in size of intercellular spaces. Large quantities of water can be accumulated in succulent tissues, to be used when soil moisture cannot supply enough for the plants requirement. To be very effective, succulents must have low transpiration rates during dry seasons. Actually, most succulents are conservative users of water, in contrast with some xerophytes (MacDougal and Spaulding, 1910). Studies by Shreve (1916) showed that stomata regulation properties of cacti and other succulents were such that they are closed during the daytime when transpiration stress is greatest.

Structural characteristics such as deep, wide-spreading root systems, small transpiring surface in proportion to root surface, reduction in leaf area when moisture stress develops, few or embedded stomata, and thick cutinous layers aid plants in avoiding or enduring periods of moisture deficiency.

The mesquite tree, *Prosopis,* and alfalfa are examples of plants with deep root systems which make contact with permanently moist subsoil. The effect of the plant's deep root system has been amply demonstrated in alfalfa during drought periods in the midwest, when forage yields remain relatively high, compared with yields of more shallow-rooted cereal crops and grasses.

Among orchard, shade, and forest trees, rooting depth has been shown to be of great importance. During the 1930's, when drought damage was widespread throughout the midwest region, Albertson and Weaver (1945) found the greatest mortality among species with shallow, poorly developed root systems.

True drought resistance, or drought hardiness, is probably based more on the degree of desiccation which a plant's protoplasm can withstand than on any other factor. A plant which shows great tolerance to desiccation is the creosote bush, *Larrea tridentata.* This species can tolerate dehydration to 50% of its dry weight (Runyon, 1936). Even in this species, however, leaves are not all alike in ability to withstand desiccation. Leaves arising at the third and fourth nodes are much more drought-tolerant than are those at the first and second nodes. Under severe moisture stress the less resistant leaves often drop off the plant.

Oppenheimer (1951) indicated that an effective basis for drought resistance was a combination of protoplasm that can endure dehydration and those morphological and anatomical features which reduce water loss and delay internal water deficits. Most drought-resistant trees appear to be in this category.

Specific responses of plants to drought have been considered by Iljin (1957) and may be stated as follows:

1. Functioning of stomata is often greatly reduced; they may remain closed during the whole day.

2. Both mesophytes and xerophytes show marked increase in sugar content during drought.

3. Photosynthesis is hampered by reduction of stomatal openings, limiting CO_2 absorption.

4. Mesophytes often show increased rates of respiration.

5. With increasing moisture stress, osmotic pressure tends to become much greater in the leaves than in the roots.

6. Cell size and shape are important in determining their resistance to desiccation.

The theory of drought injury advanced by Iljin (1953, 1957) appears to be the most adequate of all that have been proposed. It suggests that mechanical injuries to the cells cause the damage. When the vacuoles shrink, the protoplasm is pulled inward. If the cell walls are rigid, the protoplasm may be subjected to too much tension. If the cell walls are soft, they are pulled inward with the vacuoles and form wrinkles. The alternate drying and remoistening bring on mechanical stresses strong enough to cause death of the cells.

Crop Management to Reduce Drought Injury

The importance of breeding for greater water-use efficiency has been emphasized by Burton (1959). Improved varieties of Bermudagrass have proven to be exceedingly successful from the standpoint of lower transpiration ratios. Other examples may be found in barley and wheat breeding in California. The Mariout variety of barley, according to Suneson (1957), is better than other varieties in dry sections of California, and is much better adapted to high-salt soils than other varieties available in that region. In the breeding of Ramona wheat, water-use efficiency has been increased because it ripens 30 days earlier than old varieties.

Cultural practices also may aid in promoting more efficient water use. Many conservation practices, contour rows, use of stubble mulch, early planting to permit greatest utilization of winter moisture, shallow cultivation, and weed control without root damage to crops, all aid in making water use more efficient.

Fertilizer applications which increase yields may increase water-use efficiency. Stansberry, et al. (1955) showed that, by increasing the P_2O_5 applied per acre of irrigated alfalfa from 100 to 500 pounds per acre, the water required to produce a ton of hay decreased from 14.2 to 8.4 acre-inches.

Too Much Moisture

Too much water may be just as harmful to plants as too little. The maximum moisture which can be tolerated varies with different species, but the most injurious aspects of too much moisture are lack of aeration and reduction in oxygen supply. Wet soils frequently suffer the results of poor nitrification which is noticeable at times in the yellowed, sickly appearance of corn and other crops, in poorly drained soils, and at times on other soils during periods of heavy rainfall which often occur in the Corn Belt region during May or early June.

Poor aeration because of inadequate soil drainage greatly affects growth and functioning of roots. Low oxygen and high CO_2 probably have their greatest effect on the permeability of roots to water. Aeration is also highly important because of its effect on aerobic metabolism and consequent uptake and accumulation of nutrient ions in the roots (Russell, 1959b). Microbial activity in an anaerobic environment (in flooded soils) may have some positive deleterious effects on root growth.

High soil moisture and humidity conditions existing under wet irrigation regimes may increase disease damage to crops. Stockton and Doneen (1957) have demonstrated the effect of irrigation timing and extent on the yield of cotton and the prevalence of *Verticillium* wilt infection (Table 7-6).

TABLE 7-6. WILT DAMAGE IN COTTON AS RELATED TO IRRIGATION FREQUENCY AND TIMING

Treatment	A	C	B	D
Number of irrigations	3	4	7	5
Date of first irrigation	7/9	6/25	6/15	7/9
Yield, bales per acre	2.16	2.11	1.74	2.16
Percent of plants infected	48	35	71	38

It is believed that the early June irrigation supplied moist conditions resulting in rapid spread of the *Verticillium* wilt.

Moisture may be too high in the early spring, which contributes to failure in establishing stands of legumes and grasses, or killing of seedlings already established. Tolerance to flooding has been studied in Canada by McKenzie (1951). Through the use of leveled irrigation borders, which were flooded for varying periods of time in the spring, forage species were found to differ considerably in tolerance to spring flooding (Table 7-7).

An excess of moisture later in the growing season may result in delayed flowering, in poor seed setting, and often in lower quality of seed. This

TABLE 7-7. TOLERANCE OF FORAGE SPECIES TO FLOODING IN THE SPRING

Crop	Number of Days Flooding Tolerated
Red clover	0–7
Sweetclover	7–14
Alfalfa	7–14
Alsike clover	7–14
Strawberry clover	7–21
Intermediate wheatgrass	21–28
Meadow fescue	21–42
Timothy	21–56
Reed canarygrass	35–56
Slender wheatgrass	35–56
Bromegrass	35–56

is frequently a problem in the northern part of the Corn Belt, and has important effects on uniformity and quality of corn and soybeans. It is of particular importance in harvesting grain sorghum in the more humid part of the sorghum area, where rains in September and October may prevent seed from reaching a uniform and low moisture percentage before cold weather arrives in autumn.

SOME IRRIGATION PROBLEMS

At the present time, it is estimated that approximately 30 million acres are irrigated in the United States. Of these, 28 million acres are located in the western part of the nation.

Historically, the western region has been dominated by the influence of the desert. In Montana, Idaho, Wyoming, Nevada, Utah, Colorado, Arizona, and New Mexico, the eight states referred to by Webb (1957) as the desert states, the average annual precipitation is approximately 12 inches. The states bordering this region on the east have an annual precipitation of 24 inches, and the states to the west, 26.5 inches.

Extensive forested areas at relatively high elevations, in the Rocky Mountain, Cascade, and Sierra Nevada ranges, constitute the major source of irrigation water. It was suggested many years ago (Powell, 1879), that the rainfall necessary to sustain forests was similar to the amount essential for agriculture without irrigation. There is a significant relationship between forested lands and perennial streams useful for irrigation. Some of the finest western forests, Yellowstone, Yosemite, Sequoia, Rocky Mountain, and Grand Teton National Parks dominate the headwaters of large western rivers.

The President's Water Resources Policy Commission (1950) emphasized the important relationship between forest watershed and irrigated land. In the Central Valley of California, for example, the 25-inch rainfall line marks the division between grass and woodland. The main area that contributes to percolation and runoff water begins in the ponderosa pine area and extends into the much wetter region of the sequoia and red fir. Heaviest precipitation occurs at elevations of about 6000 feet. Heavy snowfall in the high Sierras, extending up to and even above the timberline, contributes significantly to total water. While the Central Valley farmer may have little or no influence on the management of these forest watersheds, their protection and management are of utmost importance to the supply of water in the future.

Some of the western irrigation areas have difficult problems to solve. For example, the Colorado River has an estimated annual flow of approximately 17,732,000 acre-feet (U. S. Bureau of Reclamation, 1946). By the terms of a 1922 compact, 7.5 million acre-feet of water are reserved for the upper basin states of Colorado, New Mexico, Utah, and Wyoming. In the lower Colorado Basin there is great competition for the remainder. Even today, according to Higbee (1958), nearly 9 million acre-feet is lost annually into the Gulf of California. This amount fluctuates greatly, from 5 to 25 million acre-feet annually, and more dams would have to be built to prevent peak spring flows, if this wastage is to be prevented. To meet the demands for water among the several states concerned, flow must be stabilized as much as possible and water apportioned equably.

An illustration of the transfer of surplus water from an area of limited soil resources to a water-deficit area of rich soils is the Colorado–Big Thompson Project (Higbee, 1958). The water is intercepted in the headwaters of the Colorado, conveyed by tunnel through the continental divide to the headwaters of the Big Thompson River, and finally distributed to irrigation districts of the South Platte River system in eastern Colorado.

Complex irrigation problems have been encountered in the Central Valley Project in California. Estimates of annual runoff into the valley show an extreme range of variability from year to year; on the average it is said to be about 33 million acre-feet. This is reported to be enough to supply all of the projected needs in the future, provided the water is properly harnessed and distributed (U. S. Bureau of Reclamation, 1949). One of the major objectives of long-term planning for an equitable distribution of water in the Central Valley is to transfer surplus waters from the Sacramento River in the north to the water-deficit districts located several hundred miles to the south. A great deal of progress has been made toward this goal, through a complex system of dams, reservoirs, canals, and pumping stations extending from the Shasta Dam and reservoir on the upper Sacramento River to the 153-mile Friant-Kern Canal which carries water as far south as Bakersfield. Many additional dams, reservoirs, canals, and pumping stations are needed, however, if the full potential of the great Central Valley is to be realized.

Less spectacular than these problems of getting adequate water, but of great importance, are irrigation practices as they relate to soil properties. If soils are highly permeable, they may be difficult to irrigate because of rapid percolation. Impermeable soils transmit water rapidly over the surface, but do not wet thoroughly. The size of soil particles, compactness and depth of the soil, organic matter content, and ground water level, are all important in determining the amount of water that can be stored by the soil for periods between irrigations.

The most effective use of irrigation water has been discussed by Hagan (1957). He believes that irrigation farmers can anticipate the response of crops to added moisture when certain conditions of weather, soil, and plant prevail. Irrigation water should be used sparingly to attain maximum use of water, minimum losses of water and nutrients through deep percolation, prevention of a drainage problem through over-irrigation, maintenance of good soil tilth, and, in some instances, to obtain high quality of product.

To assure a continuous supply of available soil moisture, the irrigation farmer cannot allow the soil to go to nearly complete moisture depletion. Probably a safety factor of 15% would be satisfactory. That is, water should be applied when available soil water is 85% depleted. This, of course, will depend on the crop grown, its rooting characteristics, the soil type, the irrigation system, and weather factors.

Salts brought in by the irrigation water often present problems. Thorne and Peterson (1949) noted three kinds of soils in western areas which present problems in management: (1) saline soils with sufficient soluble salts to interfere with crop growth, (2) saline-alkali soils containing exchangeable sodium in quantities detrimental to plants, plus appreciable amounts of soluble salts, and (3) nonsaline alkali soils with high exchangeable sodium but low in soluble salts. The so-called "white alkali" is dominated by chlorides, sulfates, nitrates, and some bicarbonates, whereas "black alkali" refers to a predominance of carbonates and bicarbonates of sodium and potassium. These salts are white but they dissolve organic matter, which gives them a black appearance.

Salt content of the surface layers of soil often fluctuates. In dry weather, salts tend to accumulate at the surface; in wet weather they may leach downward. Drainage systems may be an essential part of the irrigation system. The water from the Colorado deposits more than four tons of salts annually on each irrigated acre. In a few years salt spots develop, and the practice of flooding soils for several weeks during the cool season is resorted to in order to leach the salts downward so that crops may be grown successfully.

The action of dissolved salts on plants must be considered on two bases, the physical and chemical effects (Magistad, 1945; Hayward and Wadleigh, 1949). We have noted that in order to maintain turgor a diffusion pressure gradient must exist between the soil moisture and the cell sap moisture. Nonhalophytes begin to show reduced growth when the osmotic pressure of the soil solution exceeds about 2 atmospheres, and salt-tolerant plants will fail when osmotic pressure of the soil solution reaches 47 atmospheres. True halophytes, however, can continue to raise their internal osmotic pressure to compensate for soil solution pressures considerably above 47 atmospheres.

According to Hayward and Magistad (1946), halophytes especially adapted to saline soils include *Atriplex* species (known as saltbush), *Distichlis* species (known as salt grass), and two other grasses, *Spartina townsendii* and *Sporobolus airoides*. Some of these species excrete salt on their foliage.

Among crop species, those which tolerate saline soils include sugar beet, cotton, rape, sorghum, Bermudagrass, Rhodesgrass, western wheatgrass, and *Bromus catharticus*. Intermediate in tolerance are alfalfa, barley, flax, oats, rye, rice, wheat, sudangrass, and birdsfoot trefoil. Poorest in salt tolerance are vetch, peas, beans, potato, sweetpotato, white clover, and red clover.

Symptoms of a high degree of salinity often take the form of deep bluish-green leaves in sugar beets, alfalfa, beans, and clover. In cereals, a high concentration of salts in chloride form causes a strong reddish color as the plants approach maturity.

In most plants, germination is reduced or prevented under highly saline conditions. Chapman (1942) suggested that salinity was a limiting factor, even for halophytes. Over-irrigation, or flooding, is practiced (before planting) to leach salts downward to dilute the soil solution during the period of germination and establishment. In the San Joaquin Valley, California, soils are reclaimed by flooding for a period and then planting to rice. Abundant water is used on the rice crop and, as the root system penetrates into the soil, the channels opened up allow subsequent flooding to leach surface soils still more to reduce the salt content. Then other crops such as barley, alfalfa, and forage grasses are successfully established.

Productivity Under Irrigation

It has been estimated that productivity of crop land in the western part of the United States has been increased approximately three-fold through irrigation. Under relatively high temperatures, such as are found in the tropics and subtropics, extremely high yields of crops have been obtained under irrigation.

In sugarcane production in Hawaii, the same crop has been grown under irrigation on many plantations for 50 to 75 years. No crop rotation has been practiced, and the yield of a single 22- to 24-month crop has often averaged 12 or 13 tons of sugar per acre. In the production of forage crops, it has been shown that Napier grass (*Pennisetum purpureum*) produced 20 tons of dry matter per acre per year (Wilsie, Akamine, and Takahashi, 1940).

An irrigation experiment has been under way at Lethbridge, Alberta, for more than 50 years (Palmer, 1949). For a ten-year period, 1937–1946, average yields per acre were: oats, 109 bushels; barley, 70 bushels; sugar beets, 18 tons; and wheat, 59 bushels.

In recent years there has been a marked increase in interest in irrigation in humid areas. Present estimates indicate that approximately 2 million acres or more are being irrigated in the 31 humid eastern states. If the water supply is available, marked improvement and a much greater stability in production may be realized through supplemental irrigation, especially for crops of high acre value. In other areas, where water is costly to develop and the irrigation system difficult to maintain because of infrequent use, resorting to natural rainfall may still be preferred.

References

1. Albertson, F. W. and Weaver, J. E. 1945. Injury and death or recovery of trees in prairie climate. *Ecol. Monog.* 15: 393–433.
2. Angus, D. E. 1959. Agricultural water use. *Adv. in Agron.* 11: 19–35.
3. Ashbel, D. 1949. Frequency and distribution of dew in Palestine. *Geog. Rev.* 39: 260–288.
4. Barger, Gerald L. and Thom, H. C. S. 1949a. A method for characterizing drought intensity in Iowa. *Agron. Jour.* 41: 13–19.
5. ———. 1949b. Evaluation of drought hazard. *Agron. Jour.* 41: 519–526.

6. Bennett, O. L. and Doss, B. D. 1960. Effect of soil moisture level on root distribution of cool season forage species. *Agron. Jour.* 52: 204–206.

7. Bernstein, L. and Pearson, G. A. 1954. Influence of integrated moisture stress achieved by varying the osmotic pressure of culture solutions on growth of tomato and pepper plants. *Soil Sci.* 77: 355–368.

8. Bonner, J. and Galston, A. W. 1952. *Principles of Plant Physiology.* Freeman, San Francisco.

9. Boon-Long, T. S. 1941. Transpiration as influenced by osmotic concentration and cell permeability. *Amer. Jour. Bot.* 28: 333–343.

10. Briggs, I. J. 1914. Relative water requirement of plants. *Jour. Agr. Res.* 3: 1–64.

11. ——— and Shantz, H. L. 1912a. The wilting coefficient for different plants and its indirect determination. U. S. Dept. Agr. Bur. Pl. Ind. Bul. 230.

12. ———. 1912b. The wilting coefficient and its indirect determination. *Bot. Gaz.* 53: 20–37.

13. ———. 1912c. The relative wilting coefficient for different plants. *Bot. Gaz.* 53: 229–235.

14. ———. 1916. Hourly transpiration on clear days as determined by cyclic environmental factors. *Jour. Agr. Res.* 5: 583–651.

15. Brooks, C. E. P. and Hunt, T. M. 1930. The zonal distribution of moisture over the earth. *Mem. Roy. Met. Soc.* 3: 139–157.

16. Burton, G. W. 1959. Crop management for improved water-use efficiency. *Adv. in Agron.* 11: 104–115.

17. ———, Prine, G. M., and Jackson, J. E. 1957. Studies of drouth tolerance and water use of several southern grasses. *Agron. Jour.* 49: 498–503.

18. Chapman, V. J. 1942. The new perspective in the halophytes. *Quart. Rev. Biol.* 17: 291–311.

19. Clements, H. F. and Kubota, T. 1942. Internal moisture relations of sugarcane —the selection of a moisture index. *Haw. Pl. Rec.* XLVI: 17–35.

20. Curtis, O. F. 1936. Leaf temperatures and the cooling of leaves by radiation. *Pl. Phys.* 11: 343–364.

21. Daubenmire, R. F. 1959. *Plants and Environment.* Wiley, New York.

22. Decker, J. P. and Wetzel, B. F. 1957. A method for measuring transpiration of intact plants under controlled light, humidity and temperature. *Forest Sci.* 3: 350–354.

23. Denmead, O. T. and Shaw, R. H. 1960. The effects of soil moisture stress at different stages of growth on the development and yield of corn. *Agron. Jour.* 52: 272–274.

24. Doss, B. D., Ashley, D. A. and Bennett, O. L. 1960. Effect of soil moisture regime on root distribution of warm season forage species. *Agron. Jour.* 52: 569–571.

25. Fowells, S. A. and Kirk, B. M. 1945. Availability of soil moisture to Ponderosa pine. *Jour. Forestry* 43: 601–604.

26. Hagan, R. M. 1957. Water-soil-plant relations. *Calif. Agr.* 11: 9–12.

27. Hayward, H. E. and Magistad, O. C. 1946. The salt problem in irrigation agriculture. U. S. Dept. Agr. Misc. Publ. 607.

28. ——— and Wadleigh, C. H. 1949. Plant growth on saline and alkali soils. *Adv. in Agron.* 1: 1–38.

29. Heinicke, A. J. and Childers. 1936. Influence of respiration on the daily rate of photosynthesis of entire apple trees. *Amer. Soc. Hort. Sci. Proc.* 34: 142–144.

30. Hendrickson, A. H. and Veihmeyer, F. J. 1929. Irrigation experiments with peaches in California. *Cal. Agr. Exp. Sta. Bul.* 479. 56 pp.

31. ———. 1945. Permanent wilting percentages of soils obtained from field and laboratory trials. *Pl. Phys.* 20: 517–539.

32. Higbee, Edward. 1958. *American Agriculture: Geography, Resources, Conservation.* Wiley, New York.

33. Holzman, B. 1937. Sources of moisture for precipitation in the United States. U. S. Dept. Agr. Tech. Bul. 589.

34. Hoover, M. D. 1944. Effect of removal of forest vegetation upon water yields. *Amer. Geophys. Union Trans.* 25: 969–977.

35. Horsfall, J. G. and Harrison, A. L. 1939. Effect of Bordeaux mixture and its various elements on transpiration. *Jour. Agr. Res.* 58: 423–443.

36. Huber, B. and Miller, R. 1954. Methoden zur wasserdampf- und Transpirationsregistrierung im laufernden Luftstrom. *Ber. deut. bot. Gesell.* 67: 223–234.

37. Hunter, A. S. and Kelly, O. J. 1946. Growth and rubber content of guayule as affected by variations in soil moisture stress. *Agron. Jour.* 38: 118–134.

38. ———. 1953. Causes of death of plants as a consequence of loss of water: conservation of life in desiccated tissues. *Torrey Bot. Club Bul.* 80: 166–177.

39. Iljin, W. S. 1957. Drought resistance in plants and physiological processes. *Ann. Res. Pl. Phys.* 8: 257–274.

40. Johnston, C. O. and Miller, E. C. 1934. Relation of leaf-rust infection to yield, growth, and water economy of two varieties of wheat. *Jour. Agr. Res.* 49: 955–981.

41. Kenworthy, A. L. 1949. Soil moisture and growth of apple trees. *Amer. Soc. Hort. Sci. Proc.* 54: 29–39.

42. Klages, H. K. W. 1942. *Ecological Crop Geography.* Macmillan, New York.

43. Kramer, P. J. 1959. The role of water in the physiology of plants. *Adv. in Agron.* 11: 51–70.

44. ——— and Kozlowski, T. T. 1960. *Physiology of Trees.* McGraw-Hill, New York.

45. Kursanov, A. L. 1956. Recent advances in plant physiology in the U.S.S.R. *Ann. Rev. Pl. Phys.* 7: 401–436.

46. Levitt, J. 1951. Frost, drought and heat resistance. *Ann. Rev. Pl. Phys.* 2: 245–268.

47. ———. 1956. *The Hardiness of Plants.* Academic, New York.

48. MacDougal, D. T. and Spaulding, E. S. 1910. The water balance of succulent plants. Carnegie Inst. Wash. Publ. 141. 77 pp.

49. McKenzie, R. E. 1951. The ability of forage plants to survive early spring flooding. *Sci. Agr.* 31: 358–367.

50. Magistad, O. C. 1945. Plant growth on saline and alkali soils. *Bot. Rev.* 11: 181–230.

51. Magness, J. R., Degman, E. S., and Furr, J. R. 1935. Soil moisture and irrigation investigations in eastern apple orchards. U. S. Dept. Agr. Tech. Bul. 491.

52. Maximov, N. A. 1929. *The Plant in Relation to Water.* Trans. by R. H. Yapp. Geo. Allen and Unwin, Ltd., London.

53. Meyer, B. S. 1945. A critical evaluation of the terminology of diffusion phenomena. *Pl. Phys.* 20: 142–164.

54. ———. 1956. The hydrodynamic system. *Engel. Pl. Physiol.* Vol. 3: 596–614.

55. ———, Anderson, D. B. and Böhning, R. H. 1960. *Plant Physiology.* Van Nostrand, Princeton, N. J.

56. Miller, E. E. 1916. Comparative study of the root systems and leaf areas of corn and the sorghums. *Jour. Agr. Res.* 6: 311–332.

57. ———. 1938. *Plant Physiology.* McGraw-Hill, New York.

58. Monselise, S. P. and Turrell, F. M. 1959. Tenderness. Climate and Citrus Fruit. *Sci.* 129: 639–640.

59. Murphy, H. C. 1935. Effect of crown rust infection on yield and water requirement of oats. *Jour. Agr. Res.* 50: 387–412.
60. Nutman, F. J. 1941. Studies of the physiology of *Coffea arabica* III. Transpiration rates of whole trees in relation to natural environmental conditions. *Ann. Bot.* 5: 59–82.
61. Oosting, Henry J. 1956. *The Study of Plant Communities.* Freeman, San Francisco.
62. Oppenheimer, H. R. 1951. Summer drought and water balance of plants growing in the Near East. *Jour. Ecol.* 39: 356–362.
63. Palmer, A. E. 1949. Progress Report 1937–1946. Dominion Exp. Sta. Lethbridge, Alberta.
64. Paltridge, T. B. and Mair, H. K. C. 1936. Studies of selected pasture grasses. Australia Council for Sci. and Ind. Res. Bul. 102.
65. Parker, J. 1949. Effects of variations in the root-leaf ratio on transpiration rate. *Pl. Phys.* 24: 739–743.
66. ———. 1956. Drought resistance in woody plants. *Bot. Rev.* 22: 241–289.
67. Penman, H. L. 1948. Natural evaporation from open water, bare soil and grass. *Proc. of Royal Soc., Ser.* A 193: 120–145.
68. Powell, J. W. 1879. Report of the lands of the arid region. Second ed. Govt. Print. Office, Washington, D. C.
69. President's Water Resources Policy Commission. 1950. Ten rivers in America's future. Govt. Print. Office, Washington, D. C.
70. Richards, L. A. and Weaver, L. R. 1943. Fifteen atmosphere percentage as related to permanent wilting percentage. *Soil. Sci.* 56: 331–339.
71. ———. 1944. Moisture retention by some irrigated soils as related to soil moisture tension. *Jour. Agr. Res.* 69: 215–235.
72. Richards, L. A. and Wadleigh, C. H. 1952. Soil water and plant growth. In *Soil Physical Conditions and Plant Growth.* Academic, New York.
73. Robertson, L. S. and Kohnke, H. 1946. The pF at the wilting point of several Indiana soils. *Proc. Soil Sci. Soc. Amer.* 11: 50–52.
74. Runyon, E. H. 1936. Relation of water content to dry weight in leaves of the creosote bush. *Bot. Gaz.* 97: 518–533.
75. Russell, M. B. 1959a. Drought tolerance of plants. *Adv. in Agron.* 11: 70–73.
76. ———. 1959b. Crop responses to excess moisture. *Adv. in Agron.* 11: 74–77.
77. Schwab, G. O., Shrader, W. D., Nixon, P. R., and Shaw, R. H. 1958. Research on irrigation of corn and soybeans at Conesville and Ankeny, Iowa, 1951–1955. *Iowa Agr. and Home Ec. Exp. Sta. Res. Bul.* 458.
78. Shantz, H. L. and Piemeisel, L. N. 1927. The water requirement of plants at Akron, Colorado. *Jour. Agr. Res.* 34: 1093–1190.
79. Shimper, A. F. W. 1903. *Plant Geography on a Physiological Basis.* Clarendon, Oxford.
80. Shirley, H. L. and Meuli, L. J. 1938. Influence of foliage sprays on drought resistance of conifers. *Pl. Phys.* 13: 399–406.
81. Shreve, E. B. 1916. An analysis of the causes of variations in the transpiring power of cacti. *Physiol. Res.* 2: 73–127.
82. Slatyer, R. O. 1955. Studies of the water relations of crop plants grown under natural rainfall in northern Australia. *Austr. Jour. Agr. Res.* 6: 365–377.
83. ———. 1956. Absorption of water from atmospheres of different humidity and its transport through plants. *Austr. Jour. Biol. Sci.* 9: 552–558.
84. ———. 1957. The influence of progressive increases in total soil moisture stress on transpiration, growth and internal water relationships of plants. *Austr. Jour. Biol. Sci.* 10: 320–336.
85. Smith, James L. and Crabb, George A. 1956. Patterns and classes of rainfall

at East Lansing, Michigan, and their effect upon surface runoff. *Mich. Agr. Exp. Stat. Quart. Bul.* 39: 47–62.

86. Stanhill, G. 1957. The effect of differences in soil moisture status on plant growth. *Soil Sci.* 84: 205–214.

87. Stansberry, C. O., Converse, C. D., Huise, H. R., and Kelly, O. J. 1955. Effect of moisture and phosphate variables on alfalfa hay production on the Yuma Mesa. *Soil Sci. Soc. Amer. Proc.* 19: 303–310.

88. Stocking, C. R. 1956. Osmotic pressure or osmotic value. *Encycl. Pl. Physiol.* Vol. 2: 57–70.

89. Stockton, J. R. and Doneen, L. D. 1957. Irrigation timing and frequency as related to yield and prevalence of Verticillium wilt in cotton. *Cal. Agr.* 11 (4): 16–18.

90. Stone, E. C. 1957. Dew as an ecological factor. *Ecol.* 38: 407–422.

91. ————, Shachori, A. Y., and Stanley, R. 1956. Water absorbed by needles of ponderosa pine seedlings and its internal redistribution. *Pl. Phys.* 31: 120–126.

92. Stone, E. C., Went, F. W., and Young, C. L. 1950. Water absorption from the atmosphere by plants grown in dry soil. *Sci.* 111: 546–548.

93. Suneson, C. A. 1957. Repts. 3rd Inter. Conf. Irrig. and Drain., San Francisco.

94. Tatum, Lloyd A. and Kehr, William R. 1951. Observations on factors affecting seed-set with inbred strains of dent corn. *Agron. Jour.* 43: 270–275.

95. Taylor, C. A., Blaney, H. F., and McLaughlin, W. W. 1934. The wilting range in certain soils and the ultimate wilting point. *Trans. Amer. Geophys. Union* 15: 436–444.

96. Thorne, D. W. and Peterson, H. B. 1949. *Irrigated Soils, Their Fertility and Management.* Blakeston, Philadelphia.

97. Thornthwaite, C. W. 1931. The climates of North America according to a new classification. *Geog. Rev.* 21: 633–655.

98. ————. 1933. The climates of the earth. *Geog. Rev.* 23: 433–440.

99. ————. 1948. An approach toward a rational classification of climate. *Geog. Rev.* 38: 55–94.

100. ———— and Mather, J. R. 1955. The water balance. Publ. in Climat. Vol. 8. No. 1. Drexel Inst. Tech., Centerton, N. J.

101. Transeau, E. N. 1905. Forest centers of eastern America. *Amer. Nat.* 39: 875–889.

102. Trewartha, Glenn T. 1954. *An Introduction to Climate.* McGraw-Hill, New York.

103. Turrell, F. M. 1936. The area of the internal exposed surface of dicotyledon leaves. *Amer. Jour. Bot.* 23: 255–264.

104. United States Bureau of Reclamation. 1946. The Colorado River. Govt. Print. Office, Washington, D. C.

105. ————. 1949. Central Valley Basin. Govt. Print. Office, Washington, D. C.

106. Van Bavel, C. H. M. and Verlinden, F. J. 1956. Agricultural drought in North Carolina. N. C. Agr. Exp. Sta. Tech. Bul. 122.

107. Veihmeyer, F. J. 1927. Some factors affecting the irrigation requirements of deciduous orchards. *Hilgardia* 2: 125–291.

108. ———— and Hendrickson, A. H. 1927. Soil moisture conditions in relation to plant growth. *Pl. Phys.* 2: 71–82.

109. ————. 1928. Soil moisture at permanent wilting of plants. *Pl. Phys.* 3: 350–357.

110. ————. 1934. Some plant and soil moisture relationships. *Bul. Amer. Soil Survey Assoc.* 15: 76–80.

111. ————. 1948. The permanent wilting percentage as a reference point for the measurement of soil moisture. *Trans. Amer. Geophys. Union* 29: 887–896.

112. ———. 1949. Methods of measuring field capacity and permanent wilting percentage of soils. *Soil Sci.* 68: 75–94.

113. ———. 1950. Soil moisture in relation to plant growth. *Ann. Rev. Pl. Phys.* 1: 285–304.

114. Wadleigh, C. H., Gauch, H. G., and Magistad, O. C. 1946. Growth and rubber accumulation in guayule as conditioned by soil salinity and irrigation regime. *U. S. Dept. Agr. Tech. Bul.* 925.

115. Walter, H. 1955. The water economy and the hydrature of plants. *Ann. Rev. Pl. Phys.* 6: 239–252.

116. Warming, E. 1909. *Oecological Plant Geography.* Transl. by Grooni and Balfour. Clarendon, Oxford.

117. Weatherly, P. E. 1950. Studies in the water relations of the cotton plant: I. Field measurement of water deficit in leaves. *New Phyt.* 49: 81–97.

118. Weaver, J. E. and Mogensen, A. 1919. Relative transpiration of coniferous and broad-leaved trees in autumn and winter. *Bot. Gaz.* 68: 393–424.

119. Webb, Walter Prescott. 1957. The American west, perpetual mirage. Harpers Mag. 214 (1284): 25–31.

120. Went, F. W. 1957. *The Experimental Control of Plant Growth.* Chronica Bot. Co., Waltham, Mass.

121. Williams, R. F. 1935. An analysis of the effect of phosphorus supply on the transpiration ratio of plants. *Austral. Jour. Exp. Biol. Med. Sci.* 13: 49–66.

122. Wilsie, C. P., Akamine, E. K., and Takahashi, M. 1940. Effect of frequent cutting on the growth, yield and composition of Napier grass. *Jour. Amer. Soc. Agron.* 32: 266–273.

123. Winneberger, J. H. 1958. Transpiration as a requirement for growth of land plants. *Physiologia Plantarum* 11: 56–61.

124. Yarwood, C. E. 1947. Water loss from fungus cultures. *Amer. Jour. Bot.* 34: 514–520.

125. Zuber, M. S. and Decker, W. L. 1956. Effects of 1954 drought on corn. *Mo. Agr. Exp. Sta. Res. Bul.* 604.

Chapter 8

The Temperature Factor

INTRODUCTION

Temperature is one of the most familiar ecological factors, and one which has profound effects on most living organisms. It is a factor which can be easily measured, it is almost universal in influence, and often becomes limiting for growth and distribution of plants and animals.

As suggested by Clarke (1954), temperature is the intensity aspect of heat energy. The capacity aspect of heat energy is also of great importance, but the temperature or intensity aspect probably exerts a more predominant direct influence as an ecological factor.

Solar radiation, or insolation, is the primary source of both light and heat energy for living organisms. This radiant energy includes electromagnetic wavelengths of light (the visible spectrum), and wavelengths both shorter than light waves (ultraviolet) and longer than light waves (heat and radio waves). This chapter will be concerned with heat energy, particularly the intensity aspect, or temperature.

Thermodynamics has shown us that energy may be transformed but not destroyed. Transfer of heat energy between the plant and the environment is of great importance. To make such a transfer possible, there must be an energy gradient, a temperature, pressure, or concentration gradient. Raschke (1960) has discussed heat transfer between the plant and environment, pointing out that it takes place in three ways: (1) conduction and convection in the form of sensible heat; (2) evaporation of water (including the processes of condensation, freezing, thawing, and sublimation) in the form of latent heat; and (3) direct radiation.

When the sun's rays strike the surface of the earth, much of the radiation is degraded into heat energy. Odum (1959) has noted that only a small portion of the light energy absorbed by a green plant is used for potential or food energy; most of it goes into heat, much of which is eventually lost from the plant into the atmosphere. The dissipation of solar energy is shown diagrammatically in Figure 8-1.

Heat energy is measured in gram calories, a gram calorie being defined as the quantity of energy required to raise the temperature of one gram of water one degree Centigrade. Insolation is expressed in quantitative terms as gram calories per square centimeter per hour.

The amount of insolation is dependent primarily on latitude, altitude, season of the year, and relationship of area to large bodies of land or water. As noted by Oosting (1958), insolation at the equator varies only slightly from month to month because the angle of the sun's rays does not deviate greatly from vertical, and the days are 12 hours in length. Insolation is less at increased latitudes, because of the greater angle at which the radiation waves strike the earth's surface. However, total insolation for the growing season may be similar at different latitudes because of the

FIGURE 8-1.

Reflection, scattering, and absorption of solar rays. [*After Woodbury,* Principles of General Ecology. N. Y.: Blakiston Co., 1954.]

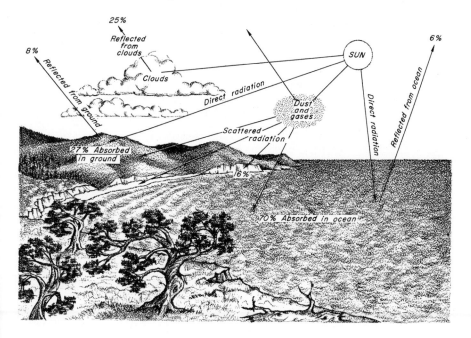

compensating factor of longer days at higher latitudes (Carder, 1957).

The sun is at zenith at noon twice each year: at the vernal equinox, March 21, and at autumnal equinox, September 21. At the time of the equinoxes, the circle of illumination reaches the North and South Poles simultaneously, days and nights are of equal length and are the same at all latitudes.

After March 21, because of the inclination of the earth's axis (23.5°), the North Pole comes nearer to the sun until June 21, after which the shift is reversed to bring it back to equinox position by September 21. The North Pole moves away from the sun until December 21, and then back to the equinox position by March 21. In the Southern Hemisphere the sequence is reversed.

The relationship between insolation from the sun, temperature, and evaporation is of great interest. Crabb (1952, 1954) has shown that the temperature of the atmosphere is highly correlated with total insolation, but that there is a time lag between peak values of insolation and temperature, which represents the average of both maximum and minimum daily temperatures and, as such, reflects the cooling effect of radiation of heat away from the earth during the night hours (Figure 8-2).

After sunrise in the morning, the temperature at the surface of the earth rises rapidly because the earth gains heat faster than it is reradiated into the atmosphere. Finally, after some hours, a relatively high surface temperature is reached, and gains through radiation are equaled by reradiation and conduction. Insolation begins to weaken in the afternoon

FIGURE 8-2.

Comparison of normal annual patterns of daily values of insolation, evaporation, and mean temperature at East Lansing, Michigan. [After Crabb, Quart. Bul., Mich. Agr. Exp. Sta. 36:406, 1954.]

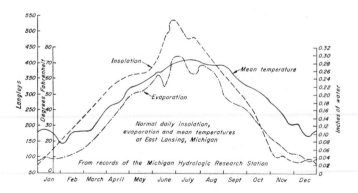

and, after sunset, radiation from the surface results in a drop of temperature during the night. Evaporation from the soil surface accelerates this cooling effect, and soil temperatures drop below air temperatures. Daily soil surface temperatures range more widely than air temperatures. Soil temperatures, except close to the surface, lag in attaining maximal and minimal points as compared with air temperatures. The data in Table 8-1 show the nature of this lag at Ames, Iowa.

TABLE 8-1. APPROXIMATE TIME OF OCCURRENCE OF MAXIMUM AND MINIMUM SOIL TEMPERATURES. (Excepting near the surface there is a lag in attaining maximal and minimal points as compared with air temperatures which usually reach maximal levels between 2 and 3 P.M. and minimal levels between 6 and 7 A.M.)[*]

Depth (inches)	Time of Occurrence (Central Standard Time)	
	Maximum Temperature	Minimum Temperature
1	Noon–2 P.M.	Shortly after sunrise
2¼	2–4 P.M.	1 hour after sunrise
4	4–6 P.M.	2 hours after sunrise
6	5–7 P.M.	3–4 hours after sunrise
8	6–8 P.M.	4–5 hours after sunrise
12	10–11 P.M.	7–8 hours after sunrise
20	Little daily change	
24	Little daily change	
40	Little daily change	
48	Little daily change	
72	Little daily change	

[*] Data from Elford and Shaw. The climate of Iowa. Spec. Rep. 24, Iowa State Univ., Agr. and Home Econ. Expt. Sta., p. 4, Apr. 1960.

The color of a soil surface affects absorption, heat storage, and reradiation back into the atmosphere. White reflects, whereas black absorbs, radiation. Color and moisture content of the soil at or near the soil surface has a marked effect on vertical gradients of temperature as has been shown by Daubenmire (1959). Within five millimeters of the surface, temperature differences exceeding 20°C may exist for adjacent dark- and light-colored surfaces.

Temperatures change more slowly in wet soil than in dry soil. The texture of soils is also important in determining the rate of temperature changes. Sandy soils warm up earlier, loams later, and muck and peat still later in the spring. In the autumn, frost damage may be greatest in coarse-textured soils because reradiation back into the atmosphere is so rapid after sunset.

Temperature is measured by means of thermometers, thermocouples, and thermistor units. The last two are based on measures of electrical potential and resistance respectively, and are particularly useful in determining temperatures in restricted spaces (Platt and Wolf, 1950). For measuring air temperatures, standardized mercury thermometers are satisfactory. Thermographs which record temperatures on a revolving drum are used when continuous temperature records are desired. Maximum and minimum thermometers are also highly useful and are part of the regular equipment of a standard weather station.

To determine the mean air temperature for a day, the United States Weather Bureau uses the average of the maximum and minimum for the day. While this gives a fair approximation of mean temperature, it ignores duration and may have limited usefulness in studies of plant-environment relations. A more satisfactory mean would be an average of the 24 hourly temperatures.

The mean temperature for 12 months likewise may have limited ecological significance. A cool, marine area, with little variability from month to month, may have the same mean annual temperature as a highly variable continental region, but the two areas constitute entirely different environments for growing plants (Figure 8-3).

The geographic distribution of air temperature is of great ecological importance. Although directly related to latitude and altitude, temperature may be influenced greatly by proximity to large bodies of water and by wind direction. The highest mean annual temperature ever recorded is 86°F at Massawa, Eritrea, in Africa, and the lowest mean annual temperature is −14°F at Framheim, Antarctica. Extremes of temperature range from lows of −90°F at Verkhoyansk, U.S.S.R., and −78°F at Fort Yukon, Alaska, to highs of 134°F at Greenland Ranch, Death Valley, California, and 136°F in Libya, North Africa.

In most climatic classifications, four major temperature belts are recognized. Extending in a poleward direction both north and south of the equator, these belts include the Tropical (Megathermal), Mesothermal, Microthermal, and Polar. These four belts are often subdivided further into still narrower temperature zones.

The annual range of mean monthly temperatures varies primarily with latitude. Near the

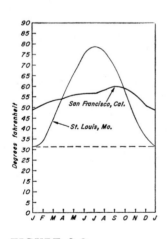

FIGURE 8-3.

Comparison of temperature range in a marine climate with that in a continental climate having a similar annual mean.

equator the mean daily temperature range from winter to summer may be less than the normal diurnal range of temperature.

EFFECTS OF ALTITUDE

Because of the fact that temperature varies with elevation, changes in altitude tend to substitute for changes in latitude. There usually is a decrease of approximately 3°F in average temperature with each 1000-foot increase in altitude. Davis (1948) noted the striking example of Quito, Ecuador, situated at an altitude of 9350 feet, just 12 miles from the equator, which has been a mean annual temperature of 55°F. In direct contrast, at Belem, Brazil, at a similar latitude, but at an elevation of 33 feet, the mean temperature is approximately 85°F.

Altitude produces a true temperature zonation, highly important in the distribution of natural species of plants as well as in crop production possibilities. Dansereau (1957), Braun-Blanquet (1932), and Raunkiaer (1934) have indicated the sharp reduction in number of species with increasing altitude. In Scotland, there were 304 species at 300 to 400 meters, but only 44 species at 900 to 1000 meters. In the Alps, 604 species were found at 850 to 1200 meters, but only 51 species above 2850 meters. The general zonation pattern, as related to altitude, has been classified by Dansereau as follows:

1. The lowlands—characteristic vegetation at low latitudes is rainforest, and at higher latitudes is summer green deciduous, evergreen hardwood, etc.

2. The montane level—cooler and more humid, this region may have temperate rainforest, deciduous, or needle-leaved forest.

3. The subalpine level—this region has clear dry atmosphere, arborescent vegetation, but smaller and more dispersed trees.

4. The alpine level—this region is cold and cloudy, with short vegetation period, and no trees, but probably some grassland or tundra.

5. The nival tier—little can live on the snows except algae, some highly specialized invertebrates, some ants, and the ice flea (*Isotomurus glacialis*).

Tropical and middle latitude mountainous regions have been classified by Sapper and James (1959) on the basis of altitude and agricultural crops. In tropical Latin America four zones are recognized: *tierra caliente* (hot lands), *tierra templada* (temperate lands), *tierra fria* (cool lands), and *tierra helada* (frost lands). Usually the *caliente* zone extends from sea level to 2000 or 3000 feet; where rainfall is sufficient tropical crops such

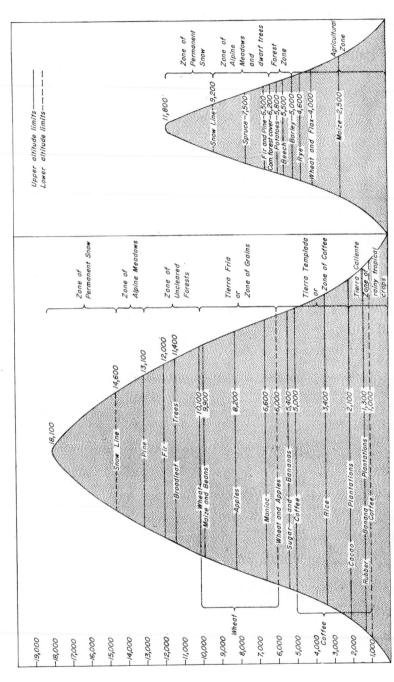

FIGURE 8-4. *Temperature zones as related to altitude in mountainous areas of both the tropics and middle latitudes.* [After Sapper, 1930, in James, A Geography of Man. 2nd Ed., Chicago: Ginn and Co., 1959.]

as rubber, cacao, bananas, and coffee may be grown. In the next zone, *templada,* which extends upward to 6000 or 6500 feet, many crops are produced, including coffee, rice, corn, cotton, and many fruits. Above this belt, the *fria* extends upward to 11,000 feet, providing conditions for production of wheat, barley, oats, potatoes, deciduous fruits, and pasture crops. In Mexico, in the Valley of Toluca, red clover and alfalfa strains developed in latitudes of 38° to 43° in the United States have been highly productive and persistent (Buller and Valdivieso, 1958). The *tierra helada* is, in general, too cold for crop production, but at the lower limits it may include alpine pastures. A graphical presentation of these temperature zones as related to adaptation of plants, both for tropical- and middle-latitude mountains, is given in Figure 8-4.

TEMPERATURE INVERSION

Altitude depresses temperatures and operates to increase the diurnal range because of the rapid heating of the earth's surface during the day and the corresponding rapid radiation from the earth's surface as night approaches. Another characteristic of mountainous areas is temperature inversion. As described by Trewartha (1954), a protected valley receives much radiant energy from the surrounding slopes during the daytime, and becomes warmer than the flanks above, where wind movement provides better ventilation. At night, the basins become reservoirs of cold air draining from the surrounding slopes. Air drainage is often accentuated in mountainous areas and temperature inversions are unusually well developed.

Typical of the marked effects of temperature inversion are those observed by the author in San Luis Obispo County, California. Atascadero is a town at the bottom of a valley between a low coastal range of mountains (2200 feet) and the main coastal range (4500 feet); here night-time temperatures in winter often dropped far below freezing point, at times as low as 10°F. At the nearby Eagle Ranch, located on the eastern slope of the hills at 1000 feet elevation, citrus and palm trees suffered little damage from frost year after year.

Temperature inversion is such a common phenomenon on the Pacific coast and in other mountainous areas that it is of great economic importance. It is basically responsible for many of the local situations in citrus production areas, where heaters and wind machines are used to prevent serious frost damage. It is one of the major contributing factors

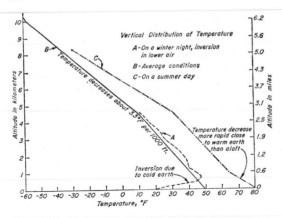

FIGURE 8-5.

Contrasts in vertical distribution of temperature (A) on a winter night, (B) under average conditions, (C) on a summer day. [After Trewartha, An Introduction to Climate, 3rd Ed. N. Y.: McGraw-Hill, 1954].

in creation of the atmospheric conditions characteristic in the Los Angeles area when smog develops. Figure 8-5 illustrates the nature of temperature inversion.

TEMPERATURE EFFICIENCY

Length of Growing Season

Various methods have been developed for evaluating the effectiveness of temperature as related to crop distribution. One of the oldest, and probably the simplest, is the length of growing season. The average period between the last killing frost in the spring and the first killing frost in the fall, the frost-free season, has been used to denote the growing season. However, weather records show that this period varies greatly from year to year. At Iowa Falls, Iowa, for example, the average frost-free season is 150 days, but it has varied from a low of 111 days to a high of 188 days (Reed, 1941). Another basis for determining the effective growing season has been to use the period between the last date in the spring and the first date in the fall on which the temperature reached a low of 28°F. At this temperature, differences in microclimate due to slope, contours, and soil types will probably not permit local areas to escape frost, which they might with a temperature of 32°F.

Klages (1942) has emphasized that a distinction should be made between the actual thermal growing season and the physiological growing season, which takes into account the base temperature at which appreciable growth can take place. If we can assume that growth does not become active under 40°F, which is not exactly correct, a new value can be determined: the effective growing season. On this basis the temperature efficiencies of different regions may be compared.

The length of the frost-free season may give some clue to the kinds of crops that can be grown successfully in an area, but it really tells little of the range of intensity and other characteristics of the temperature regime during the growing season.

A region having a short growing season is under a great handicap, for few crops can be matured in the time available. This is one of the greatest deterrents to future extension of agriculture into the colder regions. It is perhaps the most limiting of all climatic factors in the development of crop production in Alaska.

The northern limits of cultivation can be readily observed in the Scandinavian countries, Finland, Norway, and Sweden. In Finland, for example (Nuttonson, 1950), much of the country lies between 60° and 70° north latitude, the latter the northernmost point where crops are grown successfully. It is found that potatoes and barley are best adapted to the very short season characteristic at 70°, while rye, hardy perennial forages, turnips, oats, spring wheat, peas, and winter wheat successively are found to require increasing frost-free periods and more favorable seasonal temperatures. The northern limits of cultivation of many crops are determined almost entirely by temperature.

Salmon (1917) studied the limits of winter cereal production in the United States and suggested that the isotherm of 10°F for the daily minimum temperatures in January and February corresponded closely to the border between areas of extensive winter wheat and spring wheat production. Winter barley was limited approximately by the 20°F daily mean minimum for January and February, and winter oats by the 30°F minimum isotherm for the same winter period.

Temperature Summation

A positive summation of temperatures above a certain base has been proposed as a measure of thermal efficiency. This involves a summation of temperatures in excess of a certain "zero point of vital activity," such as

40°F. A daily mean temperature of 72°F gives a positive temperature of 72°–40°, or 32°F for that day. An accumulation of such positive temperatures is the basis for a number of "heat unit systems" in widespread use today.

This method has the weakness that it does not evaluate the various temperature intensities and duration in accordance with their physiological effects. As was noted by Klages (1942), it does not consider Van't Hoff's law of the velocity of chemical reactions, which indicates a doubling of the rate with an increase in temperature of 10°C, or 18°F. However, in spite of these drawbacks, temperature summation has found a considerable area of usefulness.

Temperature Efficiency Index

Thornthwaite (1931) developed a temperature efficiency index, which was a modification of the temperature summation method, with 32°F taken as the zero point. With the formula:

$$\text{T-E} = \frac{12}{\Sigma}\left(\frac{T\text{-}32}{4}\right) n,$$

in which $n = 1$, Thornthwaite obtained values similar in magnitude to those obtained by the use of his moisture effectiveness formula.

Temperature province	T-E index
A′ Tropical	128 and above
B′ Mesothermal	64–127
C′ Microthermal	32–63
D′ Tiaga	16–31
E′ Tundra	1–15
F′ Frost	0

Because of the importance of summer concentration of temperature, which varies with latitude from 25% at the equator to 100% in the permanent frost climate near the poles, subprovinces were set up as follows:

Subprovince	Percent summer concentration
a	25–34
b	35–49
c	50–69
d	70–99
e	100

Later, Thornthwaite (1948), in developing the potential evapotranspiration concept for characterizing moisture provinces, suggested that potential evapotranspiration was an index of thermal efficiency as well. It may be considered a growth index, which expresses growth in terms of the water needed. It is given in the same units as precipitation effectiveness.

The classification of temperature efficiency, according to Thornthwaite, is as follows:

Thermal efficiency index in inches P.E.T.	Climatic type		Summer concentration of T-E in %
5.61	E′ Frost		d′
111.22	D′ Tundra		d′
16.83	C′$_1$ Microthermal	88	C′$_1$
22.44	C′$_2$ Microthermal	76	C′$_2$
28.05	B′$_1$ Mesothermal	62	b′$_1$
33.66	B′$_2$ Mesothermal	56	b′$_2$
39.27	B′$_3$ Mesothermal	52	b′$_3$
44.88	B′$_4$ Mesothermal	48	b′$_4$
44.88	A′ Megathermal	33	2′

The summer concentration of thermal efficiency at the higher latitudes is inversely proportional to the log of the annual T-E index.

The megathermal climate is typified by equatorial regions where the monthly mean temperatures vary but little. A mean annual temperature of 73.4°F might be a reasonable boundary between the mega- and mesothermal areas. In the United States, areas with something like a megathermal climate include the southern portions of Florida, Texas, Arizona, and California. Even these areas do not have a truly typical megathermal climate, because the days are longer and hotter in summer and shorter and colder in winter than in the true tropics.

Mesothermal climates include large areas of the United States, especially in the eastern part. July temperatures range from a monthly mean of 85°F in southern Texas to less than 70°F in the northern states.

Microthermal regions include western mountain areas, extending from Canada to New Mexico at higher elevations, and the very northern part of Minnesota, Wisconsin, North Dakota, Michigan, New York, Maine, New Hampshire, Vermont, and northward into Canada.

Only isolated areas in the United States have a tundra climate. These include the summit of Mt. Washington, Vermont, areas in the high Sierra mountains in California, and parts of Alaska. Tundra climates are found also in the Canadian Northwest Territories. The border between tundra and frost climates is located (according to the Thornthwaite system) where the annual potential evapotranspiration is approximately 5.61 inches, which occurs in Alaska.

Physiological Index

The physiological temperature index was developed by Livingston (1916) and based on research by Lehenbauer (1914) on growth rate of maize. In this study it had been found that when young maize shoots were exposed to temperatures maintained for a period of 12 hours, hourly growth rate was 0.09 mm at 12°C, 0.45 mm at 20°C, 1.11 mm at 32°C, and dropped off drastically at 43°C. The smoothed graph of the 12-hour periods was used for the determination of physiological indices. By extrapolation the graph was extended to include the temperature range from 2°C to 48°C. Ordinates of the smoothed graph were measured for each degree of temperature, the numbers being reported in hundredths of a millimeter. To express growth rate as a physiological index, all hourly rates of elongation were divided by the value obtained at 4.4°C as unity. Livingston mapped the United States on the basis of these physiological units. He emphasized that growth-rate data were obtained from one crop only, that young seedlings only were used, and that the specific conditions of the experiment were seldom found under natural conditions for anything more than a very short period of time.

Although the several methods discussed would appear to have limited usefulness when applied to studying response of plants to temperature, Klages (1942) showed a rather high degree of correlation between average frost-free season and other methods of expressing thermal efficiency of a region, such at Thornthwaite's T-E index and Livingston's physiological index. All of these methods have general value in relation to plant distribution problems.

Hopkins' Bioclimatic Law

Hopkins (1938) attempted to express the importance of latitude, longitude, and altitude in the distribution and rate of development of plants by means of a "Bioclimatic Law." This law established bioclimatic zones, with recognition of the effects of oceans, continents, and other physiographic features, and was expressed in terms of a periodic event in the life of a plant. In brief form, the bioclimatic law may be stated as follows: "A biotic event in temperate North America will, in general, show a lag of four days for each degree of latitude, 5° of longitude, and 400 feet of altitude, northward, eastward, and upward, in spring and early summer."

Evans (1931), after studying blooming dates of timothy, said that Hopkins' law did not give proper emphasis to increasing day length with higher latitudes. The day-length factor tends to compensate in part for the delay in growth caused by an increase in latitude. However, this compensatory effect of longer days is difficult to evaluate precisely.

Phenological data for all important crop plants would be highly useful. Much has been done in recent years to obtain such data, but for many crops we have only fragmentary phenological information. Such data, indicating with considerable accuracy just when the plant reaches certain stages of development as the season progresses, are useful in the following ways (Daubenmire, 1959):

1. In farming for determining planting dates in the spring, for comparing growth stages in any given year with long-term averages for the same species, and for predicting harvesting dates.

2. In range management for making decisions as to when the range should be ready to graze.

3. In forestry for determining transplanting dates, time of seed dispersal and germination, and measures of seasonal growth rates.

4. In irrigated agriculture for regulating the application of water according to stage of development of the plant.

5. In production of canning crops for regulating planting dates and predicting harvesting dates.

6. In medicine for predicting hay fever season, especially for those who react specifically to pollen of certain species.

Efforts have been made to characterize seasons by the use of phenological data from certain wild plants. Caprio (1957) found that the date of lilac bloom in Montana was a good indication of the thermal environment, indicating relative earliness or lateness of a given season.

Heat-Unit Systems

In a report on relations between climates and crops, Abbe (1905) pointed out that according to the doctrine of thermal constants a given stage in the development of any plant is reached when that plant has received a certain amount of heat, regardless of the time required. In each successive stage of growth there was assumed to be a definite heat requirement, generally expressed in some form of "heat units." Modifications of this concept have been recognized from time to time, particularly as related to the temperature at which activity is said to begin.

A summation of positive temperatures above a base or "zero point of vital activity," is the working basis for most heat-unit systems. This base temperature has been determined by experimental methods, and may differ in different crops. For most early-sown crops such as wheat, oats, barley, and peas, the base temperature of 40°F is used. At this temperature it is known that appreciable growth usually occurs. For corn, a base temperature of 50°F has been used, and for cotton possibly 60°F would be preferable.

The number of heat units for one day is obtained by subtracting the base temperature from the actual mean temperature for that day. A summation of daily heat units gives the total in heat units for any specified period from planting to maturity. This system has also been called the "remainder index system" and values have been expressed in terms of "day-degrees," "degree-days," "heat units," and "thermal units."

The canning industry has made extensive use of heat-unit systems in arranging planting dates and predicting harvesting schedules. Early work by Boswell (1927, 1929) and Magoon and Culpepper (1932) suggested promising possibilities. Boswell found that if he used summations above a base of 40°F a fairly constant amount of heat was required to reach blooming stage, regardless of the time interval. He showed also that later plantings required less time to reach maturity than did earlier plantings. Magoon and Culpepper found that corn grown in Maine and New York required a far smaller heat-unit summation than corn grown in Virginia, indicating the important influences of day length, insolation, and possibly respiration of the plant.

In commercial canning operations, especially for peas and sweet corn, heat-unit systems have been used successfully in Wisconsin, Minnesota, New York, Pennsylvania, Ontario, Illinois, and Iowa for regulating planting schedules and harvesting dates (Barnard, 1948; Bomalaski, 1948; Seaton and Huffington, 1950; Katz, 1952; and Sayre, 1953). An example of a characteristic pattern of cumulative heat units showing progressive increase in growing degree days as used in the pea canning industry is given in Figure 8-6.

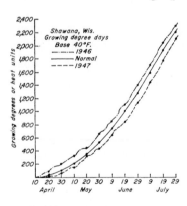

FIGURE 8-6.

Example of progressive increase in growing degree days at Shawano, Wisconsin, for two individual years and computed average. [After Bomalaski, in Daily Weather Map, U. S. Weather Bureau, Aug. 24, 1950.]

For greatest success, long-time records of air and soil temperatures on farms making up the canning district are needed. In a given year, adjustments for abnormal seasonal conditions can be made, even changes as the season progresses. Experience has shown that, prior to planting time, soil temperatures are more important; after planting time, and especially after seedling emergence, air temperatures are of greater importance. When the flowering stage is reached it may be possible to use a new and more accurate base for computing the date of maturity of the crop.

At the canning stage, a tenderometer reading (force required to puncture the seed coat) is used to determine proper date of harvest, in order to insure a quality product. It has been found that peas will remain in good harvest condition twice as long at 62°F than at 80°F. It is obvious, then, that cool weather is desirable for peas, which explains why commercial pea canning areas are concentrated in such states as Minnesota, Wisconsin, and New York.

The merits of a heat-unit system may include the following points:

1. Characterizes the length of the growing period for different varieties.
2. Makes for more orderly harvests.
3. Prevents bunching of harvests and eliminates slack periods.
4. Aids in forecasting labor needs for factory operations.
5. Helps to cut harvesting and factory costs.
6. Aids in quality control.

Data obtained in Wisconsin and New York have indicated the average number of heat units required to bring certain varieties of peas to the proper canning stage.

Location	Variety	Heat units required	
Wisconsin	Alaska	1100–1200	100 Tenderometer
Wisconsin	Perfection	1400–1600	100 Tenderometer
New York	Thos. Laxton	1350	85 Tenderometer
New York	Perfection	1520	85 Tenderometer

These values are not to be considered as absolute. They will vary from farm to farm and from season to season. But, in spite of this, each variety may be characterized by a rather definite range of heat units required to reach proper stage for canning.

Limitations of heat-unit systems are many. Although temperature, as measured by accumulated heat units, is one of the most important factors in determining development toward maturity, other factors must be considered.

1. Soil fertility may affect maturity, high phosphorous hastening it and high nitrogen delaying it.
2. Soil type is important, for heavy soils warm up slowly, whereas sandy soils warm up rapidly.
3. Topography, slope, and drainage are important, since they affect temperature and moisture conditions.

4. Altitude and latitude influence the number of heat units required to bring a crop to maturity.

5. Frost and drought damage are not accounted for by the system.

6. Wind, hail, storms, insects, and diseases may influence the heat-unit values necessary to bring a crop to a given stage of maturity.

7. Sunlight intensity measured in gram calories per square centimeter includes more than just temperature accumulation.

Probably the greatest weakness of any temperature-summation system lies in the fact that growth and development are not directly proportional to temperature, especially to supraoptimal values. Also, these systems provide no consideration for the effect of alternating day and night temperatures and the diurnal range of temperature.

It was shown by Madariaga and Knott (1951) that heat-unit accumulation was not a good basis for determining maturity of lettuce in California. Growth rate was found to vary greatly according to whether planting was in spring or fall. Heat units predicted maturity fairly well for spring plantings, but very poorly for fall plantings.

Data presented by Wiggans (1956) indicated that the number of heat units required for a specific variety of oats to reach maturity varied little from year to year. Early or late planting had little effect on heat units required, but a spread of eight weeks in the planting season narrowed to two weeks spread in time of maturity.

A modification of the heat-unit system was suggested by Reath and Wittwer (1952). They found that for peas the multiple of day-degree summations and the average duration of daylight was a less variable expression than heat summation alone. Day-length was included also by McCall and Voigt (1953, cited by Nuttonson, 1953) in studying phenological data of wheat from a number of different areas in the United States.

Several extensive reports on the use of heat-unit systems for wheat, barley, and rye have been prepared by Nuttonson (1953, 1955, 1957a, 1957b). He used extensive data obtained over a period of years from the United States, Czechoslovakia, and the U.S.S.R. Analyses of many data led him to conclude that photothermal units, obtained by multiplying day-degrees by day-length, were more satisfactory than simple day-degree summations for classifying wheat, barley, and rye varieties on a physiological-thermal basis and for predicting dates of heading and maturity.

On the basis of day-degrees summation, Nuttonson (1955) found that at similar elevations increases in latitude resulted in decreases in day-degrees. However, the photothermal-unit system tends to eliminate such differences because of inclusion of day-length in its computation.

In working with winter wheat Nuttonson (1955) found that for comparing varieties and seasons the period from March 1 to date of heading, and the period from March 1 to date of maturity, were quite as satisfactory for total day-degree or photothermal-unit summations as were more extended periods computed from the date sown through the winter to March 1. Analyses of many data, obtained in various parts of the world, have shown the importance of consideration of other factors, including soil moisture, fertility, latitude, and altitude.

A refinement of the heat-unit system was proposed by Decker (1953) who developed a formula in which temperatures were given efficiency ratings, in recognition of the acceleration in growth rate with increases in temperature.

Sunlight Degrees and Sugarcane Production

As was pointed out by Clements (1940), most of the dry matter of a plant is derived from the atmosphere about the plant, and from water, through the process of photosynthesis—"a process which is paced almost wholly by temperature and light intensity, becoming more important as the temperatures reach the optimum range."

In the production of sugarcane in Hawaii it had been noted that sunny areas often produced much higher yields than were produced in cloudy areas (Clements, 1940). In two experimental areas, Waipio and Kailua, the same variety of sugarcane, 31-1389, was studied for growth rate and final yield under similar conditions of temperature, fertilizer, and moisture. At the end of 22 months, the cane at Kailua produced 65 tons of stalks per acre and 7.2 tons of sucrose per acre, whereas the cane at Waipio produced 134 tons of stalks per acre and 18.6 tons of sucrose per acre. The main differences between the two areas appeared to be in solar radiation and its absorption (Figure 8-7).

This discovery led to the use of a value known as "sunlight degrees," a measure of insolation, in addition to, or in the place of, a summation of heat units. Whereas daily sunlight degrees were computed from differences between recorded temperatures obtained with "black bulb" and

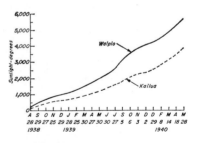

FIGURE 8-7.

Record of accumulated sunlight-degrees for Waipio and Kailua, Hawaii, two locations differing markedly in intensity of sunlight. [After Clements, Hawaiian Planter's Record 44:204, 1940.]

"white bulb" thermographs, these values were in the same direction (although weaker) as gram-calories per cm² per second obtained by a pyrheliometer.

Later work by Clements and Kubota (1943) showed that solar radiation was highly correlated with total sugar content of the young leaf sheath. This correlation was used in a complex formula for computing growth units, by which date of maturity and an estimate of final yield could be predicted.

RESPONSE OF PLANTS TO TEMPERATURE

Cardinal Points of Vital Activity

Every physiological plant process operates with a more or less well defined range of limits or tolerances. For temperature, there must be at least a minimum essential to the initiation of activity; the activity will proceed at the highest rate when the optimum temperature is reached; eventually activity will come to a close at the maximum temperature point. These three points are known as the cardinal temperature points. They may vary widely with the age or stage of development of the plant, and they vary considerably for different species. Grafe (1914) has given a table of cardinal temperature points for germination of crop seeds (based on data collected by F. Haberlandt) which gives some idea of the differences among crops as to their temperature requirements (Table 8-2).

It should be emphasized that such values for cardinal temperatures are not absolute, but should be considered as relative values only. Some crops' seeds will germinate at temperatures just above freezing, yet at later growth stages they may require much higher temperatures.

A general relationship exists between temperature and planting dates in temperate climates, which may be roughly approximated as follows:

Crop	Daily mean temperature at planting time
Spring wheat	37°–40°F
Oats	43°F
Potatoes	45°F
Corn	55°–57°F
Cotton	62°–64°F

Minimum temperatures for growth of peas, rye, and wheat range from 29° to 41°F, whereas sorghum and melons require temperatures of 59° to 64°F to make any appreciable growth. It was shown by Lundegardh

TABLE 8-2. CARDINAL TEMPERATURE POINTS FOR GERMINA-
TION OF CERTAIN CROP SEEDS*

Crop	Cardinal Points in Degrees Fahrenheit			Days Required for Germination at Indicated Temperatures			
	Minimum	Optimum	Maximum	40°F	54°F	60°F	66°F
Red clover	34	86	99	7.5	3.0	1.75	1.0
Alfalfa	34	86	99	6.0	3.75	2.75	2.0
Hemp	34–36	95	113	3.0	2.0	1.0	1.0
Peas	34–36	86	95	5.0	3.0	1.75	1.75
Rye	34–36	77	86	4.0	2.5	1.0	1.0
Vetch	34–36	86	95	6.0	5.0	2.0	2.0
Flax	35–37	77	86	8.0	4.5	2.0	2.0
Timothy	37–39	79	86	—	6.5	3.25	3.0
Wheat	39–40	77	86–90	6.0	3.0	2.0	1.75
Barley	39–40	68	82–86	6.0	3.0	2.0	1.75
Oats	39–41	77	86	7.0	3.75	2.75	2.0
Carrot	39–41	77	86	—	6.75	4.25	3.25
Sugar beet	39–41	77	82–86	22.0	9.0	3.75	3.75
Lentils	39–41	86	97	6.0	4.0	2.0	1.75
Maize	46–50	89–95	104–111	—	11.25	3.25	3.0
Sorghum	46–50	89–95	104	—	11.25	4.75	4.0
Rice	50–53	86–90	97–101	—	—	—	—
Tobacco	55–57	82	95	—	—	9.0	6.25
Pumpkin	54	89–93	104	—	—	10.75	4.0
Melon	54–59	95	104	—	—	15.0	17.0

* Adapted from data by F. Haberlandt in Grafe *Ernahrungsphysiologisches Practicum höherer Pflanzen*. Berlin, Paul Parey, 1914.

(1931) that for most plants the optimal temperature for photosynthesis was considerably lower than the optimum for respiration. The common white potato shows an optimum photosynthesis at about 68°F, but the respiration rate will increase until the temperature reached is about 118°F, at which photosynthesis is zero. The photosynthesis-respiration relationship may be ecologically important in determining limits of adaptation to temperature.

For most temperate-zone crops, the optimum temperature for growth ranges from 75°–85°F, with a maximum of 95°–105°F. For corn the minimum temperature for appreciable growth is 50°F, the optimum 86°–95°F, and the maximum approximately 113°F.

The minimum temperature at which growth starts or ceases may not be the same as the minimum a species can endure without injury. Likewise, the maximum temperature for growth may be considerably less than the temperature which causes heat damage. For example, 105°F may be the temperature at which growth ceases, but 130°–140°F might be the lethal temperature, if maintained for some time.

We have emphasized the existence of tolerance limits for all environmental factors. As already noted, the principle of physiological limits for growth has been employed in the physiological temperature index developed by Livingston (1916) and based on the work of Lehenbauer (1914). The effect of temperature on the growth rate of shoots of young seedlings of maize was determined with the roots in nutrient solution and the shoots in circulating air at 95% relative humidity. Lehenbauer found that in order to define the temperature with which a given growth rate is to be expected, it is essential to state the length of time during which the plant is subjected to the action of that temperature. Temperature coefficients for growth rates of shoots of maize seedlings were obtained for various 10°C ranges of temperature through a time period of 12 hours. These Q_{10} values did not follow the Van't Hoff Law, which states that the rate of a chemical reaction is doubled by increasing the temperature 10°C, for they ranged from 6.56 with a temperature change from 12°–22°C to 0.06 for a temperature change from 33°–43°C. For an exposure of three hours or longer, the greatest mean hourly growth rate was achieved at temperatures from 29°–32°C.

Similar studies using peas were conducted by Leitch (1916). The Q_{10} values ranged from 8.25 with a temperature change from 0°–10°C to 2.00 with a temperature change from 19°–29°C. Four cardinal points for temperature were suggested:

1. Minimum temperature—the lowest temperature at which growth takes place.

2. Maximum temperature—the highest temperature at which the process takes place.

3. Optimum temperature—the highest temperature at which there is no time-factor operating.

4. Maximum-rate temperature—the temperature at which the process attains the highest intensity. For the pea plant Leitch found that the minimum temperature for growth was −2°C, the maximum temperature was 44.5°C, the optimum range was 28°–30°C, and the maximum-rate temperature was 30.3°C.

The concept of optimum temperature must be considered with caution. It may be thought of as that value at which a process goes on at the fastest rate. However, as Lehenbauer emphasized, there is no rate at which growth will proceed indefinitely, and a specific time period must be taken into consideration. Among most plants, the optimum temperature for germination usually differs considerably from the optimum value for flowering or seed setting, and the optimum temperature for photosynthesis may be still another value.

Adaptation to Temperature

The ecological effect of temperature values must be examined from another viewpoint: shall maximum and minimum temperature limits be applied to individual plants or to populations of biotypes or ecotypes? The optimum for the population can be only a very general concept, and may be thought of best as a range within which the species or variety maintains its ecological position.

The limits of range must be determined by ecological factors operating on individuals of a population. These individuals, at least at higher latitudes, are usually not exposed to the mean temperature of a region for very many hours at a time. Rather, they are subjected to highly variable temperatures, diurnal and seasonal—in fact, temperature extremes. Near the equator, however, vegetation may actually be exposed to a temperature range which is rather similar to the mean.

The greatest range of temperatures in which all vegetation survives may be something like 220°F. Some conifers in the subarctic regions can withstand a temperature of −80°F, while certain desert shrubs can survive 140°F (Oosting, 1958). In general, the northern limits of trees are thought to be established by low temperature, whereas the altitudinal limits are probably set by either low temperature or wind, or possibly both in combination.

A careful evaluation of the various thermal influences shows that for the permanent life of a species the temperature must never be so high or so low at any time as to kill the organism, and yet it must be high enough, or in some instances low enough, for a period long enough to permit reproduction and growth of the species (Clarke, 1954).

Some plants require a certain amount of low temperature before their life cycle can be completed. Flowering plants like tulips and daffodils are planted in the fall, go through a low-temperature period in the winter, emerge and bloom in the spring. Dormant buds of certain fruit trees and berries require a period of chilling before they flower successfully. Some blueberries require an exposure of 800 hours of cool temperatures before dormant buds develop (Clarke, 1954). Seeds often must be chilled under either dry or moist conditions to overcome dormancy. Low-temperature treatment to cause floral induction is the basis for vernalization, a process which accelerates flowering, especially in crops such as winter cereals.

Plants that are not frost hardy and that have no mode of escape are limited in altitude and latitude by the damaging effects of freezing. Palm trees are a notable example: their natural range does not extend north of Florida, the Gulf Coast, and southern Arizona and California.

Low temperature injury to plants may be dependent on the degree and duration of the minimum temperature reached, the moisture content of the tissues, the general physiological conditions, and adaptational characteristics of the species. Temperatures far above the freezing point may be limiting to normal growth in tropical species. Burr, et al. (1957) have reviewed research on response of sugarcane to temperature. Root temperatures below 70°F definitely limit growth, whereas 80°F appears to be optimum for growth and absorption of nutrients. Practically no growth takes place at 50°F, and at 62°F growth is greatly reduced. If root temperatures are dropped from 74°F to 66°F, phosphorus intake is reduced to one-third and nitrogen intake is reduced about one-half. Cool nights are also limiting for growth of sugarcane: growth with night temperatures of 57°F was only half that produced with night temperatures at 73°F.

Sugarcane is propagated by planting stalks as "seed pieces" and the minimum temperature required for germination is about 70°F. Optimum temperature is from 90° to 100°F; above 100° is detrimental. Experiments have shown that dropping soil temperature from 78°F to 71.5°F resulted in a delay of 10 days in seed-piece germination.

Brown (1939) reported on response of three temperate and one tropical species of forage grasses to temperature. The lower limit for growth of Kentucky bluegrass, Poa pratensis, Canada bluegrass, Poa compressa, and orchardgrass, Dactylis glomerata, was 40°F air temperature. Optimum growth of the bluegrass was attained at air temperatures from 80° to 90°F. Orchardgrass, however, grew best at 70°F air temperature. Bermudagrass showed a lower limit for growth of 50°F and an optimum of 100°F air temperature. Root temperatures for optimum growth were 50°F for Canada bluegrass, 60°F for Kentucky bluegrass, 70°F for orchardgrass, and 100° for Bermudagrass.

In a study of turf grasses, Carroll (1943) found that soil temperatures were much more limiting than were air temperatures. In a series of trials, exposures to soil temperature of −15°C resulted in more injury to Lolium perenne, L. multiflorum, Cynosurus cristatus, and Agrostis canina than to Poa pratensis, Poa nemoralis, and Agrostis tenuis. High temperatures of 50° to 60°C caused heat injury by direct thermal effect on the protoplasm.

The growth of cotton is definitely limited by temperatures far above freezing. Holekamp, Hudspeth, and Ray (1960) have shown that seedlings emerge earlier and grow faster if planting is delayed until the minimum temperature at 8 inches below the surface averages from 60° to 70°F for about 10 days. When soil temperature was below 60°F, emergence required 14 days instead of 5 to 9 days at the more favorable temperature. In the High Plains area near Lubbock, Texas, the planting date for cotton varies from April 23 to May 16, with an average date of May 3.

Cold Injury and Cold Resistance

Exposure to low temperature may cause injury to plants in a number of ways:

1. *Suffocation.* Low-growing plants such as winter cereals and forage crops may suffer from a deficient oxygen supply when covered for long periods during the winter with an ice sheet or densely packed or encrusted snow. Sprague and Graber (1940) found that injuries to alfalfa covered by an ice sheet were due to internal accumulations of toxic products of aerobic and anaerobic respiration. Ice in contact with roots and crowns tends to inhibit diffusion of CO_2, and concentration of it and other respiratory products may become harmful to plants.

2. *Physiological drought and desiccation.* Two conditions may cause plant injury through excessive transpiration. If the autumn is dry and soil moisture is not brought up to somewhere near field capacity by the time of fall freeze-up, normal transpiration of coniferous trees and shrubs may result in a total soil moisture stress that reduces water absorption rate below that essential to meet transpiration requirements. Another condition, sometimes called "winter drought," often occurs in coniferous forests. This condition was particularly serious in the winter of 1947–48, as described in Wisconsin by Voigt (1951) and Patton and Riker (1954). Excessive transpiration and a lag in absorption of moisture from the soil, caused by a warm period when the soil was still frozen, resulted in an internal moisture deficit sufficient to cause needle droop and in some instances marked leaf loss and death of twigs. In the Adirondacks, Curry and Church (1952) observed winter injury through desiccation of foliage which resulted in a browning effect with much defoliation. Red spruce, hemlock, white pine, and balsam fir showed much greater injury from this "winter drought" than was suffered by white spruce, blue spruce, white cedar, and red pine. It was estimated that approximately 10% of the trees had one-fourth of their crowns killed by desiccation. Kramer (1940) reported that the cause of decreased water absorption by plants at low soil temperature is the combined effect of decreased permeability of the root membranes and increased viscosity of the water itself. This results in increased resistance to water movement across the living cells of the roots.

3. *Heaving.* Injury to plants is caused by a lifting upward from their normal position, causing roots to loosen or break and at times the plant

crowns to push completely above the soil surface. After heaving, it may be difficult for the roots to become firmly established again and the plant may die from desiccation plus mechanical damage. Heaving is not caused by expansion of soil water freezing *in situ* in the soil interstices, but by free water progressively segregated from the soil (Schramm, 1958). Heaving pressure increases with a decrease in soil particle size to a point at which the soil is practically impervious to water. The free water takes the form of ice filaments grouped in columns oriented vertically to the soil surface. It was estimated by Taber (1930) that heaving often exerted a lifting force as great as 200 pounds per square inch.

McCool and Bouyoucos (1929) felt that heaving was caused by ice crystals oriented vertically in the surface layer of soil. The free water below, through repeated nights of freezing, tends to increase the ice crystals from below, and the upper layers are lifted.

Post and Dreibelbis (1942) found a high concentration of moisture at or near the surface of frozen soils. In the heaving process, three types of frost structure were found. **Concrete** structure included many very thin ice lenses, small ice crystals, and an extremely dense complex, found in soils previously frozen and thawed. **Honeycomb** structure was loose and porous, permitting vapor movement, and was found under shallow freezing conditions, sometimes in soils filled with grass roots. **Stalactite** structure included many small icicles connecting the heaved surface to the soil below.

A study of heaving of forage seedlings was conducted by Biswell, *et al.* (1953) on burned chamise brushlands in California. In general, heaving was greater on north-facing slopes than on slopes facing south. Legumes showed a much higher percentage of heaved seedlings than did grasses. Among grasses, *Bromus catharticus* and *Dactylis glomerata* suffered much more serious heaving than did *Festuca elatior* and *Phalaris tuberosa*. Under the conditions of this trial, a mulching with plant material scattered on the surface greatly reduced heaving damage.

In Canada, Holmes and Robertson (1960) observed that heaving of alfalfa was associated with conditions of partially bare soil and fluctuating temperatures. Under these conditions, water tended to accumulate at or near the soil surface, a condition favorable to heaving. Snow cover offered a highly protective effect against heaving, as did long periods of steady cold weather.

Decker and Ronningen (1957) in Maryland found that uniform plant cover was a deterrent to heaving. Damage to Ladino clover by heaving closely paralleled the upward movement of wooden dowels placed in the forage plot area. Less heaving damage was caused in plots of alfalfa, and virtually none in a Kentucky bluegrass sod.

4. *Chilling.* This type of injury is caused by low temperatures above the freezing point. Plants were classified by Sellschop and Salmon (1928) as to their reaction to chilling:

a. Plants killed by exposure for 60 hours to temperatures of 0.5°C to 5°C included rice, cotton, cowpea, and velvet beans.

b. Plants injured by the above conditions but recovering after being placed back in favorable conditions included sudangrass, Spanish peanut, and Valencia peanut.

c. Plants not likely to suffer serious injury from exposure to chilling temperatures included corn, sorghum, pumpkin, and Virginia bunch peanut.

d. Plants injured by prolonged chilling, but likely to recover, included buckwheat, soybeans, and tepary beans.

e. Plants not injured by chilling as far as is known included sunflower, potato, tomato, and flax.

Some effects of chilling are chlorotic areas, or bands, on leaves of sugarcane, sorghum, and corn when exposed for 60 hours at 2° to 4°C. These have been called Faris bands (Klages, 1942).

5. *Freezing injury.* Plant parts or whole plants may be killed or damaged beyond repair as a result of actual freezing of the tissues. It is well established that freezing damage is caused by the formation of ice crystals within the plant. These ice crystals probably form first in the intercellular spaces and then within the cells. In very rapid freezing, ice may form within the cells almost as soon as it forms between cells. Ice within the cells probably causes most freezing injury, and this is thought to be caused mainly by the mechanical effects of ice crystals disrupting the physical structure of the protoplasm and plasma membrane (Scarth, 1944; Levitt, 1951; Bonner and Galston, 1952).

The mechanical effects of freezing and thawing of intercellular ice crystals may be another type of freezing injury, according to Scarth (1944).

Formation of ice in the intercellular spaces also results in withdrawal of water from the cells, causing them to dry out at ordinary temperatures. Levitt (1951) noted that tissues shrink when they freeze. The decrease in cell volume caused by cell dehydration may result in cell collapse. Continued removal of water from the cell sap, with greater and greater dehydration, may cause the cells to die, a third kind of freezing damage (Scarth, 1944; Levitt, 1951).

Siminovitch and Scarth (1938), in experiments conducted in the laboratory with red cabbage, found that in freezing tissues both extracellular and intracellular ice crystals were formed.

Stuckey and Curtis (1938) reported that in freezing tissue small ice crystals form in the cytoplasm and through a lacerating action disorganize the protoplasmic structure. The order of freezing observed was (1) the cytoplasm, (2) the vacuole, and (3) the plastids.

In spite of the lack of complete agreement on which is more important, or which occurs first, ice formation within or between the cells, the accepted concept of injury from freezing is that it is basically caused by mechanical effects of ice formation either within or between the cells, rather than to dehydration *per se* or to chemical effects (Meyer and Anderson, 1952).

Hardening of Plants

Many perennials and biennials of the temperate regions are conditioned to attain a considerable degree of frost-hardiness. According to Harvey (1930), the threshold for hardening is approximately 6°C. Hardening may be considered as a temporary adaptation of the protoplasm which gives the plant resistance to low-temperature injury. For example, trees which can withstand temperatures of −50°C in winter may be killed by 0°C if artificially frozen in midsummer. Such trees become hardened naturally through gradually decreasing temperatures and short photoperiods. Alfalfa is a crop which naturally undergoes considerable hardening each autumn, and may be hardened artificially by exposure to temperatures just above freezing for a number of days. Bonner and Galston (1952) indicated that both alfalfa and cabbage may be hardened experimentally by subjecting plants to 0°C for a few hours of each 24 hours for a few days. Intermittent periods of relatively low night temperatures appear to be responsible for inducing frost-hardening.

The changes that accompany hardening include an increase in sugar concentration and an increase in the osmotic pressure of the cell sap. Also there is evidence of an increase in permeability of the plasma membranes, an increase in soluble proteins, and an increase in bound water as a result of "osmotic hardening" (Levitt and Scarth, 1936; Levitt, 1941; Scarth, 1944).

Studies of expected minimum winter temperatures have been used as a basis for designating plant hardiness zones (Skinner, 1958). Zones of plant hardiness for the United States and Canada are shown in Figure 8-8.

Proper management of perennial forage legumes has been shown by many workers to be a most important aspect of reducing low-temperature injury. Time of last cutting, soil moisture level, surface cover, and fertility level all may influence rate of attaining maximum hardiness in the fall, and consequent ability to withstand low-temperature damage.

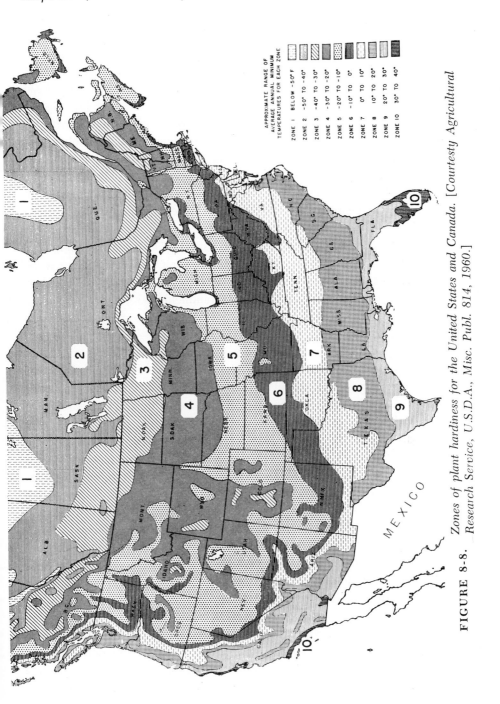

FIGURE 8-8. Zones of plant hardiness for the United States and Canada. [Courtesy Agricultural Research Service, U.S.D.A., Misc. Publ. 814, 1960.]

Bula and Smith (1954) found that maximum cold resistance in alfalfa, red clover, and sweet clover was reached by late November and early December, or shortly after the soil surface was permanently frozen and air temperature began to remain below freezing. The high level of cold resistance was maintained through December, January, and early February. Cold resistance began to decrease after February 15, but was not lost rapidly until the soil surface was thawed in late March. Total available carbohydrates in the roots and crowns were at a high level by mid-October, and were mainly starch. After that date, and during November when starch was being converted into sugars, cold resistance increased rapidly. The highest level of total sugars was found in sweetclover and the lowest in red clover. It appeared that cold resistance developed more slowly in red clover than in alfalfa or sweetclover. Resistance, in their studies, was determined by the electroconductance method used by Dexter, Tottingham, and Graber (1932). Late summer and fall cutting practices have shown to be highly important in preventing low-temperature injury in alfalfa (Graber, et al. 1927; Rather and Harrison, 1938; Grandfield, 1935; and others).

Plant Characteristics and Cold Resistance

It would be highly useful if certain easily identifiable morphological characters were positively correlated with cold resistance. A search for such characters has been underway for generations, but with only limited success. Nilsson-Ehle (1912), the famous Swedish plant breeder, stated that "winter hardiness of wheat stands is no definite relation to the ordinary morphological characteristics of varieties." Some features of plants, however, have given clues to differences in hardiness. A German investigator, Bühlert (1906), noted that winter-hardy rye had narrower and thicker leaves than the less hardy varieties. Sinz (1914) reported that wheat of hardy varieties had narrower leaves which were firmer and more cutinized. Salmon (1917) found that the most hardy cereals had narrower leaves and a more prostrate growth habit, whereas soft winter wheats, winter barley, and winter oats had broad leaves and a more upright fall growth.

In the northern states, growth habit has been found to be associated with winter-hardiness in forage crops as well as cereals. Following a fall cutting in September, winter-hardy varieties of alfalfa, Ladak, Ranger, and Vernal, develop a low rosette type of growth under short photoperiod and cool temperature. In contrast, Kansas Common and Du Puits, considerably less winter-hardy, lack this early fall dormancy habit and continue to produce a tall, erect growth until temperatures stop growth in late autumn.

Root systems too may reflect differences in hardiness. Canadian studies by Southworth (1921) and Heinrichs (1954) have indicated a high degree of correlation between degree of branching of the root system and winter-hardiness.

The relationship between fall growth habit and hardiness has been the basis for the development of "trueness-to-type" tests which have been used to check performance of seed lots of winter-hardy varieties of alfalfa (Canode, 1958; Elling, 1959).

High Temperature Injury

High temperature is a limiting factor in the production of crops in many semiarid and arid climates. While the effects are often associated with drought, temperature itself may be high enough to cause direct injury to the cell protoplasm. Direct temperature effects are noticeable especially in young seedlings and in young transplants. The thermal death point of active cells ranges from 50° to 60°C for most plant species, but varies with species, age of tissue, and time of exposure to the high temperature (Meyer and Anderson, 1952). Miller (1938) has suggested that most plant cells are killed by temperatures of 45° to 55°C, but that some tissues withstand from 62° to 105°C. Sapper (1935) found that the lethal limit for most aquatic and shade plants was 40°C, and for most xerophytes 50°C, when the plants were exposed to a saturated atmosphere for one-half hour.

Direct effects of high temperatures include stem lesions, heat cankers, and sunscald damage. Winter sunscald in fruit trees has been studied by Mix (1916) and Eggert (1944). It was found that in winter or early spring the sun warms the surface of the exposed side of the tree and that a difference of 30° to 50°F may exist between the cambium temperatures on the north and south sides of peach and apple tree trunks. Damage may be caused by the rapid changes in temperature, and the accompanying metabolic disturbances, especially the increase in rate of respiration. Winter damage to Ladino clover stolons may be caused in a similar manner. Sprague, *et al.* (1954) measured temperatures of stolons at midday in winter and found that they often reached 65° to 70°F, although air temperatures remained close to the freezing point. At night the temperatures of these stolons often were actually below air temperatures.

The effect of high temperatures on tolerance of corn to heat was studied by Heyne and Laude (1940). Corn seedlings, from 10 to 14 days after emergence, were held for 5 hours at 130°F and a relative humidity of 25% to 30%, and found to be more tolerant to heat than older plants.

The response of perennial ryegrass stubble and roots to temperature was reported by Sullivan and Sprague (1949). Sods of ryegrass were clipped at

one and one-half inches and allowed to recover at four different temperatures. New top growth was most rapid in development at 60° to 70°F and
least rapid at 80° to 90°F. The damaging effect of high temperature appeared to be caused by the rapid dissipation of reserve carbohydrates, a
slowing down of new leaf production, and poor recovery from defoliation.

Julander (1945) found that when stolons of range grasses in the soil were
held at 48°C for periods varying from 0 to 16 hours, recovery after planting
showed that high soil temperatures may be a direct cause of death in a
long drought period. Buffalograss and Bermudagrass were more resistant to
heat than Bluestems, wheat grasses, and Kentucky bluegrass. Heat resistance appeared to be a measure of drought resistance.

Certain indirect effects of high temperatures include the apparent drop in
photosynthesis as respiration mounts, although actual photosynthesis may
not drop. Also, dry winds promote desiccation of leaves through high rates
of water loss by transpiration. Wilted leaves may cause stomatal closure and
this may actually lower photosynthesis.

Heat resistance, according to Levitt (1951), appears to depend on specific protoplasmic properties. There appears to be a similarity among
drought, heat resistance, and frost resistance. Tissues low in water content
generally can endure high temperatures better than those of high water
content (Meyer and Anderson, 1952). Temporary heat resistance may be
increased by a gradual dehydration process. Dry seeds and spores are far
more resistant to heat damage than some of the vegetative tissues. Protection from high-temperature injury is achieved in part by such characteristics
as waxy bloom or pubescence, corky layers of bark serving as insulation, vertical orientation of leaf blades, and, at times, a high transpiration rate.

Thermoperiodism

The responses of plants to a rhythmic fluctuation in temperature is known
as thermoperiodism. A number of physiological processes, including germination, stem elongation, fruiting, floral development, and increase in
frost-hardiness, may proceed most satisfactorily under a rhythm of alternating temperatures. Especially striking have been the results obtained by
Went (1944, 1945, 1950) in the production of tomatoes grown under conditions of both constant and alternating temperatures. The tomato was found
to be sensitive to night temperatures. With young seedlings the optimum
night temperature was 26° to 30°C. As the plant grew older the optimum
night temperature dropped, finally reaching a range of 13° to 18°C, depending on the variety. Fruit set abundantly with daylight temperatures of
26.5°C and nighttime temperatures of 15° to 20°C. A high optimum day

temperature is effective because it increases the photosynthetic rate. Tomatoes grow mainly at night, and with temperatures above 18°C translocation of sugars become a limiting factor. Actually little fruit sets in the field with night temperatures above 22°C or below 10°C. In southern California, in winter and early spring, night temperatures are often below 10°C, but late afternoon temperatures may be between 15° and 20°C. By covering plants at 3 P.M., an optimum dark (night) temperature exists for a few hours and fruit set is improved considerably.

In another study Went (1957) emphasized the diurnal temperature range at various latitudes as related to the growth of plants at night. It had been pointed out by Sachs (1875) that tomatoes, corn, peppers, and potatoes appeared to grow primarily during the night hours. The term, "effective" night temperature, or "nyctotemperature," was computed by Went as follows:

$$t_{nycto} = t_{min} + \tfrac{1}{4}(t_{max} - t_{min}).$$

The daylight temperatures or "phototemperature," was computed as:

$$t_{photo} = t_{max} - \tfrac{1}{4}(t_{max} - t_{min}).$$

Went (1957) noted that in Java, at 7° south latitude, there is but 0.9°C difference between the nyctotemperatures of the coolest and the warmest months. In Puerto Rico, at 18° north latitude, the difference is 3.9°C; at Palo Alto, California, at 37° north latitude, 10.0°C; at Alamosa, Colorado, at 37° north latitude, 28.3°C; and at Fairbanks, Alaska, at approximately 65° north latitude, 45.0°C. Effective night temperatures at several locations in California are given in Figure 8-9.

Some plants such as *Lupinus* and *Clarkia* species are rather intolerant of high night temperature. Germination, establishment, and development to maturity may be restricted to certain favorable temperatures, and thus diurnal range of temperatures may be a factor of considerable importance in controlling plant distribution.

This concept of the importance of the effective day and night temperatures has been elaborated further by Kimball and Brooks (1959) in a tentative zonation of the state of California into five main groups of plant climates. These zones, with emphasis on mean effective day and mean effective night monthly temperatures, include (1) direct ocean and coastal areas; (2) coastal valleys; (3) intermediate valleys; (4) interior valleys; and (5) foothills to 3000 feet.

Within the Central Valley it is of interest to note that effective night temperatures in July and August are lower in the middle portion (Davis, for example) than at either the northern end (Red Bluff) or the southern end (Bakersfield) of the valley.

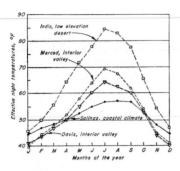

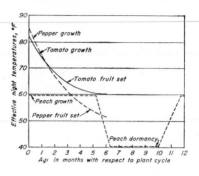

FIGURE 8-9.

Representation of 12 months of effective night temperatures at a number of locations in California. [After Kimball and Brooks, Calif. Agr. 13(5):12, 1959.]

FIGURE 8-10.

Change in night temperature requirements with age of plant or stage of growth, for pepper, tomato, and peach. [After Went in Kimball and Brooks, Calif. Agr. 13(5):12, 1959.]

For a number of plants—lupines, peppers, tomatoes, zinnias, and others—a night temperature which changes with age or stage of development of the plant is required (Figure 8-10). In commercial production of zinnia seed, it has been found that an effective night temperature in midsummer only two or three degrees warmer than optimum for seed setting will result in partial to complete failure to produce seed. Kimball and Brooks point out that once accurate data are accumulated on the specific plant requirements for temperature, and accurate data are accumulated on the temperature conditions in the respective plant zones, this information will furnish a basis for comparing current season conditions with average conditions, for predicting crop maturity dates, and for determining the most favorable areas for the production of various field and horticultural crops.

Vernalization

While vernalization has been considered a phenomenon related to both temperature and light, it appears certain that in its original meaning it was restricted to a chilling, or low temperature, effect. It is a well known fact that in all temperate-zone countries seed of winter cereals must be planted before the end of winter in order to fruit successfully within a year of the time of sowing. Spring cereals, on the other hand, come into flower and produce seed not many weeks after they are sown in the spring.

The earliest report on vernalization probably was that by Klippart (1857) in Ohio. He observed that winter wheat could be made to behave as spring wheat by allowing the seed to germinate slightly in the fall, then storing it at low temperature until planting time in the spring.

The work of Klebs (1918) and Gassner (1918) indicated the importance of temperature as related to the reproductive phase of certain plants. Klebs suggested that development toward flowering proceeded in three stages, (1) the "ripeness-to-flower" condition, (2) formation of floral primordia, and (3) development of floral structures and their expansion.

Gassner germinated winter and spring rye at different temperatures from just above the freezing point to 24°C. Later, when well established, the seedlings were transplanted into the field. The temperature during germination had no effect on flowering of the spring rye, but with the winter rye only the plants that were germinated at low temperatures, at 1° or 2°C, flowered regularly and completely, regardless of the date of appearance above ground in the spring. Gassner concluded that spring rye was independent of any low temperature requirement to achieve flowering, but that winter rye must pass through a chilling period either during or at some stage following germination.

In a recent review paper on vernalization, Chouard (1960) pointed out that two main groups of workers have studied the physiology of vernalization on an accurate experimental basis: the British group, particularly Gregory and Purvis, working with Petkus winter rye; and the German group, Lang, Melchers, *et al.*, working with the biennial strain of henbane, *Hyoscyamus niger*. As used by Chouard, and for purposes of this discussion, vernalization is defined as the acquisition or acceleration of the ability to flower by a chilling treatment.

Undoubtedly influenced by the earlier work of Gassner, the Russian worker, Lysenko (1928, 1935) reported on results of the pretreatment of seed with low temperature. Partially soaked and slowly germinating seeds of winter cereals were subjected to a temperature just above freezing for 15 to 60 days, the period varying with the variety. Such seed, when sown in early spring, produced a yield of grain the same summer, possibly even earlier than spring varieties planted at the same time. Lysenko called the process *jarovizacija*, translated vernalization, and encouraged farmers to use it extensively, thus extending northward the growing areas of winter wheat and winter rye.

The theoretical basis for vernalization was found in Lysenko's phasic development theory (Whyte, 1946), which stated that (1) growth and development are not identical; (2) the entire process of development consists of individual phases or stages; (3) these stages proceed in strict sequence —a subsequent stage cannot begin until the previous stage is completed;

and (4) different stages of development require different environmental conditions for completion.

Research in London by Gregory and Purvis (1936a, 1936b, 1938, 1948), Purvis (1934, 1939, 1944, 1947, 1948, 1954) and by Purvis and Gregory (1937, 1938, 1952) has given a rather complete picture of the physiology of vernalization of Petkus winter rye. When the spring form of rye is grown under long days, the primary axis produces seven leaf primordia and then forms the young ear, recognizable by double ridges on the sides of the apex. Under short days, spring rye produces 25 leaves before earing; thus it is a quantitatively long-day plant.

Winter rye is a biennial rosette plant which, if planted in spring under long days, produces 25 leaf primordia before earing. If grown under short days, it produces 16 leaf primordia before earing. However, if seed is previously vernalized, winter rye develops just like the spring variety (under long days), producing ear primordia after seven leaves have developed.

It appears, therefore, that in both strains the first six or seven lateral primordia formed by the apex are predetermined as leaves, and the "ripeness to flower" condition is reached at the sixth or seventh leaf. The subsequent primordia are "labile" and will produce leaves or tillers depending on photoperiod in spring rye and on degree of vernalization and subsequent photoperiod in winter rye. After vernalization, winter cereals are quantitatively long-day plants.

To achieve vernalization several conditions must be met (Chouard, 1960):

1. Sufficient imbibition of water to allow the vernalizing process but low enough to hinder seedling growth.

2. A period of activation (necessary to induce respiratory exchanges in the imbibed seeds) of about 10 to 24 hours at 15° to 18°C after the beginning of soaking.

3. Oxygen absolutely required.

4. An appropriate duration and temperature of chilling (The effective low temperature is between +1° and 5° or 6°C with a wide optimum).

In the studies of vernalization a number of workers showed that short days could substitute (in part at least) for the chilling effect in promoting or accelerating flowering. This led to a concept, accepted by many, that vernalization be defined loosely as any treatment applied in the early growth stages that results in promoting or hastening the reproductive phase.

The process of vernalization is reversible within limits. Purvis and Gregory (1938, 1952) and Gregory and Purvis (1936b) showed that in winter rye devernalization was accomplished by: (1) exposure to about 20°C in a damp atmosphere lacking oxygen for one to five days; and (2) exposure in ordinary damp atmosphere at about 35°C for a period of eight to twelve

days. The effectiveness of devernalization depends on the time interval between completion of vernalization and the beginning of devernalization. If
vernalization is thoroughly achieved, a return to 15°C or 20°C fixes the
vernalized state in a few days.

Extensive studies of vernalization of the biennial henbane, *Hyoscyamus
niger*, have been reported by Lang (1952, 1957), Liverman and Lang
(1956), Lang and Melchers (1943, 1947), and Lang, Sandoval, and Bedri
(1957). Henbane exists in two races, a winter and a spring form. In vernalization experiments with this plant, important differences were found
relative to the responses obtained in winter cereals, as follows:

1. Neither the seed nor immature embryos have been vernalized. The
chilling treatment is effective only on plants at least ten days old and in
the rosette stage.

2. The leafy plant is strictly a long-day plant.

3. The winter strain of henbane has an obligate requirement for vernalization.

4. Partial replacement of vernalization by previous exposure to short days
is not possible.

5. Henbane shows a remarkable ability for grafting and for transmission
of vernalization from donor to receptor through grafts.

As with winter cereals, henbane can be devernalized if the treatment is
applied immediately after the end of chilling, but an interval of three or
four days at 20°C is enough to fix the vernalized state definitely.

A basic requirement for vernalization of any plant is an hereditary prop-
erty transmitted as a physiological characteristic. Vavilov (1951) considered
that this characteristic was associated with the plant's evolutionary development, and related to the climate of its origin. As indicated by Chouard
(1960), the vernalization characteristic is borne by a few genes, and in henbane probably only one gene.

Information on vernalization has helped to develop a clearer picture of
the difference between winter and spring cereals. Genetic differences between winter and spring wheats have been studied by Nilsson-Ehle (1917),
Aamodt (1923), Florell (1925), Powers (1934), Vavilov (1951), and
others. In general, the spring habit has been dominant over winter habit,
but segregation in different material has shown varying degrees of complexity. Vavilov believed that "the study of growth stages shows that there
is no fundamental difference between winter and spring varieties."

In Germany Voss (1938) found that winter wheat would flower at temperatures above 20°C when exposed to continuous light without vernalization, if given sufficient time. An experiment in Great Britain by Gregory
(cited by Whyte, 1948) included two well known spring wheat varieties,

Little Joss and April Bearded. When seeds of these were vernalized, Little Joss behaved as a winter variety while April Bearded behaved as a true spring variety. Gregory concluded that the reason Little Joss had been used successfully by farmers as a spring variety was that it is an early-planted variety. Early planting resulted in a low temperature treatment in the field during the early growth stages.

According to Vavilov (1951), when extensive world wheat collections were studied in Russia, it was found that the proportion of varieties which came into bloom normally the same year sown decreased as the date of sowing became later in the season and temperatures were consequently higher.

In Switzerland, Büchli (1943) studied the performances of spring wheat varieties from Canada, Germany, and a local Swiss strain. Planting was started on February 2, with additional plantings at weekly intervals until April 30. One of the German varieties was found to require a certain amount of cold before normal development took place. Early planting allowed this necessary exposure to low temperature during the germination period. Farmers were advised to plant as early as possible, unless they were sure that the variety they sowed had no low-temperature requirement.

Pal and Murty (1941) found that Indian winter wheats did not require any low-temperature treatment, even when grown at high summer temperatures, whereas English varieties under those same conditions would not bloom normally without a chilling pretreatment.

Evidence has been cited to show that in addition to vernalization brought about by a chilling treatment applied to germinating seeds, a partial vernalization can take place in the field through early planting. Also, there is evidence to show that vernalization can be effected in the ripening seed on the mother plant. Experiments by Kostjucenko and Zarubailo (1937) indicated that winter wheat of identical varieties which was ripened at Hibiny (67° 44′ north latitude) and at Kirovobad (40° 41′ north latitude), when planted at Hibiny the following year, showed marked differences in development. In September, following spring planting, plants from Hibiny seed had flowered and many had set seed, whereas plants from Kirovobad seed were at the tillering stage. This difference was explained on the basis that under the low temperatures at the more northern latitude the preceding autumn, partial to complete vernalization had taken place before harvest. That embryos can be vernalized on the mother plant has been definitely confirmed by Gregory and Purvis (1936a). Whyte (1946) has suggested the importance of this phenomenon in conducting variety trials using wide collections of seed, and also in the location of seed production areas for certain crops.

A practical example of the importance of vernalization on the developmental physiology of crops may be found in the sugar beet industry. For many years, until World War I, the United States was dependent on Europe for sugar beet seed. Difficulties in obtaining sufficient seed resulted in efforts to develop our own seed production. As was reported by Owen, Carsner, and Stout (1940), Coons (1943), and Stout (1945, 1946) careful attention was given to the factors that determine whether the growth of the plant was to be purely vegetative or reproductive. It was found that the sugar beet requires a period of low-temperature exposure (13–19°C probably most effective) to induce normal seed stalk formation. Also, the effect of photoperiod was found to be intimately associated with and dependent on the temperature of exposure. In the breeding of new varieties for disease resistance, this whole problem was brought into sharp focus. Two varieties, U. S. No. 1 and U. S. No. 33, developed for resistance to curly-top virus, were found to bolt and produce seed stalks in high percentages during the first year, particularly in winter plantings in California. It is reported that in one such field, from which 16 tons of beets per acre were harvested, 9 tons of seed stalks had to be removed before the roots were dug. The genetic make-up of these varieties was such that only a slight cold exposure was required to induce flowering.

A situation nearly the opposite prevailed in the production of sugar beet seed in southern California and Arizona in the warmer winter areas. Seed fields in some seasons had too few low temperatures to permit more than a minor percentage of plants to form seed stalks, with the result that seed yields were poor. This resulted in a genetic drift in the population such that when this seed was used for root production, heavy bolting often occurred in seasons of cold wet springs. After much research on this problem, it was found that in certain areas of the Pacific Northwest weather conditions were extremely favorable for the production of sugar beet seed. Winter temperatures were sufficiently low that nonbolting types would undergo induction and produce good seed yields in the next season. Also it was found that seed production could still be successful in warm winter climates, providing certain precautions were taken. Early planting and dense stands favored profuse bolting and good seed production.

References

1. Aamodt, O. S. 1923. Inheritance of growth habit and resistance to stem rust in a cross between two varieties of common wheat. *Jour. Agr. Res.* 24: 457–469.

2. Abbe, C. 1905. Report on relations between climates and crops. U.S.D.A., Weather Bur. Bul. 342.

3. Barnard, J. 1948. Heat units as a measure of canning crop maturity. *The Canner* 106: 28.

4. Biswell, H. H., Schultz, A. M., Hedrick, D. W., and Mallory, J. I. 1953. Frost heaving of grass and brush seedlings on burned chamise brushlands in California. *Jour. Range Mgt.* 6: 172–180.

5. Bomalaski, H. H. 1948. Growing-degree days—How to apply this unit to a measure of crops. *Food Packer* 29 (8): 51; 29 (9): 57.

6. Bonner, J. and Galston, A. W. 1952. *Principles of Plant Physiology.* Freeman, San Francisco.

7. Boswell, V. R. 1927. Influence of temperature on the growth and yield of garden peas. *Amer. Soc. Hort. Sci. Proc.* 23: 162–168.

8. Boswell, V. R. 1929. Factors influencing yield and quality of peas. *Md. Agr. Exp. Sta. Bul.* 306.

9. Braun-Blanquet, Josias. 1932. *Plant Sociology, the Study of Plant Communities.* McGraw-Hill, New York.

10. Brown, E. M. 1939. Some effects of temperature on the growth and chemical composition of certain pasture grasses. *Mo. Agr. Exp. Sta. Res. Bul.* 299.

11. Büchli, M. 1943. Untersuchungen uber den Einflusz der saatzeit auf ertrag und Qualitat des Sommerweizens. *Ber. Schweig. Bot. Ges.* 53A: 334–368.

12. Bühlert, K. 1906. Untersuchungen über das Auswintern des Getreides. *Landw. Jahrb.* 35: 837–888.

13. Bula, R. J. and Smith, Dale. 1954. Cold resistance and chemical composition in overwintering alfalfa, red clover and sweetclover. *Agron. Jour.* 46: 397–401.

14. Buller, R. E. and Valdivieso, Rene G. 1958. Comportamients de leguminosas forrajeras en los Valles de Mexico y de Toluca. Oficina de Estudios Especiales, Mexico, Folleto Tecnico 34.

15. Burr, G. O., Hartt, C. E., Brodie, H. W., Tanimoto, T., Kortschak, H. P., Takahashi, D., Ashton, F. M., and Coleman, R. E. 1957. The sugarcane plant. *Ann. Rev. Plant Phys.* 8: 275–308.

16. Canode, C. L. 1958. Natural selection within Ranger alfalfa. *Idaho Agr. Exp. Sta. Res. Bul.* 39.

17. Caprio, J. M. 1957. Phenology of lilac bloom in Montana. *Sci.* 126: 1344–1345.

18. Carder, A. C. 1957. Growth and development of some field crops as influenced by climatic phenomena at two diverse latitudes. *Can. Jour. Sci.* 37: 395–406.

19. Carroll, J. C. 1943. Effects of drought, temperature and nitrogen on turf grasses. *Plant Phys.* 18: 19–36.

20. Chouard, P. 1960. Vernalization and its relations to dormancy. *Ann. Rev. Pl. Physiol.* 11: 191–238.

21. Clarke, G. L. 1954. *Elements of Ecology.* Wiley, New York.

22. Clements, H. F. 1940. Integration of climatic and physiologic factors with reference to the production of sugarcane. *Haw. Planter's Rec.* 44 (3): 201–233.

23. ———— and Kubota, T. 1943. The primary index, its meaning and application to crop management with special reference to sugarcane. *Haw. Planters' Rec.* 47 (4): 257–297.

24. Coons, G. H. 1943. The development of sugar beet seed production. *Imp. Agr. Bur., Joint Publ.* 5, 37–47.

25. Crabb, G. A., Jr. 1952. Insolation: a primary factor in evaporation from a free water surface in Michigan. *Mich. Agr. Exp. Sta. Quart. Bul.* 35: 186–192.

26. ————. 1954. The normal annual pattern of mean daily temperature at East Lansing, Michigan. *Mich. Agr. Exp. Sta. Quart.* 36: 401–407.

27. Curry, J. R. and Church, T. W. 1952. Observations on winter drying of conifers in the Adirondacks. *Jour. Forestry* 50: 114–116.
28. Dansereau, P. 1957. *Biogeography*. Ronald, New York.
29. Daubenmire, R. F. 1959. *Plants and Environment*. Wiley, New York.
30. Davis, H. D. 1948. *The Earth and Man*. Macmillan, New York.
31. Decker, A. M. 1953. Ph.D. Thesis. University of Maryland, College Park.
32. Decker, A. M. Jr. and Ronningen, T. S. 1957. Heaving in forage stands and in bare ground. *Agron. Jour.* 49: 412–415.
33. Dexter, S. T., Tottingham, W. E., and Graber, L. F. 1932. Investigations of hardiness of plants by measurement of electroconductivity. *Plant Phys.* 7: 63–78.
34. Eggert, R. 1944. Cambium temperatures of peach and apple trees in winter. *Amer. Soc. Hort. Sci. Proc.* 45: 33–36.
35. Elling, L. J. 1959. Trueness-to-type tests. *Minn. Farm and Home Science* 16 (2): 4, 6.
36. Evans, M. W. 1931. Relation of latitude to time of blooming in timothy. *Ecol.* 12: 182–187.
37. Florell, V. H. 1925. Studies on the inheritance of earliness in wheat. *Jour. Agr. Res.* 29: 333–347.
38. Gassner, G. 1918. Beiträge zur physiologischen Characteristik sommer- und winterannueller Gewächse, inbesondere der Getreidepflanzen. *Zeit. Bot.* 10: 417–430.
39. Graber, L. E., Nelson, N. T., Leukel, W. A., and Albert, W. B. 1927. Organic food reserves in relation to the growth of alfalfa and other perennial herbaceous plants. *Wis. Agr. Exp. Sta. Res. Bul.* 80.
40. Grandfield, C. O. 1935. The trend of organic food reserves in alfalfa roots as affected by cutting practices. *Jour. Agr. Res.* 50: 697–709.
41. Gregory, F. G. and Purvis, O. N. 1936a. Vernalization of winter rye during ripening. *Nature* 138: 973.
42. ———. 1936b. Devernalization of winter rye by high temperatures. *Nature* 138: 1013–1015.
43. ———. 1938. Vernalization of excised mature embryos and developing ears. *Ann. Bot. London* 2: 753–764.
44. ———. 1948. Reversal of vernalization by high temperature. *Nature* 161: 859–861.
45. Harvey, R. B. 1930. Time and temperature factors in hardening plants. *Amer. Jour. Bot.* 17: 212–217.
46. Heinrichs, D. H. 1954. Developing creeping rooted alfalfa for pasture. *Can. Jour. Agr. Sci.* 34: 269–280.
47. Heyne, E. G. and Laude, H. H. 1940. Resistance of corn seedlings to high temperatures in laboratory tests. *Jour. Amer. Soc. Agron.* 32: 116–126.
48. Holecamp, E. R., Hudspeth, E. B., and Ray, L. L. 1960. Soil temperature guides cotton growers. *Agr. Res.* 9 (4): 12.
49. Holmes, R. M. and Robertson, G. W. 1960. Soil heaving in alfalfa plots in relation to soil and air temperatures. *Can. Jour. Soil Sci.* 40: 212–218.
50. Hopkins, A. D. 1938. Bioclimatics, a science of life and climate relations. *U. S. Dept. Agr. Misc. Publ.* 280.
51. Julander, O. 1945. Drought resistance in range and pasture grasses. *Pl. Phys.* 20: 573–599.
52. Katz, Y. H. 1952. Relation between heat units accumulated and planting and harvesting of canning peas. *Agron. Jour.* 44: 74–78.
53. Kimball, M. H. and Brooks, F. A. 1959. Plant climates of California. *Calif. Agr.* 13: 7–11.

54. Klages, H. K. W. 1942. *Ecological Crop Geography.* Macmillan, New York.

55. Klebs, G. 1918. Über die Blütenbildung von *Sempervivum. Flora* 111–112: 128–151.

56. Klippart, J. H. 1857. Treatment to convert winter wheat to spring wheat. *Ann. Rept. Ohio State Board Agr., Sec.* 12: 562–816.

57. Kostjucenko, I. A. and Zarubailo, T. 1937. Vernalization of seed during ripening and its significance in practice. *Herbage Rev.* 5: 146–157.

58. Kramer, P. J. 1940. Root resistance as a cause of decreased water absorption by plants at low temperature. *Pl. Phys.* 15: 63–79.

59. Lang, A. 1952. Physiology of flowering. *Ann. Rev. Pl. Physiol.* 3: 265–303.

60. ——. 1957. Effect of gibberelin on flower formation. *Proc. Natl. Acad. Sci. U. S.,* 43: 709–717.

61. —— and Melchers, G. 1943. Die photoperiodische Reaktion von *Hyoscyamus niger. Planta* 33: 653–702.

62. ——. 1947. Vernalisation und Devernalisation bei einer zweijahrigen Pflanze. *Zeit. Naturforsch.* 2b. 444–449.

63. Lang, A., Sandoval, J. A., and Bedri, A. 1957. Induction of bolting and flowering in henbane by a gibberelin-like material from a seed plant. *Proc. Natl. Acad. Sci., U. S.* 43: 960–964.

64. Lehenbauer, P. A. 1914. Growth of maize seedlings in relation to temperature. *Phys. Res.* 1: 247–288.

65. Leitch, I. 1916. Some experiments on the influence of temperature on the rate of growth in *Pisum sativum. Ann. Bot.* 30: 25–46.

66. Levitt, J. 1941. *Frost Killing and Hardiness of Plants.* Burgess, Minneapolis.

67. ——. 1951. Frost, drought and heat resistance. *Ann. Rev. Plant Phys.* 2: 245–268.

68. —— and Scarth, G. W. 1936. Frost hardening studies with living cells. *Can. Jour. Res.* C 14: 267–305.

69. Liverman, J. L. and Lang, A. 1956. Induction of flowering in long day plants by applied indoleacetic acid. *Pl. Physiol.* 31: 147–150.

70. Livingston, B. E. 1916. Physiological temperature indices for the study of plant growth in relation to climatic conditions. *Physiol. Res.* 1: 399–420.

71. Lundegardh, H. 1931. *Environment and Plant Development.* Edward Arnold, London.

72. Lysenko, T. D. 1928. A study of the effect of the thermic factor upon the duration of development stages of plants. *Azerbaijan Plant Breeding Station Bul.* 3: 169. (English Summary.)

73. ——. 1935. *Theoretical Basis of Vernalization.* Gov't Publ. of Collective and State Farm Literature, Moscow.

74. McCool, M. M. and Bouyoucos, G. S. 1929. Causes and effects of soil heaving. *Mich. Agr. Exp. Sta. Spec. Bul.* 192.

75. Madariaga, F. J. and Knott, J. E. 1951. Lettuce growing rates. *Calif. Agr.* 5: 4.

76. Magoon, C. A. and Culpepper, C. W. 1932. Response of sweet corn to temperatures from time of planting to canning maturity. U.S.D.A. Tech. Bul. 312.

77. Meyer, B. S. and Anderson, D. B. 1952. *Plant Physiology.* Van Nostrand, New York.

78. Miller, E. C. 1938. *Plant Physiology.* McGraw-Hill, New York.

79. Mix, A. J. 1916. Winter sunscald injury to fruit trees. Cornell Univ. Agr. Exp. Sta. Bul. 382.

80. Nilsson-Ehle, H. 1912. Zur Kenntnis der Erblichkeits- verhältnisse der Eigenschaft Winterfestigkeit beim Weizen. *Zeit. fur Pflanzenzüchtung* 1: 3–12.

81. ——. 1917. Selection of spring wheat in Sweden. *Sveriges Utsädesförenings Tidskrift* 28: 51–76.

82. Nuttonson, M. Y. 1950. Ecological crop geography of Finland and its Agro-climatic analogues in North America. Amer. Inst. Crop Ecol., Washington, D. C.

83. ———. 1953. Phenology and thermal environment as a means for physiological classification of wheat varieties and for predicting maturity dates of wheat. Amer. Inst. Crop Ecol., Washington, D. C.

84. ———. 1955. Wheat-climate relationships and the use of phenology in ascertaining the thermal and photo-thermal requirements of wheat. Amer. Inst. of Crop Ecol., Washington.

85. ———. 1957a. Barley-climate relationships and the use of phenology in ascertaining the thermal and photo-thermal requirements of barley. Amer. Inst. of Crop Ecol., Washington.

86. ———. 1957b. Rye-climate relationships and the use of phenology in ascertaining the thermal and photo-thermal requirements of rye. Amer. Inst. of Crop Ecol., Washington, D. C.

87. Odum, E. P. 1959. *Fundamentals of Ecology.* Saunders, Philadelphia and London.

88. Oosting, Henry J. 1958. *The Study of Plant Communities.* Freeman, San Francisco.

89. Owen, F. V., Carsner, E., and Stout, M. 1940. Photothermal induction of flowering in sugar beets. *Jour. Agr. Res.* 61: 101–124.

90. Pal, B. P. and Murty, G. S. 1941. Studies in the vernalization of Indian crop plants. *Indian Jour. Gen. Pl. Breed.* 1: 61–86.

91. Patton, R. F. and Riker, A. J. 1954. Needle droop and needle blight of red pine. *Jour. Forestry* 52: 412–418.

92. Pelletier, J. R. *et al.* 1958. Experimental Farm Ste. Anne de la Pocatiere, Quebec. Progress Report, Exp. Farm Service, Ottawa.

93. Platt, R. B. and Wolf, J. N. 1950. General uses and methods of thermistors in temperature investigations. *Pl. Phys.* 25: 507–512.

94. Post, F. A. and Dreibelbis, F. R. 1942. Some influence of frost penetration and microclimate on water relationships of woodland, pasture and cultivated soils. *Soil Sci. Soc. Amer. Proc.* 7: 95–104.

95. Powers, LeRoy. 1934. The nature and interaction of genes differentiating habit of growth in a cross between varieties of *Triticum vulgare. Jour. Agr. Res.* 49: 573–605.

96. Purvis, O. N. 1934. Analysis of influence of temperature during germination on subsequent development of certain winter cereals. *Ann. Bot. (London)* 48: 919–955.

97. ———. 1939. Inheritance of spring and winter habit in hybrids of Petkus rye. *Ann. Bot. (London)* 3: 719–731.

98. ———. 1944. Role of carbohydrate and nitrogen supply in the vernalization of excised embryos of Petkus rye. *Ann. Bot. (London)* 8: 285–314.

99. ———. 1947. Effect of depletion of carbohydrates on the growth and vernalization response of excised embryos. *Ann. Bot. (London)* 11: 269–283.

100. ———. 1948. Effect of date of sowing and of excising embryos on the responses of Petkus winter rye to different periods of vernalization treatment. *Ann. Bot. (London)* 12: 183–206.

101. ———. 1954. Mechanism of vernalization with reference to the temperate cereals. *Eighth Inter. Bot. Cong., Paris Sec.* 11: 286–288.

102. ——— and Gregory, F. G. 1937. A comparative study of vernalization of winter rye by low temperature and by short days. *Ann. Bot.* 1: 569–592.

103. ———. 1938. Devernalization by high temperature. *Nature* 155: 113.

104. ———. 1952. Reversibility by high temperature of the vernalized condition in Petkus winter rye. *Ann. Bot. (London)* 16: 1–21.

105. Raschke, K. 1960. Heat transfer between the plant and the environment. *Ann. Rev. Pl. Phys.* 11: 111–126.

106. Rather, H. C. and Harrison, C. M. 1938. Alfalfa management with special reference to fall treatment. *Mich. Agr. Exp. Sta. Spec. Bul.* 292.

107. Raunkiaer, C. 1934. *The Life Forms of Plants and Statistical Plant Geography.* Clarendon, Oxford.

108. Reath, A. N. and Wittwer, S. H. 1952. Effects of temperature and photoperiod on the development of pea varieties. *Amer. Soc. Hort. Sci. Proc.* 60: 301–310.

109. Reed, W. W. 1941. The climate of the world. In *Climate and Man,* Yearbook of Agriculture, U. S. Dept. of Agriculture, Washington, D. C.

110. Sachs, J. 1875. *Textbook of Botany, Morphological and Physiological.* Transl. by A. W. Bennett and W. T. T. Dyer. Clarendon, Oxford.

111. Salmon, S. C. 1917. Why cereals winterkill. *Jour. Amer. Soc. Agron.* 9: 353–380.

112. Sapper, I. 1935. Versuche zur Hitzeresistenz der Pflanzen. *Planta:* 23: 518–556.

113. Sapper, Karl and James, P. 1959. *A Geography of Man.* 2nd ed., Ginn, New York.

114. Sayre, C. B. 1953. Forecasting maturity of peas. Farm Research. N. Y. State Agr. Exp. Sta., Geneva. 19 (4): 12.

115. Scarth, G. W. 1944. Cell physiological status of frost resistance: a review. *New Phyt.* 43: 1–12.

116. Schramm, J. R. 1958. The mechanism of frost heaving of tree seedlings. *Amer. Phil. Soc. Proc.* 102: 333–350.

117. Seaton, H. L. and Huffington, J. M. 1950. Application of the heat unit system of crop control in the canning industry. Continental Can Co., Inc. Presented at Amer. Soc. Hort. Sci. Sept. 11, 1950.

118. Sellschop, J. P. F. and Salmon, S. C. 1928. The influence of chilling, above the freezing point, on certain crop plants. *Jour. Agr. Res.* 37: 315–338.

119. Siminovitch, D. and Scarth, G. W. 1938. A study of the mechanism of frost injury to plants. *Can. Jour. Res. c* 16: 467–481.

120. Sinz, E. 1914. Beziehungen zwischen Trockensubstanz und Winterfestigkeit bei verscheidenen Winterweizen Varietäten. *Jour. f. Landw.* 62: 301–335.

121. Skinner, H. T. 1958. The geographic charting of plant climatic adaptability. Fifteenth Inter. Hort. Congr. Rept.

122. Southworth, W. 1921. A study of the influence of the root system in promoting hardiness in alfalfa. *Sci. Agr.* 1: 5–9.

123. Sprague, M. A., Havens, A. V., and Biel, E. R. 1954. Winter temperatures fluctuations of Ladino clover in the field in relation to survival. Paper presented at meeting of American Society of Agronomy, St. Paul, Minnesota, Nov. 10.

124. Sprague, V. G. and Graber, L. F. 1940. Physiological factors operative in ice-sheet injury of alfalfa. *Pl. Phys.* 15: 661–673.

125. Stout, M. 1946. The relationship of temperature to reproduction in sugar beets. *Jour. Agr. Res.* 72: 49–55.

126. Stuckey, Irene H. and Curtis, O. F. 1938. Ice formation and the death of plant cells by freezing. *Plant Phys.* 13: 815–833.

127. Sullivan, J. T. and Sprague, V. G. 1949. The effect of temperature on growth and composition of the stubble and roots of perennial ryegrass. *Pl. Phys.* 24: 706–719.

128. Taber, S. 1930. The mechanism of frost heaving. *Jour. Geol.* 38: 303–317.

129. ———. 1931. The climates of North America according to a new classification. *Geog. Rev.* 26: 633–655.

130. Thornthwaite, C. W. 1948. An approach toward a rational classification of climate. *Geog. Rev.* 38: 55–94.

131. Trewartha, G. T. 1954. *An Introduction to Climate.* McGraw-Hill, New York.

132. Vavilov, N. I. 1951. *Origin, Variation, Immunity and Breeding of Cultivated Plants.* Ronald, New York.

133. Voigt, G. K. 1951. Causes of injury to conifers during the winter of 1947–48 in Wisconsin. *Wis. Acad. Sci. Lett. Trans.* 40: 241–242.

134. Voss, J. 1938. Weitere untersuchen über Entwicklungsbeschleunigung an Weizensorten, insbesondere an Winterweizen. *Pflanzenbau* 15: 1–35, 49–79.

135. Went, F. W. 1944. Thermoperiodicity in growth and fruiting of the tomato. *Amer. Jour. Bot.* 31: 135–150.

136. ———. 1945. Relationships between age, light, variety and thermoperiodicity of tomatoes. *Amer. Jour. Bot.* 32: 469–479.

137. ———. 1950. The response of plants to climate. *Sci.* 112: 489–494.

138. ———. 1957. *Experimental Control of Plant Growth.* Chronica Botanica, Waltham, Mass. 1957.

139. Whyte, R. O. 1946. *Crop Production and Environment.* Taber and Taber, London.

140. ———. 1948. Research in vernalization. In *Vernalization and Photoperiodism.* Ed. by A. E. Murneek and R. O. Whyte. Chronica Botanica, Waltham, Mass.

141. Wiggans, S. 1956. The effect of seasonal temperatures on maturity of oats planted at different dates. *Agron. Jour.* 48: 21–25.

142. Woodbury, A. M. 1954. *Principles of Ecology.* Blakiston, New York.

Chapter 9

The Light Factor

INTRODUCTION

Light is the primary source of energy, without which living organisms could not exist. However, direct exposure of living protoplasm to light may soon cause injury or death (Pearse, 1939). Structural patterns and behavioral characteristics of plants and animals, therefore, are concerned with the solution of this dilemma (Odum, 1959). Light is a vital factor to all living things, but it is often also a limiting factor at both the maximum and minimum levels.

Green plants obtain the energy necessary for life directly from sunlight, which, through the connecting link, chlorophyll, is converted into chemical energy contained in simple sugar molecules. Light also serves plants in other ways, especially in its stimulating effects upon differentiation of tissues and organs (Daubenmire, 1959).

In the previous chapter, total insolation from the sun was considered. Of the total range of electromagnetic wavelengths in the solar spectrum, light, or luminous energy, includes wavelengths between approximately 400 and 750 mμ. Ultraviolet is below 390 and infrared above 750 mμ. It is believed that approximately one-half of the solar radiation is in the range of wavelengths of 750 mμ or greater and almost half is visible light.

Ecologically, light quality (wavelength or color), light intensity (measured in foot-candles), and light duration (day length) all are important to plants. Day length and intensity probably are the ecological aspects of light of greatest importance in plant distribution.

MEASUREMENT OF LIGHT

The unit of energy is the gram-calorie, which includes the effects of invisible as well as visible radiation. When very small quantities of light energy are measured, the joule or erg is used, one gram-calorie being equal to 4.18 joules, or 41.8 million ergs.

The intensity of light itself is measured by comparison with a **standard candle.** The amount of light received at a distance of one meter from a standard candle is known as a **meter-candle** or **lux.** The light intensity at one foot from a standard candle is called a **foot-candle.** A foot-candle equals 10.764 luxes, and the measurement in lux units is now accepted as the standard international unit of light intensity.

DISTRIBUTION OF LIGHT

The intensity and quality of light received at the earth's surface depend upon the solar constant, the distance of the sun from the earth, and the absorption and diffusion of light by the atmosphere. The solar constant is the magnitude of solar radiation at the outer atmosphere for the sun at zenith (directly overhead) and at its mean distance from the earth. This value is about 1.94 gram-calories per square centimeter per minute. Actual values of solar radiation at the surface of the earth have ranged from about 1.75 gr/cal/cm^2/min on high mountain tops (12,000 foot-candles) to 1.5 gr/cal/cm^2/min (10,000 foot-candles) at sea level (Shirley, 1935, 1945; Clarke, 1954).

Atmospheric conditions exert a marked effect on the amount of light received at the earth's surface. Smoke, dust, and gases cause a scattering of light. Water vapor absorbs considerable infrared light and ozone absorbs ultraviolet (Shirley, 1935).

In the winter much light is diffused because of the increased solar zenith distance (or angle of incidence), with the result that a higher percentage of red light and a lower percentage of blue light reaches the earth than in summer.

Owing to absorption of light by water vapor, light intensity is less in humid than in arid climates. In areas where clouds and fog are prevalent, such as the central and northern Pacific coast of North America, light may be reduced to as little as 4% of its potential intensity (Daubenmire, 1959).

Hourly values and yearly totals of light are much higher in the tropics than in the arctic. However, during the growing season the amount of light received during the average day in the tropics may be but slightly greater than the amount received in arctic regions. The angle of incidence is of great importance in determining light intensity, causing sharp seasonal differences with changes in latitude. At high latitudes in summer, however, the greater length of day serves as a compensating factor (Kimball, 1935).

Vegetation itself may be one of the greatest factors in limiting light intensity at the earth's surface. Oosting (1956) reported a high degree of variability in light measurements taken in a mixed pine-hardwood forest at noon when full sunlight was 9500 foot-candles in intensity. Readings taken at three-foot intervals, at a height of three feet above ground, showed a range of light intensity of from 100 to 4400 foot-candles throughout the forest area.

Clarke (1954) compared different forest tree species as to their effects on light intensity received on the forest floor. Poplar trees tend to grow rather widely spaced and allow considerable light to reach the ground. In Illinois, measurements showed that the portion of the forest floor exposed to direct sunlight was 84% for poplar, 77% for pine, and 35% for oak. In maple-elm forests and in many tropical rainforests, practically no direct sunlight reaches the ground surface. Other measurements showed that if the forest canopy was complete, less than 1% of the total light reached the ground.

The quality of light which has filtered through leafy foliage may be quite different from normal full sunlight. Atkins (1932) found that such light was lower in blue and violet wavelengths and higher in red than normal light. However, the reduction in intensity of light at the forest floor probably is of much greater importance than any changes in quality, from the ecological standpoint (Shirley, 1935, 1945). The accompanying effects of reduced light upon other environmental factors, humidity, soil moisture, air movement and temperature again make clear the importance of the holocoenotic action of the environment. Some of these effects are shown in a comparison of habitat factors in a virgin forest and an adjacent clearing in Table 9-1.

Different kinds of forests have markedly different seasonal influences on the light intensity near the forest floor. A stand of pine reduces light nearly the same all year round, so illumination at lower levels will depend mainly on seasonal light intensity. Deciduous trees such as maples, however, cause quite a different light situation as seasons change, with a minimum intensity on the forest floor in July and a maximum probably in April just before leaves develop.

The effect of the foliage of the cotton plant on light intensity at levels below the top of the plants has been studied by Eaton and Ergle (1954).

TABLE 9-1. COMPARISON OF CERTAIN FACTORS OF THE HABI-
TAT IN A VIRGIN PINE FOREST AND IN AN ADJACENT
CLEARING IN NORTHERN IDAHO DURING THE
MONTH OF AUGUST *

Habitat Factor		Forest	Clearing
	Maximum	25.9	30.0
Air temperature, °C	Minimum	7.4	3.9
	Range	18.5	26.1
Mean relative humidity at 5 P.M., %		38.8	35.2
Mean daily evaporation,† ml		14.1	36.1
Mean soil temperature at 15 cm, °C		12.8	17.0
Mean soil moisture at 15 cm, %		32.0	42.3

* Data from Larsen. *Ecol.* 3:302–305, 1922.
† Livingston atmometer mounted 15 cm above the ground.

In a stand of cotton 110 cm in height, the light intensity was 30% as great at half-height, and less than 5% as great as that above the plants at ground level.

Measurements of light intensity under a small-grain companion crop (oats), as related to legume establishment, were made by Bula, Smith, and Miller (1954). They used a device known as a light-averaging instrument (Miller 1951), which determined the ratio of the time average of two fluctuating quantities of light. The percentages of light penetrating to three inches above the soil surface were determined in plots sown to Clinton oats planted at the rate of $2\frac{1}{2}$ bushels per acre. When they had reached the three-leaf stage, light intensity was 100% at the three-inch level. When heads were emerging, light intensity at three inches was 40%. When the crop was fully headed, light intensity three inches from ground level was but 25%. These data indicate clearly the changing pattern of available light intensity for young seedlings of legumes being established in a small-grain crop.

DURATION OF LIGHT

The amount of light received by plants is determined by the intensity of light and its duration. In natural environments the length of day may have an even greater effect on the total amount of light received than does light intensity. The effect of latitude has been mentioned. With an increase in latitude a smaller angle of incidence results, with a consequent reduction in solar intensity. However, at latitudes up to 55° or more, the greater length of day during much of the growing season may more than compensate for the smaller angle of incidence of the sun's rays. It was shown by Carder (1957) that total insolation at Beaverlodge, Alberta (55° north latitude), was about the same as that at Madison, Wisconsin (43° north latitude) during the growing season. However, the effective heat supply at Beaver-lodge was only about 60% of that at Madison.

LIGHT IN WATER

About 10% of the light that strikes the surface of a body of water is reflected back into the atmosphere. The remaining light, passing downward, is modified by the water medium in intensity, quality, angular distribution, and time distribution (Clarke, 1954). In the first place, reduction in the various wavelengths of light varies greatly, even in distilled water. Red light is diminished rapidly with depth of water, while the blue component penetrates to much lower depths. The suspended material in natural waters exerts a strong influence on the reduction in light at various depths. Beds of kelp, submerged or floating vascular plants, phytoplankton, and algae are very effective in curtailing penetration of light.

EFFECTS OF LIGHT ON PLANTS

Light is of basic importance as the primary source of energy for the photosynthetic process. Plants which convert radiant energy to chemical energy constitute the first step in the ecological cycle of every complete ecosystem. The basic structure of green plants, with leaves arranged so as to intercept large quantities of light, facilitates efficient photosynthesis. As noted by Daubenmire (1959), the structure of the spongy mesophyll and the stomatal apparatus allows rapid gas exchange. The visible wavelengths of light, so significant in photosynthesis, also have the greatest energy values. But, in spite of this apparent efficiency, most actively growing land plants use only about 1% of visible radiation for photosynthesis (Rabinowitch, 1951).

In order that a plant can grow, its photosynthesis during the day must build up enough organic matter to more than compensate for the losses by respiration during both night and day. The amount of light required for photosynthesis to equal the respiratory compounds is called the **compensation** point (Spoehr and Smith, 1936). In many higher plants this varies from about 27 to 4200 luxes. For tree seedlings the compensation point usually lies between 2% and 30% of full sunlight.

For individual leaves of most plants, much less than full sunlight is needed for optimum photosynthesis. However, for a large plant with many leaves, there may be sufficient shading by other leaves that full sunlight on the whole plant may be highly desirable. It has been shown in apple trees, for example, that the rate of photosynthesis increases to its maximum with full sunlight, even though single leaves function at optimum rate with 25% to 33% of full sunlight (Christopher, 1934; Heinicke and Childers, 1937; Heinicke and Hoffman, 1933).

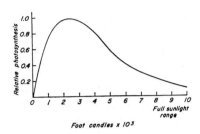

FIGURE 9-1.

Relationship between light intensity and photosynthesis in marine phytoplankton. [*After Ryther, Limnol. and Oceanogr. 1:61–70, 1956.*]

Minimum light intensities for maximum photosynthesis of several plant species include 76 foot-candles for radishes, 3000 and 1000 foot-candles for eastern red oak and white oak, 9000 foot-candles for loblolly pine, and full daylight for tomato plants (Singh and Kumar, 1935; Kramer and Decker, 1944; Porter, 1937).

In the production of sugarcane in Hawaii, as has been discussed in Chapter 8, under temperature, it was found by Clements (1940) that cane tonnage and yield of sugar may be limited by light intensity in some mountainous cloudy areas.

With most crops, the rate of photosynthesis at low light intensities tends to be directly proportional to light intensity, up to possibly 10% to 20% of full sunlight. The general relationship between light intensity and photosynthesis in some of the lower plants (phytoplankton) is illustrated in Figure 9-1.

The efficiency of plants in converting light energy into plant products has been illustrated by Went (1957) as follows:

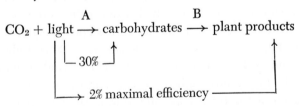

The reason for this low efficiency is not due to process "A" but rather to process "B" which results in the transformation of the primary products of photoreduction of CO_2, the sugars, into materials for cell walls, protoplasm, and plant products in general.

In studies of cotton, Eaton and Ergle (1954) found that artificial shading with muslin cloth in late June (at the start of flowering) resulted in a marked reduction in yield. With light reduced to 32% of full sunlight, bolls dropped off and final yield was reduced by 47%. The concentration of sugars and starch was reduced by 24% in the leaves, 38% in the main stems, and 8% in 14-day-old bolls.

Blackman and Wilson (1951, 1954) determined the reduction in net assimilation caused by shading in ten plant species. The response among species was similar, both in plants adapted to conditions of full sunlight and those considered to be shade plants. The compensation point for eight species, including buckwheat, sunflower, tomato, and peas, ranged from 6% to 9% of full sunlight; in barley and *Vicia faba,* the other two, the compensation point was 14% to 18%. The authors concluded that these species could not be grouped into "sun" and "shade" plants based on the reduction in net assimilation due to shading, or based on their respective compensation points.

Adaptation to Light

Local distribution of plant species is influenced by available light. Some plants tolerant to reduced light include spruce, hemlock, beech, sugar maple, spicebush, and bloodroot. The maple can grow satisfactorily where illumination is reduced to less than 2% of full sunlight. In contrast, birch, poplar, willow, Ponderosa pine, sumac, *Andropogon* grasses, and sunflowers are intolerant of shade. Intolerant species cannot develop in the shade of a dense population of either their own or other species (Clarke, 1954).

Of the tropical crops, coffee is known to be tolerant to low light intensity. Many varieties are, in fact, more productive when grown in partial shade, especially in equatorial regions. Young plantations may be established under the shade of tropical trees, especially trees of species of *Inga* and *Erythrina*. In the Sao Paulo and Paraná areas of Brazil, where temperatures are somewhat lower, shade is unnecessary. In Hawaii, coffee growing is restricted to the Kona district, located on the leeward slopes of the two mountains, Hualalai and Mauna Loa. Here, between 800 and 2200 feet above sea level, lies a humid zone with an equable climate. Trade winds from the east are deflected by the mountains, with the result that a cloud blanket covers the Kona area much of the time. Especially during the flowering and ripening season, natural cloudiness and abundant rainfall promote high yields of good quality coffee.

In Puerto Rico, Arrilaga and Gomez (1942) found that Arabian coffee production was best under conditions of 33% to 50% of full sunlight. Cacao, another tropical crop, has been found to produce optimum growth in approximately 25% of full sunlight (Cobley, 1942).

It is not easy to explain why shade-tolerant species, **sciophytes,** do not require more light, nor why sun-loving species, **heliophytes,** require intense light for normal development. It is believed that in some species the light requirement for photosynthesis may in itself explain their high light requirements. Insufficient light intensity may curtail root development, as was demonstrated in alfalfa by Gist and Mott (1957). Under similar conditions red clover root and top growth suffered less at low light intensities than did alfalfa.

It is well known that in the seedling stages low light intensity may determine the failure of legumes or grasses established with companion crops. Klages (1942) showed that more light usually was available to young seedlings of alfalfa and red clover established with a companion crop of Alaska (early) peas than with most small grains. Flax was judged a desirable companion crop where summer rainfall was high, but in northern Idaho, where summers were dry, flax was undesirable. Pritchett and Nelson (1951) reported that the choice of variety (as well as species) of small grain to be used as a companion crop was extremely important under Iowa conditions, and suggested that many failures to establish stands of forage species were owing to low light intensity caused by the competing companion crop.

To determine more precisely the effect of light intensity on gross morphology and vigor of seedlings of alfalfa and bromegrass, Pritchett and Nelson (1951) exposed seedlings in the greenhouse to light intensities ranging from 2833 foot-candles to 157 foot-candles, the latter similar to light conditions under heavily fertilized oats. With decreasing light intensity, the dry weight of plants decreased, roots being affected more seriously than tops. The ratio of roots to tops was reduced from 2.12 to 0.37 under exposure to red light which was decreased from 2833 foot-candles to 157 foot-candles. The response of bromegrass seedlings to nitrogen decreased with red light and stopped at intensities below 422 foot-candles. The nodulation of alfalfa seedlings decreased as light intensity decreased, and was inhibited at 257 foot-candles. Percentage nitrogen in seedlings decreased under decreased light except at the very lowest light intensity used.

There may be several reasons for superior growth at high light intensities. One reason may be that some species have high heat requirements. A retardation of infestation by certain pathogenic fungi, and a more favorable nitrogen release in the soil because of more rapid decomposition, have been mentioned as other reasons for better growth at high light intensities.

The reasons why sciophytes are shade tolerant seem to be no more simple. These plants actually do have low light requirements (Böhning and Burnside, 1956). Shade-tolerant plants possess the ability to increase their chlorophyll contents at low light intensity, according to Shirley (1935, 1945). Bright light apparently is actually injurious to some species, for an internal water deficit develops rapidly when they are exposed to full sunlight. This

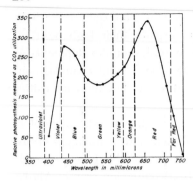

FIGURE 9-2.

Relative rates of photosynthesis of wheat in different wavelengths of light of equal intensities. [Modified after Hoover, Smithsonian Misc. Coll. 95, 1937.]

results in closure of the stomates and a consequent greatly reduced rate of photosynthesis.

To counteract the effects of intense light, the disk-shaped chloroplasts tend to become oriented against vertical walls, leaving only one edge exposed to direct light (Daubenmire, 1959).

The Quality of Light

When white light is passed through a prism, it is dispersed into wavelengths of different colors: violet, 400 to 435 millimicrons; blue, 435 to 490; green, 490 to 574; yellow, 574 to 595; orange, 595 to 626; red, 626 to 750. All of these wavelengths affect photosynthesis, but yellow and green are absorbed to only a small degree. The principal wavelengths absorbed in photosynthesis are in the violet-blue and in the orange-red regions (Figure 9-2).

The fact that there is a greater absorption of energy for photosynthesis in the blue and red regions is demonstrated clearly by the work of Rabideau, French, and Holt (1946). They studied three genera of plants, *Lactuca*, *Brassica*, and *Ficus*, using light of three specific wavelengths and determining reflection, transmission, absorption, and relative photosynthesis in one layer of leaves. It was assumed that every quantum of energy absorbed was equally efficient in photosynthesis. The data are presented in Table 9-2.

TABLE 9-2. COMPARATIVE EFFICIENCY OF PHOTOSYNTHESIS FOR THREE SPECIES IN THE BLUE, GREEN AND RED SPECTRAL REGIONS

Plant	Wavelength (mμ)	Reflection	Transmission	Absorption	Relative Photosynthesis
Lactuca	450	.17	.01	.82	1.03
	550	.35	.25	.40	.50
	670	.18	.02	.80	1.00
Brassica	450	.14	.06	.80	.99
	550	.30	.20	.50	.62
	670	.13	.06	.81	1.00
Ficus	450	.06	.01	.93	.99
	550	.12	.03	.85	.90
	670	.06	.00	.94	1.00

In *Lactuca* and *Brassica* there was evidence of about twice the efficiency of photosynthesis from radiation in the blue and red regions than in the green. However, in *Ficus* there was apparently only slightly less efficiency from radiation in the green region.

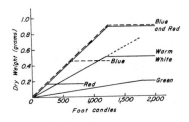

FIGURE 9-3.

Dry-matter production in young tomato plants as a function of light intensity, for different wavelengths. [After Dunn and Went, Environmental Control of Plant Growth. *Waltham, Mass.: Chronica Botanica, 1957.]*

Experiments by S. Dunn in the Earhart Plant Research Laboratory (cited by Went, 1957) have shown the effects of both light intensity and quality on dry matter production in young tomato plants. This is illustrated in Figure 9-3, in which the light energy is given in foot-candles for white light, and the colored light scale on the abscissa denotes light energy in calories or microwatts.

At intensities below 1200 foot-candles, growth was proportional to light, indicating that at low light intensities process "A," the photoreduction of CO_2, may be limiting. At higher intensities, however, process "B," the transformation of sugars into plant products, is limiting. Furthermore, the curves indicate that either blue or red light alone is less effective than white light, but the combination of blue and red light resulted in dry matter production much greater than occurred in white light. It has been shown that the green light present in the white light prevents maximal growth rate (Went, 1957).

Wavelengths shorter than 390 mμ are invisible, but may be very active in chemical reactions. Popp and Brown (1936) suggested that these ultraviolet wavelengths were not necessary for normal growth of plants, but probably were not injurious to any but some of the lower forms. Much of the ultraviolet is screened out by the ozone layer in the upper atmosphere, so that radiation at the earth's surface contains only about 2% of these wavelengths. When dust and smoke are abundant, the short waves are reduced still further. Clarke (1954) has pointed out that, to be effective in bringing about the production of vitamin D, the ultraviolet must be in the range of 295 to 310 mμ. In the winter in most cities there is practically no measurable radiation shorter than 310 mμ, and therefore no action of ultraviolet can take place.

Wavelengths of light shorter than the ultraviolet, including x-rays and gamma rays, are definitely injurious to plants.

Wavelengths longer than 750 mμ are not visible to the eye, and are called infrared. Such waves are detected by the sensation of heat, which becomes more intense with the longer wavelengths. In addition to heating effects, stimulating effects on growth and on germination have been reported by Wassink and Stolwijk (1956). These workers reported also that, whereas white light tends to produce short, stocky growth, blue and violet wavelengths tend to do this even more definitely, and yellow and red tend to cause stem elongation.

The wavelengths of light from approximately 720 to 780 mμ are known as far-red and are known to be of great importance in the photochemical reactions governing the promotion or retardation of flowering.

Orientation and Light

Light plays an important role in orienting the growth of plants. This movement or orientation, if caused by light, is called **phototropism**. The primary orientation of the plant refers to the position of the main axis, which is the result of gravity or geotropism. Secondary responses may occur, such as the tops of green plants growing toward the light, an example of positive phototropism. Leaves are usually oriented at right angles to the incident light, in a position to receive maximum radiation. The characteristics of the sunflower plant are well known; its response to changes in turgor is such that the top and leaves tend to remain in the direction of the sun throughout the daylight hours. In regions of excessive heat and intense light some plants, such as *Silphium laciniatum*, have their leaves so oriented that their leaf edges face the sun.

Germination of Seeds

The influence of light on seed germination has been studied extensively by Crocker (1936), Evenari (1956), Thompson (1938) and Toole, *et al.* (1956). Seeds of many plants are sensitive to light, especially when they have imbibed water. Lettuce (*Lactuca sativa*) and Kentucky bluegrass (*Poa pratensis*) will not germinate without the stimulation of light. The germination of the carrot (*Daucus carota*), *Rumex crispus*, and black spruce (*Picea abies*) is favored by light. Other species, including the primrose, *Primula spectabilis*, many of the *Liliaceae*, and *Vanilla fragrans* require darkness for germination, and still others, American elm (*Ulmus americana*), *Bromus tectorum*, and many of the cucurbits germinate better in the dark.

Tobacco seed requires a slight stimulation from light, possibly just a fraction of a second, for good germination (Kincaid, 1935). Seeds which normally have a light requirement for germination should not be planted deeply, or they will not emerge. However, soaked seeds given an adequate light treatment retain the light stimulation and, when dried, have been found to germinate successfully where deprived of light.

The relationship of light to seed germination is made complex by the influence of other environmental factors. Many seeds which require light for germination may gradually lose this requirement after storage under dry conditions (Toole, *et al.* 1956). It has been demonstrated also that by manipulation of temperature and/or addition of oxygen, acids, or nitrates, the requirement for light may be changed.

Light and Reproduction

Low light intensity has been shown to favor vegetative growth. Crops harvested for their leaves and stems are favored by climates having considerable cloudiness, whereas crops harvested for fruit, grain, or seed are favored by more intense light (Daubenmire, 1959). In the production of greenhouse crops, adequate sunlight is of great importance. Orientation of a greenhouse in an east-west direction allows the most effective use of sunlight, especially in the wintertime when the sun's rays strike the glass roof at a rather low angle.

Effect of Light on Growth Form

Light intensity exerts an influence on morphological characteristics of plants. Full sunlight, as compared to reduced light intensity, results in thicker stems, well-developed xylem, and shorter internodes (Vinson, 1923; Popp, 1926; Shirley, 1929; Penfound, 1932). Leaves, too, may be affected, developing smaller but thicker leaf blades or segments of blades (Hanson, 1917; Gourley and Nightingale, 1921; Shirley, 1929). Stomata are likely to be smaller and more numerous (Helmers, 1943; Penfound, 1932). Cuticle and cell walls are thicker. This explains why some tobacco varieties as well as tea may produce a more desirable leaf in partial shade (Cain and Miller, 1933; Helmers, 1943; Korstian, 1925). Chloroplasts may be fewer in full sunlight, according to Rabinowitch (1945). Palisade cells are better developed, but sponge mesophyll is more weakly developed (Duncan, 1933; Hanson, 1917; Isanogle, 1944; Korstian, 1925). Penfound showed that full sunlight resulted in a lower ratio of total leaf area to vascular tissue of the supporting stem, and Shirley found that roots were longer and more branched, with a higher root/shoot ratio. Larger and more numerous nodules are found on legume roots under intense light conditions, as are a greater total fresh weight and dry weight of both roots and shoots (Burkholder, 1936). In Indiana, Rhykerd, Langston, and Mott (1959) found that an increase in light energy resulted in a decrease in leafiness in seedlings of alfalfa and red clover, but tended to increase (or hold constant) the leafiness of birdsfoot trefoil. Later, as the plants became older, the leaf-stem ratios of the three forage species tended to become similar.

Light and Physiological Features

The effect of light intensity on physiological features of plants is just as pronounced as it is on morphological features. Chlorophyll content is usually lower in full sunlight, and carotinoid pigments are more apparent (Gourley and Nightingale, 1921; Rabinowitch, 1945; Shirley, 1929). Full sunlight may cause a lower photosynthetic rate, a high respiration rate, and a high compensation point in many plants (Brett, 1944; Pickett, 1934; Spoehr and Smith, 1936). High light intensity results in a lower percentage of water on a dry basis and a high transpiration rate (Hanson, 1917; Marsh, 1941; Martin, 1935; Penfound, 1932; Shirley, 1929). Other effects of full sunlight include higher salt content, sugar content, and osmotic value, as well as a decrease in pH of cell sap and high carbohydrate/nitrogen ratio (Korstian, 1925; Marsh, 1941; Loehwing, 1930; Vinson, 1923). Flowering and fruiting are usually enhanced by increased light intensity (Dunlap, 1943; Gourley and Nightingale, 1921; Shirley, 1929). Full sunlight also tends to develop greater resistance to temperature injury (Tysdal, 1933), to drought (Shirley, 1935, 1945), and to parasites (Heald, 1933).

PHOTOPERIODISM

As has previously been mentioned, at the time of the equinoxes, March 21 and September 21, the respective lengths of days and nights are approximately equal at all latitudes. On June 21, however, day length at the equator is 12 hours; at 40° north latitude, 15 hours; at 60° north latitude, 19 hours; and at the North Pole, 24 hours. This difference in length of days and nights, as related to latitude, is a factor of great importance in the natural distribution of plants (Allard, 1932, 1948). The response of plants to the relative length of day and night is known as **photoperiodism**. Plants which develop and reproduce normally only when the photoperiod is greater than a critical minimum are called long-day plants, whereas those which develop normally only when the photoperiod is less than a critical maximum are called short-day plants.

Present concepts of photoperiodism were developed largely through the extensive studies of Garner and Allard (1920, 1923, 1930, 1931) and Allard (1932). They reported in 1920 that a variety of tobacco, Maryland Mammoth, continued to grow (out of doors) in a purely vegetative state at the latitude of Washington, D. C., but flowered profusely when grown in the greenhouse in the winter under short days. Later, Biloxi soybeans were found to behave in a similar manner, and these crops were called short-day plants. Further, research suggested that there was a critical photoperiod, between 12 and 14 hours, by which species might be divided into two groups, long-day and short-day plants. Some plants were found to be unaffected by photoperiod and were called day-neutral.

Long-day plants included small grain cereals, potato, timothy, biennial sweetclover, and red clover. Short-day plants included certain varieties of tobacco and soybeans, millet, hemp, lespedeza, chrysanthemum, and poinsettia. Tomato, early peas, sweetpotato, pineapple, apple, dandelion, buckwheat, cotton, and squashes are considered relatively day-neutral. It is now known also that some plants are intermediate in photoperiodic requirement, an important example being one of the sugarcane species, *Saccharum spontaneum*.

Through natural selection over many generations species, varieties, and ecotypes have developed responses to photoperiods corresponding to the latitudes where they are found and the season of the year in which they reproduce. This kind of adaptation has been clearly shown in studies of geographic or latitudinal races of side-oats grama by Olmsted (1943, 1944, 1945), forest trees by Vaartaja (1954) and Pauley and Perry (1954).

Studies of timothy by Evans and Allard (1934) indicated that among 16 strains, mostly American, earliness or lateness was associated with inherently different responses to seasonal length of day following renewal of growth in the spring. In another study, two American hexaploid strains, Marietta and Huron, and three European diploid strains, Harpenden, Moscow, and Welsh S50, were observed. Both American strains were early, but Marietta flowered under a 12-hour day, whereas Huron required a 13.5-hour photoperiod. The European strains behaved as typical long-day plants. They did not flower at Washington, D. C. (longest days:14.9 hours), but did flower under 16- and 18-hour days. These strains are grown normally in Europe at latitudes between 50° and 60°, which is considerably farther north than the Timothy Belt in the United States.

Among short-day species, soybeans have been studied extensively. When grown at the latitude of Washington, D. C. under natural day length, early plantings of Mandarin, Peking, Tokyo, and Biloxi varieties averaged 25, 55, 65, and 95 days respectively from germination to flowering. However, under short days (12 hours or less) flowering in all varieties was attained in from 23 to 27 days. Year-to-year variations in date of flowering under field conditions appeared to be caused by differences in temperature. Day length, however, is considered the primary external factor responsible for the fact that one variety is always relatively early and another late in attaining flowering.

Recent studies by Johnson, Borthwick and Leffel (1960) have shown that present-day varieties of soybeans vary greatly in degree of response to photoperiod, both during the period from emergence to floral initiation and during post-flowering stages of development. Differences in the period from emergence to maturity resulted from fixed photoperiods of 14.5, 14.0, 13.5, and 13.0 hours, and from different planting dates under one photoperiod. Under natural conditions, both northern and southern varieties, adapted to full season development and planted at the optimum date, initiate floral primordia during or just after the longest days of the season. Northern varieties complete post-flowering stages of development under day lengths that are changing rapidly and that are a smaller fraction of the day length at the time of floral initiation than is true for southern varieties. To characterize a variety of soybeans as to response to photoperiod, it is necessary to know the optimum day lengths, both for flowering and for the later stages of development.

Maize is a plant of tropical origin but is grown widely over a considerable range of latitude. Native varieties in South America, Central America, and Mexico consist mainly of short-day plants. Strains from Guatemala were subjected by Thomas (1948) to a photoperiod of 11 hours at Ames, Iowa (42° north latitude), as well as to the normal Iowa day length (about 15 hours during June). The short days promoted flowering, but under the normal photoperiod flowering occurred too late in the season for grain maturity.

Kiesselbach (1950) reported a study of seasonal variation in development of the corn crop in Nebraska. The latitudinal adaptation of varieties and hybrids was found to be associated with the progressively longer photoperiod from the southern to the northern part of the state. Standard varieties were found to flower 13 days sooner when planted in the states farther south than when grown in Nebraska. Southern-adapted varieties, on the other hand, required 18 days longer to flower in Nebraska than in their home environment.

IMPORTANCE OF DARKNESS

Through critical studies of short-day plants, particularly Biloxi soybean and cocklebur (*Xanthium pennsylvanicum*), Hamner and Bonner (1938) concluded that the photoperiodic stimulus was brought about during both the light and dark periods. A continuous dark period of 8.5 to 9 hours, after previous exposure to a favorable photoperiod, was essential for normal flowering. The intensity, rather than the duration of the light period, was important, but most critical of all was the absolute length of the dark period. It is believed also that the length of the dark period is critical in long-day plants, because of its inhibiting effect.

It was demonstrated by Snyder (1938) and by Borthwick, Hendricks, and Parker (1948) that a continuous long day is not essential for some long-day plants. Flowering in winter barley was promoted by either an intermittent flash lighting for periods of 0.5 to 1 minute, followed by equal or longer dark periods, or by an interruption in the middle of a dark period, with lighting for a few minutes only. It has been found that such interruption of the dark period by brief exposure to light will result in initiation of flowers in many long-day plants.

FROM VEGETATIVE TO REPRODUCTIVE PHASE

Floral induction in many perennial forage grasses takes place in the autumn, under short days and low temperatures. The importance of this change from the purely vegetative phase to the reproductive phase, as related to agronomic management practices, has been emphasized by Peterson and Loomis (1949), Gardner and Loomis (1953), Hanson and Sprague (1953), and others.

After the ripe-to-flower condition (or induction) has been achieved, the visual transition from the vegetative to the reproductive phase is marked by the differentiation of floral primordia. A minimal number of leaves must be present, and environmental conditions favorable for initiation of flowers may include higher temperatures and longer days than are most favorable for induction. By means of microdissection of growing points, detailed studies of this phase of reproduction have been made possible (Bonnett, 1936, and Sharman, 1945). Approximate dates of differentiation of floral primordia in winter annuals and perennials are of considerable interest. Observations among selections of bromegrass, *Bromus inermis*, by Sass and Skogman (1951) at Ames, Iowa, indicated that the first date of appearance of floral primordia ranged from April 4 to April 19. Primordia differentiated in the autumn did not survive through the winter season. In the warm-season native species, big bluestem (*Andropogon gerardi*), Holt (1952) observed that floral primordia were not found until the latter part of June.

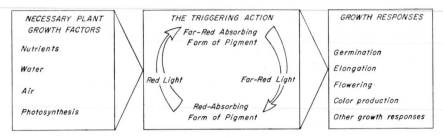

FIGURE 9-4.

Effect of two forms of light-sensitive pigment in controlling plant-growth responses through reaction to the color and intensity of light they receive. [After Borthwick, et al, Agricultural Research, U. S. Dept. of Agr. 8:5, 1959.]

Because of the discovery of the importance of the dark period for both short-day and long-day plants, Borthwick, Parker and Hendricks (1950) suggested that the accepted classification of plants into long-day and short-day groups was hardly appropriate. Rather, they proposed that plants be categorized on the basis of the length of the favorable dark period. The older system had become well accepted by plant scientists, however, and it is still common practice to call plants in which flowering is promoted by long days and short nights as long-day plants.

Although the exact mechanism of photoperiodic induction is not completely understood, it is now known that the stimulus is received through the leaves by a light-sensitive blue pigment (Hendricks, 1956; Borthwick, Hendricks, and Parker, 1956, and Borthwick, et al 1959). This pigment occurs in two reversible forms, the conversion from one form to the other being brought about by exposure to different wavelengths of light in the red region of the spectrum. In one form, the pigment absorbs red light, with a maximum in the 630 to 670 $m\mu$ range; the other form absorbs light in the far-red region, 720 to 780 $m\mu$. The form of the blue pigment which predominates depends on the color of light to which the plant was last exposed. These relationships are suggested in the diagram in Figure 9-4.

The two major controlling photoreactions have been described as follows (Borthwick, Hendricks, and Parker, 1956; Hendricks, 1956):

$$P \quad + \quad RX \quad \underset{\text{Red radiation}}{\rightleftharpoons} \quad PX \quad + \quad R$$

P	RX		PX	R
(pigment absorption maximum 640–660 $m\mu$)	(another reactant)	(far-red radiation or darkness)	(pigment absorption maximum 720–740 $m\mu$)	(changed reactant)

It is suggested that in the daytime the amount of PX is controlled in part by the amount of red and far-red radiation, and in part by the relative level of the associated reactant. At night PX drifts back toward the red-absorbing form P. Whether the plant blooms or fails to bloom with long nights depends on the level of demand for flowering of the materials arising from the reaction controlled by PX.

In addition to the effect of this reversible photoreaction on flowering response, red light in the range of 640 to 670 mμ promotes the germination of lettuce and other seeds, and promotes red coloring in apples. Exposure to far-red light, in the region of 720 to 780 mμ, nullifies or reverses the action of the red light (Borthwick, *et al.*, 1952).

LIGHT AND TEMPERATURE INTERRELATIONS

Specific requirements of light and temperature are often difficult to determine because of interacting effects and the partial replaceability of one factor by the other. Ladino clover, *Trifolium repens* var. *latum,* is known to be composed of a heterogeneous population of plants having varied combinations of temperature and light requirements for normal reproduction. Space-planted populations in breeding nurseries at 42° north latitude have been found to include plants which bloom freely in early summer, in late summer, and sparsely, if at all. Some of the sparse-blooming plants bloom freely under 18- to 20-hour days, and some require both long days and low temperatures. Ladino clover breeders are faced with the problem of finding desirable selections for use in synthetic varieties which will bloom freely in the geographical areas where the seed will be produced. Most of the seed is now produced in California, Oregon, and Idaho.

Greenhouse studies with bromegrass have shown that late-flowering selections from Kansas bloomed freely only with an 18-hour day (or longer) and at a relatively high temperature and high level of soil fertility. Other selections, however, flowered freely over a wide range of photoperiod, temperature, and soil fertility (Evans and Wilsie, 1946). In central Iowa, several varieties of bromegrass, including both northern and southern ecotypes, often bloom within a day or two, about June 1. At Saskatoon, Canada, as has been noted by Knowles and White (1949), southern varieties bloom two to four days later than northern, usually about July 1. Although bromegrass is considered a long-day plant, it is apparent that the critical factor in determining the time it blooms is temperature.

In orchardgrass, Gardner and Loomis (1953) showed that, whereas both low temperature and short days were essential for floral induction, the two factors could be applied separately, providing exposure to short days came first and was followed immediately with low temperature.

The interacting effects of temperature and photoperiod were shown in a striking manner by Carder (1957) in a field investigation at two latitudes, Madison, Wisconsin, 43° north, and Beaverlodge, Alberta, 55° north. Ten annual crops, including wheat, oats, barley, peas, and millet, were grown for two years at these different latitudes. Growth and phenology of the several varieties were correlated with meteorological conditions. Insolation was approximately equal at the two locations, but the effective heat supply at Beaverlodge was only 60% of that at Madison. Photoperiods were quite different, the daily photoperiod for 21 days following emergence of the crops averaging 16.2 hours at Madison and 20.1 hours at Beaverlodge. In addition, the civil twilight at Beaverlodge was much longer than at Madison.

Crops grew taller at the southern location, and ripened earlier. The earlier-maturing varieties yielded relatively better under cool temperatures than did the later ones. The wheat varieties yielded better at Beaverlodge, but barley and peas yielded better at Madison. Millet did not head at Beaverlodge, but the other varieties produced heavier kernels at the northern latitude than at the location farther south. Both temperature and length of day were considered responsible for the different growth behavior of the crop varieties at the two latitudes.

In England, Cooper (1960) found that floral induction in a number of outbreeding populations of perennial ryegrass, *Lolium perenne*, could be brought about by either low temperature (0–3°C) or short day (8 hours) independently, but short day exposure at low temperatures was ineffective. The induction requirement appeared to vary with the climatic origin of the population concerned. The summer annual Westerwold's ryegrass showed a need for neither short days nor low temperatures, whereas the winter annual Wimmera ryegrass showed a quantitative response to both environmental factors. Most strains of perennial ryegrass showed an obligate requirement for cold or short days, the more persistent varieties such as Kent or S101 having the greatest requirement for floral induction.

In the discussion in Chapter 8, vernalization was presented as basically a temperature phenomenon, although the importance of light-temperature interactions and the possibility of replacement of low temperature by short day was noted.

In Wisconsin, Roberts and Struckmeyer (1938) observed that under greenhouse conditions, red clover grew most rapidly and flowered best with long days and cool temperatures. Sweetclover responded best to long days and warm temperatures. Alfalfa grew and flowered satisfactorily under long, warm days, but did not set seed well if nights were too warm.

Went (1945), and more recently Verkerk (1955), have studied interactions of light and temperature under accurately controlled environmental conditions. From results obtained by Verkerk, it appeared that relatively weak light had the same effect as relatively high temperature, resulting in thinner stems, lighter colored leaves, fewer flower buds, and fewer, smaller fruits containing less starch and sugars. A comparison of two light intensities at different temperatures showed that stem length was not strongly affected by light intensity, nor was leaf weight, but total dry weight, leaf area, sturdiness of stem, and weight of fresh fruit were much reduced by lowering light intensity, the degree of reduction being different at different temperatures.

A number of important applications of the phenomenon of photoperiodic response are possible. In the production of onions, long days promote bulb formation whereas short days promote flowering and seed production. This situation poses a problem to the plant breeder who may wish to use germplasm from varieties not adapted to a particular latitude.

In potato breeding, the production of seed is promoted by growing plants in the greenhouse, or at a latitude sufficiently far north (or south) that the photoperiodic requirements can be obtained.

The whole problem of adaptation, and especially the introduction of new species or new varieties illustrates the importance of a knowledge of photoperiodic response. This has been demonstrated conclusively in the sugar beet industry, in which the balance between beet root production and the tendency to bolt and produce seed are so intimately tied to the temperature-light climate of a region. Specialized areas for producing seed, or the timing of planting to promote flowering, is possible, once the requirements of the species is understood (Coons, 1943).

In corn improvement, the extreme differences in photoperiodic response between Central American strains adapted to short days and Corn Belt strains adapted to long days have created problems in the incorporation of desired traits from one type into the other.

A notable example of response to day length in tobacco is that of the variety Maryland Mammoth, the one used first in the explanation of photoperiodism by Garner and Allard (1920). In the latitude of Maryland this variety produces only leaves, a characteristic desirable for the production of commercial tobacco. For seed production this variety must be grown under shorter days, such as in Florida, where it reproduces successfully but produces a poor size and quality of leaf.

Manipulation of day-length has facilitated the hybridization of varieties or species of crops which normally bloom at different times of the year. Such techniques have been used successfully by sugarcane breeders for making crosses between the wild species *Saccharum spontaneum,* which normally blooms in July, and the cultivated sugarcane, *Saccharum officinarum,* which blooms in November or December.

References

1. Allard, H. A. 1932. Length of day in relation to the natural and artificial distribution of plants. *Ecol.* 13: 221–234.

2. ———. 1948. Length of day in the climate of the past geological eras and its possible effect upon changes in plant life. In Murneek, A. E. and Whyte, R. O., eds. *Vernalization and Photoperiodism.* Chronica Botanica, Waltham, Mass.

3. Arrilaga, J. G. and Gomez, L. A. 1942. Effect of solar radiation intensity on the vegetative growth and yield of coffee. *Jour. Agr. Univ. Puerto Rico* 26: 73–90.

4. Atkins, W. R. G. 1932. The measurement of daylight in relation to plant growth. *Empire For. Jour.* 11: 42–52.

5. Blackman, G. E. and Wilson, G. L. 1951. Physiological and ecological studies in the analysis of plant environment VI. *Ann. Bot.* 15: 63–94.

6. ———. 1954. Physiological and ecological studies in the analysis of plant environment IX. *Ann. Bot.* 18: 71–94.

7. Böhning, R. H. and Burnside, C. A. 1956. The effect of light intensity on rate of apparent photosynthesis in leaves of sun and shade plants. *Amer. Jour. Bot.* 43: 557–561.

8. Bonnett, O. T. 1936. The development of the wheat spike. *Jour. Agr. Res.* 53: 445–451.

9. Borthwick, H. A., Hendricks, S. B., and Parker, M. W. 1948. Action spectrum for photoperiodic control of floral initiation of a long-day plant, winter barley. *Bot. Gaz.* 110: 103–118.

10. ———. 1956. Photoperiodism. In Vol. III, *Radiation Biology.* McGraw-Hill, New York.

11. ———, Toole, E. H., and Toole, V. K. 1952. A reversible photoreaction controlling seed germination. *Proc. Natl. Acad. Sci. U. S.* 38: 662–666.

12. Borthwick, H. A., Hendricks, S. B., Siegelman, H. W., Norris, K. H., and Butler, W. L. 1959. How light controls plant development. *Agr. Res.* 8 (5): 3–5.

13. Borthwick, H. A., Parker, M. W., and Hendricks, S. B. 1950. Recent developments in the control of flowering by photoperiod. *Amer. Nat.* 84: 117–134.

14. Brett, C. H. 1944. An electrically regulated humidity control. *Jour. Econ. Entom.* 37: 552–553.

15. Bula, R. J., Smith, Dale, and Miller, Edward E. 1954. Measurements of light beneath a small-grain companion crop as related to legume establishment. *Bot. Gaz.* 115 (3): 271–278.

16. Burkholder, P. R. 1936. The role of light in the life of plants. *Bot. Rev.* 2: 1–52, 97–172.

17. Cain, S. A. and Miller, J. D. O. 1933. Leaf structure of *Rhododendron catawbiense* Mich. grown in Picea-Abies forest and in heath communities. *Amer. Midl. Nat.* 14: 69–82.

18. Carder, A. C. 1957. Growth and development of some field crops as influenced by climatic phenomena at two diverse latitudes. *Can. Jour. Pl. Sci.* 37: 392–406.

19. Christopher, E. P. 1934. The intensity of light striking leaves of apple trees at different times of day. *Amer. Soc. Hort. Sci. Proc.* 32: 86–92.

20. Clarke, G. L. 1954. *Elements of Ecology.* Wiley, New York.

21. Clements, Harry F. 1940. Integration of climatic and physiologic factors with reference to the production of sugar cane. *Haw. Sugar Planters' Rec.* 44 (3): 201–233.

22. Cobley, L. S. 1942. The effect of shade on the growth rate of cacao cuttings. *Trop Agr.* (*Trinidad*) 19: 227–233.

23. Coons, G. H. 1943. Development of sugar beet seed production in the United States. Imp. Agr. Bur. Joint Publ. 5: 37–47.

24. Cooper, J. P. 1960. Short-day and low-temperature induction in *Lolium*. *Ann. Bot.* 24 (94): 232–246.

25. Crocker, W. 1936. Effect of the visible spectrum on the germination of seeds and fruits. In B. M. Duggar, *Biological Effects of Radiation* 1: 791–828.

26. Daubenmire, R. F. 1959. *Plants and Environment.* Wiley, New York.

27. Duncan, W. H. 1933. Ecological comparison of leaf structures of *Rhododendron punctatum* Andr. and the ontogeny of the epidermal scales. *Amer. Midl. Nat.* 14: 83–96.

28. Dunlap, A. A. 1943. Low light intensity and cotton boll-shedding. *Sci.* 98: 568–569.

29. Eaton, F. M. and Ergle, D. R. 1954. Effects of shade and partial defoliation on carbohydrate levels and the growth, fruiting and fiber properties of cotton plants. *Plant Phys.* 29: 39–49.

30. Evans, M. W. and Allard, H. A. 1934. Relation of length of day to growth in timothy. *Jour. Agr. Res.* 48: 571–586.

31. Evans, Marshall and Wilsie, C. P. 1946. Flowering of bromegrass, *Bromus inermis,* in the greenhouse as influenced by length of day, temperature and level of fertility. *Jour. Amer. Soc. Agron.* 38: 923–932.

32. Evenari, M. 1956. Seed Germination. In A. Hollaender, *Radiation Biology.* 3: 515–549. McGraw-Hill, New York.

33. Fowle, F. E. 1927. *Smithsonian Physical Tables.* Smithsonian Misc. Coll. Publ. 2539. 458 pp.

34. Gardner, F. P. and Loomis, W. E. 1953. Floral induction and development in orchardgrass. *Plant Physiol.* 28: 201–217.

35. Garner, W. W. and Allard, H. A. 1920. Effect of the relative length of day and night and other factors of the environment on growth and reproduction of plants. *Jour. Agr. Res.* 18 (11): 553–605.

36. ———. 1923. Further studies of photoperiodism, the response of the plant to relative length of day and night. *Jour. Agr. Res.* 23: 871–920.

37. ———. 1930. Photoperiodic response of soybeans in relation to temperature and other environmental factors. *Jour. Agr. Res.* 41: 719–735.

38. ———. 1931. Duration of the flowerless condition of some plants in response to unfavorable lengths of day. *Jour. Agr. Res.* 43: 439–443.

39. Gist, George R. and Mott, G. O. 1957. Some effects of light intensity, temperature and soil moisture on the growth of alfalfa, red clover and birdsfoot trefoil seedlings. *Agron. Jour.* 49: 33–36.

40. Gourley, J. H. and Nightingale, G. T. 1921. The effects of shading some horticultural plants. N. H. Agr. Exp. Sta. Tech. Bul. 18.

41. Hamner, K. C. and Bonner, J. 1938. Photoperiodism in relation to hormones as factors in floral initiation and development. *Bot. Gaz.* 100: 388–431.

42. Hanson, A. A. and Sprague, V. G. 1953. Heading of perennial grasses under greenhouse conditions. *Agron. Jour.* 45: 248–250.

43. Hanson, H. C. 1917. Leaf structure as related to environment. *Amer. Jour. Bot.* 4: 533–560.

44. Heald, F. D. 1933. *Manual of Plant Diseases.* McGraw-Hill, New York.

45. Heinicke, A. J. and Childers, N. F. 1937. The daily rate of photosynthesis during the growing season of 1935 of a young apple tree of bearing age. N. Y. (Cornell) Agr. Exp. Sta. Mem. 201.

46. Heinicke, A. J. and Hoffman, M. B. 1933. Rate of photosynthesis of apple leaves under natural conditions. I. Cornell Agr. Exp. Sta. Bul. 577.

47. Helmers, A. E. 1943. The ecological anatomy of ponderosa pine needles. *Amer. Midl. Nat.* 29: 55–71.

48. Hendricks, S. B. 1956. Control of growth and reproduction by light and darkness. *Amer. Scient.* 44: 226–247.

49. Holt, I. V. 1952. Initiation and development of the inflorescence in *Phalaris arundinacea, Dactylis glomerata* and *Andropogon Gerardii.* M. S. Thesis. Library, Iowa State University, Ames, Iowa.

50. Hoover, W. H. 1937. The dependence of carbon dioxide assimilation in higher plants on wave length of radiation. Smithsonian Misc. Coll. 95. 13 pp.

51. Isanogle, I. T. 1944. Effects of controlled shading upon the development of leaf structure in two deciduous tree species. *Ecol.* 25: 404–413.

52. Johnson, H. W., Borthwick, H. A., and Leffel, R. C. 1960. Effects of photoperiod and time of planting on rates of development of the soybean. *Bot. Gaz.* 122: 77–95.

53. Kiesselbach, T. A. 1950. Progressive development and seasonal variations of corn crop. Nebr. Agr. Exp. Stat. Res. Bul. 166.

54. Kimball, H. H. 1935. Intensity of solar radiation at the surface of the earth and its variations with latitude, altitude, season and time of the day. *Mon. Wea. Rev.* 63: 1–4.

55. Kincaid, R. H. 1935. Effect of certain environmental factors on germination of Florida cigar-wrapper tobacco seeds. Fla. Agr. Exp. Sta. Bul. 277.

56. Klages, H. K. W. 1942. *Ecological Crop Geography. Macmillan,* New York.

57. Knowles, R. P. and White, W. J. 1949. Performance of southern strains of bromegrass in western Canada. *Sci. Agr.* 29: 437–450.

58. Korstian, C. F. 1925. Some ecological effects of shading coniferous nursery stock. *Ecol.* 6: 48–51.

59. Kramer, P. J. and Decker, J. P. 1944. Relation between light intensity and rate of photosynthesis of loblolly pine and certain hardwoods. *Pl. Phys.* 19: 350–358.

60. Loehwing, W. F. 1930. The effect of light intensity on tissue fluids in wheat. *Iowa Acad. Sci. Proc.* 37: 107–110.

61. Marsh, F. L. 1941. Water content and osmotic pressure of sun and shade leaves of certain woody prairie plants. *Bot. Gaz.* 102: 812–815.

62. Martin, E. V. 1935. Effect of solar radiation on transpiration of *Helianthus annuus. Pl. Phys.* 10: 341–354.

63. Miller, E. E. 1951. Averaged measurements of optical transmission. *Rev. Sci. Instrum.* 22: 56–57.

64. Odum, E. P. 1959. *Fundamentals of Ecology* (2nd Ed.). Saunders, New York.

65. Olmsted, C. E. 1943. Growth and development in range grasses. III. Photoperiodic response in the genus *Bouteloua. Bot. Gaz.* 105: 165–187.

66. ———. 1944. Photoperiodic response of 12 geographic strains of side-oats grama. *Bot. Gaz.* 106: 46–74.

67. ———. 1945. Photoperiodic response of clonal divisions of three late strains of side-oats grama. *Bot. Gaz.* 107: 382–401.

68. Oosting, Henry J. 1956. *The Study of Plant Communities.* Freeman and Co., San Francisco.

69. Pauley, S. S. and Perry, T. O. 1954. Ecotypic variation of the photoperiodic response in *Populus. Jour. Arnold Arbor.* 35: 167–188.

70. Pearse, A. S. 1939. *Animal Ecology* (2nd Ed.). McGraw-Hill, New York.

71. Penfound, W. T. 1932. The anatomy of the castor bean as conditioned by light intensity and soil moisture. *Amer. Jour. Bot.* 19: 538–546.

72. Peterson, M. L. and Loomis, W. E. 1949. Effects of photoperiod and temperature on growth and flowering of Kentucky bluegrass. *Pl. Physiol.* 24: 31–43.

73. Pickett, W. F. 1934. Photosynthesis activity and internal structure of apple leaves are correlated. *Amer. Soc. Hort. Sci. Proc.* 32: 81–85.

74. Popp, H. W. 1926. A physiological study of light of various ranges of wavelength on the growth of plants. *Amer. Jour. Bot.* 13: 706–735.

75. ——— and Brown, F. 1936. The effect of ultraviolet radiation upon seed plants. In B. M. Duggar, *Biological Effects of Radiation* 2: 853–887.

76. Porter, A. M. 1937. Effect of light intensity on the photosynthetic efficiency of tomato plants. *Pl. Phys.* 12: 225–252.

77. Pritchett, W. L. and Nelson, L. B. 1951. The effect of light intensity on the growth characteristics of alfalfa and bromegrass. *Agron. Jour.* 43: 172–177.

78. Rabideau, G. S., French, C. S., and Holt, A. S. 1946. Absorption and reflection spectra of leaves, chloroplast suspensions, and chloroplast fragments as measured in an Ulbricht sphere. *Amer. Jour. Bot.* 33: 769–777.

79. Rabinowitch, E. I. 1945. *Photosynthesis and its Related Processes.* 1: 602. Interscience, New York.

80. ———. 1951. *Photosynthesis and Related Processes.* 2: 603–1208. Interscience, New York.

81. Rhykerd, C. L., Langston, R., and Mott, G. O. 1959. Influence of light on foliar growth of alfalfa, red clover and birdsfoot trefoil. *Agron. Jour.* 51: 199–201.

82. Roberts, R. H. and Struckmeyer, B. E. 1938. Effects of temperature and other environmental factors upon photoperiodic responses of some of the higher plants. *Jour. Agr. Res.* 59: 699–709.

83. Ryther, J. H. 1956. Photosynthesis in the ocean as a function of light intensity. *Limnol. and Oceanog.* 1:61–70.

84. Sass, J. E. and Skogman, J. 1951. The initiation of the inflorescence in *Bromus inermis* Leyss. *Iowa State Coll. Jour. Sci.* 25: 513–519.

85. Sharman, B. C. 1945. Leaf and bud initiation in the Gramineae. *Bot. Gaz.* 106: 269–289.

86. Shirley, H. L. 1929. The influence of light intensity and light quality upon the growth and survival of plants. *Amer. Jour. Bot.* 16: 354–390.

87. ———. 1935. Light as an ecological factor and its measurement. *Bot. Rev.* 1: 355–381.

88. ———. 1945. Light as an ecological factor and its measurement. *Bot. Rev.* 11: 497–532.

89. Singh, B. N. and Kumar, K. 1935. The reactions of the assimilatory system to alterations of light intensity. *Proc. Indian Acad. Sci.* 81: 754–762.

90. Snyder, W. E. 1938. Effect of light and temperature on floral initiation in the cocklebur and Biloxi soybean. *Bot. Gaz.* 100: 388–431.

91. Spoehr, H. A. and Smith, J. H. C. 1936. The light factor in photosynthesis. In B. M. Duggar, *Biological Effects of Radiation* 2: 1015–1058.

92. Thomas, R. O. 1948. Photoperiodic responses in maize. Iowa State Coll. Jour. Sci. 23: 86–88.

93. Thompson, R. C. 1938. Dormancy in lettuce seed and some factors influencing its germination. U.S.D.A. Tech. Bul. 655.

94. Toole, E. H., Hendricks, S. G., Borthwick, H. A., and Toole, V. K. 1956. Physiology of seed germination. *Ann. Rev. Plant Physiol.* 7: 299–324.

95. Tysdal, H. M. 1933. Influence of light, temperature and soil moisture on the hardening process in alfalfa. *Jour. Agr. Res.* 46: 483–515.

96. Vaartaja, Olli. 1954. Photoperiodic ecotypes of trees. *Can. Jour. Bot.* 32: 392–399.

97. Verkerk, K. 1955. Interaction of photosynthetic light and temperature. Meded. Landb Hogesch., *Wageningen* 55: 175–224. (Original not seen; cited in Wellensiek, 1957.)

98. Vinson, C. G. 1923. Growth and chemical composition of some shaded plants. *Amer. Soc. Hort. Sci. Proc.* 20: 293–294.

99. Wassink, E. C. and Stolwijk, J. A. J. 1956. Effects of light quality on plant growth. *Ann. Rev. Plant Physiol.* 7: 373–400.

100. Wellensiek, S. J. 1957. The plant and its environment. In *Control of the Plant Environment*, ed. J. P. Hudson, Academic, New York.

101. Went, F. W. 1945. Simulation of photoperiodicity by thermal periodicity. *Sci.* 101: 97–98.

102. ———. 1957. *The Experimental Control of Plant Growth.* Chronica Botanica, Waltham, Mass.

The Atmosphere and
Air Movement

NATURE AND COMPOSITION OF
THE EARTH'S ATMOSPHERE

The free atmosphere surrounding the earth is composed of a mechanical mixture of a few gases which exist in relatively constant proportions. By volume (in percent) the composition of air includes nitrogen, 78.09; oxygen, 20.93; argon, 0.93; carbon dioxide, 0.03; and miscellaneous, 0.02. Variations from this may be found over industrial plants which release quantities of gaseous fumes such as SO_2, CO_2, and CO, as well as water vapor and solid particles.

The portion of the lower atmosphere, which is subject to differential heating, thereby causing convection currents and turbulences, is called the **troposphere.** This may extend to a height of ten miles in the tropics, but at 60° latitude such turbulences may reach a height of not more than six miles (Woodbury, 1954).

Beyond the lower atmosphere, extending out into space, is the **stratosphere,** in which the temperature remains relatively constant at from $-45°C$ to $-75°C$. At the lower edge of this layer, conditions are quiet, but in the upper stratospheric region the air may be quite turbulent. One of the characteristics of the stratosphere is the occurrence of a well-marked layer having an increased concentration of ozone (O_3). This layer occurs at approximately 20 miles above sea level as a result of the action of ultraviolet light from the sun, and it results in reducing the cooling rate of the earth. Actually, while it is often called the ozone layer, the composition of ozone probably does not exceed ten parts per million (Newell, 1960).

The gaseous mixing in the atmosphere is, in general, similar at sea level and at heights up to 50 miles. Above that the action of ultraviolet and x-radiation from the sun causes the formation of innumerable ions and the dissociation of oxygen. Above 60 or 70 miles, gaseous mixing is no longer effective and much of the oxygen is in the atomic form.

These layers (above 60 or 70 miles), extending from 40 or 50 miles outward for great distances, are known collectively as the *ionosphere*. The ionosphere is characterized by being electrified, mainly through electromagnetic radiations from the sun. The concentration of electrons in the upper atmosphere may reach a maximum somewhere between 200 and 500 miles from the earth. Also, the ionosphere contains heavy ions in numbers roughly equivalent to the number of electrons (Newell, 1960). Energy relations are by no means uniform in the upper atmosphere. The Van Allen radiation belt, discovered by J. A. Van Allen and his associates in 1958, is thought to include at least two separate high-energy zones. These zones carry energies from 20,000 electron volts to several million electron volts, with a maximum intensity of the inner zone at 2500 miles, and of the outer zone at 10,000 miles.

Although the upper atmosphere may at some future date be of great ecological significance to man, at the present time it is the lower atmosphere with which we are most concerned from the ecological viewpoint.

AIR POLLUTION

The injurious effects of air pollution have been known for many years, but it is only recently that the extent and seriousness of the problem have attracted widespread public attention. Disasters such as the 1952 London black fog period, in which 4000 deaths occurred, and others in Donora, Pennsylvania, Poza Rica, Mexico, and Belgium's Meuse Valley attracted the attention of the whole world (Absolom, Wilkins, and Oswald, 1954; Drinker, 1956; Haagen-Smit, 1959).

In metropolitan areas one of the most common causes of air pollution is smoke from burning dumps, steel mills, foundries, and other industrial plants. Large-sized particles of soot and dust are rather easily removed from smoke, but very fine dust of .5 to 1 micron in size and the still smaller gas molecules present a much greater problem.

Sulfur dioxide was considered for many years to be one of the most injurious air pollutants. It was always present in smoke and fumes from industrial plants, at times in rather heavy concentrations. Studies of injury to plants by SO_2 were reviewed by Thomas (1951). Acute injury was characterized by collapsed marginal leaf areas, the first symptom being dull water-soaked spots. Later these spots bleached to an ivory or brownish appearance. Less severe damage appeared as chlorotic areas or a general yellowing of the leaf, which occasionally turned reddish in color as chlorophyll and carotenoids disappeared. Alfalfa was readily damaged by SO_2 fumes, and it was shown experimentally that this type of injury could be simulated by clipping off leaf areas similar to those destroyed by the gas (Stanford Research Institute, 1949).

A unique type of air pollution is that known as smog. This term, a word coined from *smoke* and *fog*, has come to mean obnoxious concentrations of air pollutants which cause eye-irritation, plant damage, and greatly reduced visibility. Actually, fog is not an essential part of smog, although it is often present. Condensation nuclei, including particles of smoke, dust, spores, and salt, are always present in the atmosphere. These nuclei facilitate the development of smog.

According to Neiburger (1957), three conditions are essential for the production of smog of the Los Angeles type: (1) sources emitting pollution into the air, (2) atmospheric conditions which prevent rapid transport of these pollutants, and (3) solar radiation for photochemical reactions which transform the pollutants into substances causing irritation to the eyes and respiratory system and damage to plants.

The first condition is always present and includes smoke and fumes from industrial plants, incinerators, and automobiles. The second condition is typical of the Los Angeles Basin, extending at times from San Diego on the south to Oxnard on the north. The surface wind pattern in summer and autumn is a southwest or west wind from the ocean during the day, and calm or light land breezes from the north and east at night. This pattern often results in temperature inversion, the inversion layer beginning at about 475 meters above sea level. Below this level, temperature decreases with height, but above 475 meters, and extending up to possibly 1050 meters, temperature increases with height (Neiburger, 1957). The cool air near the surface tends to become stagnant and, if fog forms in this layer, it becomes more dense because of the many condensation nuclei present. If winds do not remove such air masses, the smog condition may stabilize for days. Air pollutants in this area include carbon monoxide, sulfur dioxide, oxides of nitrogen, hydrocarbons, aldehydes, and organic acids (Haagen-Smit, 1958).

In typical Los Angeles smog, the concentration of sulfur dioxide is low, but that of oxidizing pollutants is high. These include ozone and peroxides formed by the atmospheric oxidation of organic material. Haagen-Smit believes that these organic peroxides are responsible for the severe irritating effect on the eyes and respiratory system, as well as for much of the plant damage which occurs. Other irritants contributing to the injurious nature of smog are secondary products such as formaldehyde and acrolein, a tear-gas ingredient (Nicholson, 1959).

Total damage from smog to plants in southern California has been estimated to be as high as six to eight million dollars per year (Hull and Went, 1952; Nicholson, 1959). It is believed that in addition to losses apparent from plant symptoms, some reduction in yield probably occurs in many crops which show no visible effects.

Agricultural crops differ in sensitivity to smog injury. According to Hull and Went, some of the sensitive crops include alfalfa, endive, spinach, oats, sugar beets, and tomatoes. Further studies of sensitivity to smog by Middleton, Kendrick, and Darley (1955) provided a basis for a more complete classification of crops. Rated as most sensitive were alfalfa, oats, table beets, spinach, endive, and Swiss chard. Plants considered sensitive-to-intermediate included sugar beets, sweetclover, and celery. Those intermediate-to-resistant included barley, lettuce, peas, rhubarb, and tomato. Most resistant to smog injury were common beans, wheat, corn, Bermudagrass, and cabbage.

The nature of visible damage to plants by smog has been investigated. Middleton, Kendrick, and Darley (1953) found that injury identical to that observed under field conditions was obtained when plants were exposed to the reaction products of ozone and unsaturated hydrocarbons. Chlorotic leaf markings, banding, silvering, or bronzing of leaves is typical of smog damage (Middleton, Kendrick, and Darley, 1953; Todd, Middleton, and Brewer, 1956; Faith, 1959).

Controlled experiments by Middleton, Kendrick, and Darley (1953) showed that the severity of plant damage varied with ecological conditions under which the crop was grown. Spinach grown at 75°F was damaged much more severely than when it was grown at 55°F. Romaine lettuce and endive responded in a similar manner. A high level of nitrogen fertilization increased susceptibility to damage in spinach by 40% and to oats and barley by a lesser degree. High soil moisture was found to favor greater plant damage from smog than low soil moisture.

Varietal differences in susceptibility to smog damage were noted by Middleton, Kendrick, and Darley (1953). Among common beans, Golden Cluster and Pink were susceptible, but Bountiful and Kentucky Wonder were resistant. Among lima bean varieties, Fordhook 242 was susceptible, but Concentrated Fordhook was highly resistant.

Specific affects of air pollutants on physiological processes were studied by Todd, Middleton, and Brewer. A number of plant species, including *Lemna* (duckweed), red kidney bean, grapes, citrus, Kentia palm, and avocado, were exposed to controlled concentrations of ozone and ozonated hexane, two of the most injurious pollutants in smog. Visible damage to duckweed occurred after a one-hour exposure to ozonated hexane at an oxidant concentration of 0.2 ppm. Photosynthesis was reduced drastically after an exposure of 24 hours. Ozone produced a somewhat smaller reduction in photosynthesis. Both ozone and ozonated hexane exposure resulted in marked losses in chlorophyll after 24 hours.

The process of respiration was also observed by Todd, Middleton, and Brewer. In lemon fruits a stimulation of respiration rate resulted from treatment with ozone and ozonated hexane, but the possible harm caused by this change was not evaluated.

A third process, the maintenance of cell membrane permeability, was found to be affected by air pollutants. In table beet, bean leaf, and potato tuber tissue exposed to ozonated hexane, there were indications of changes and in some instances disruption of membrane permeability.

In studies with woody plants, Kentia palm and avocado, evidence of reduction in growth due to exposure to air pollutants was obtained.

Some progress toward reducing the smog problem has been made through the tremendous efforts of many foundations and state agencies. Stringent controls on smoke from industrial plants, banning of ordinary open-flame incinerators, and equipping of automobiles with smog-eliminating devices have shown promise of reducing the immediate smog hazard in the Los Angeles area. However, with an ever-increasing concentration of population in metropolitan areas, a rapid rise in the number of automobiles, and a continued increase in concentration of industry, the problem of smog is one of great importance not only to West Coast areas but to the whole United States and the world.

Other sources of air pollutants of a distinctly injurious nature are sprays, particularly those used as herbicides. Wind drift of sprays has become so injurious to sensitive crops that strict regulations and controls have become necessary. Faith (1959) cites the example of the effects of a spray operation using 2,4-D in the ester form for weed control in a rice field. Due to serious wind drift, 2,4-D was blown 15 to 20 miles and caused considerable injury to a cotton crop at that distant location.

CARBON DIOXIDE AND OXYGEN BALANCE

It is remarkable that a compound so essential to the ecological relationships of organisms, CO_2, is present in such a small amount. Carbon dioxide in the air constitutes but .03% of the air medium, or approximately 1/700 as much as oxygen. However, it is well distributed and often rather efficiently used.

Green plants release O_2 in photosynthesis and, although this process occurs only during daylight periods, its results are so much greater than those of respiration (which releases CO_2) that the net effect is an increase of O_2 and a decrease of CO_2 in the atmosphere.

To counterbalance this effect, animals and nongreen plants continually use O_2 and liberate CO_2 into the air. In spite of this, however, the normal concentration of CO_2 in the air is often considered suboptimal for photosynthesis. Experiments have shown that the accumulation of carbon compounds can be increased by increasing the CO_2 concentration. This is a basis for the theory held by some physiologists that CO_2 may at times be the limiting factor in the production of corn, sugarcane, and tropical forage grasses. It was shown by Chapman, Gleason, and Loomis (1954) that the CO_2 concentration in the air declines below average when photosynthesis is very active, and may build up above average when little photosynthesis takes place. Evidence by Lemon (1959) suggests that in sunny weather photosynthetic rate is largely dependent upon turbulent CO_2 exchange between the atmosphere and the crop. A factor which tends to keep up the concentration of CO_2 in the atmosphere is the large quantity liberated from the soil. In a forest, as Daubenmire (1959) has noted, the lower layers of the atmosphere may contain from six to ten times the average concentration of CO_2. This excess CO_2 near the soil surface in a forest undoubtedly tends to compensate for low light intensity available to the layers of vegetation near the surface of the ground.

The use of CO_2 by plants may be influ-

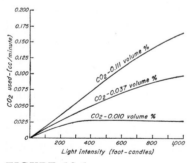

FIGURE 10-1.

Relationship between rate of photosynthesis in wheat plants and light intensity at normal atmospheric, at decreased and at increased concentrations of carbon dioxide. [After Hoover, et al, Smithsonian Misc. Coll. 18 (16), 1933.]

enced greatly by the light intensity present. It was shown by Hoover, Johnson, and Brackett (1933) that under low light intensity the rate of photosynthesis may be controlled by light, whereas under high light intensity the photosynthetic rate may be controlled by the CO_2 present. This relationship is shown in Figure 10-1.

THE SOIL AIR

The respiration of soil organisms, including plant roots, results in a high concentration of CO_2 and a low concentration of O_2 in the soil. This sets up a steep diffusion gradient between the gases in the upper soil layers and those in the atmosphere above the soil. Temperature, barometric pressure, and moisture contribute to the changing composition of soil air, but diffusion is the principal process by which soil air is renewed (Baver, 1956).

The O_2 content of the soil air tends to fluctuate widely, whereas the CO_2 content remains relatively stable. Page and Bodman (1951) showed that loams with moisture at field capacity contain approximately 19% O_2 in the main root horizons, which is reduced, temporarily at least, by frequent rains. Several factors operate to keep the oxygen content of soil air below that of the air above. One of these factors is the activity of microorganisms, which tends to keep the concentration of oxygen low and CO_2 high. This is so universal that Wallis and Wilde (1957) noted that the rate of evolution of CO_2 from the soil is a good measure of the rate of decomposition. Respiration of plant roots during rapid growth, however, may contribute more to the total CO_2 in the soil than is produced by the microorganisms (Turpin, 1920).

Other factors influencing the ratio of O_2 to CO_2 in the soil are the amount of pore space and the size of the pores. Aeration is increased by porosity, which results from good aggregation, root channels, and animal burrows. Tillage also, especially plowing when the moisture content of the soil is at or near field capacity, may improve soil structure and porosity, but working the soil when too wet will, of course, destroy good aggregation.

The size of pores also plays an important role in soil aeration. Daubenmire has noted that a coarse sand with a total porosity of 55.5% is 1000 times more permeable to air than a fine sand with a pore volume of 37.9%.

A high degree of porosity is of little advantage if most of the pores are so small that they hold capillary water. Roots of most upland plants will not penetrate deeply under such conditions. Schuster and Stephenson (1940) demonstrated that for the best distribution of roots in nut trees, a favorable distribution of pore space, possibly half capillary and half noncapillary pores, was necessary.

Finally, good drainage is essential if the oxygen content of soil air is to be kept at a favorable level. In moist climates, for example the Piedmont Plateau in southeastern North America, the growth rate and height of pines was closely correlated with the depth to the least impermeable soil horizon (Coile, 1940).

If the concentration of CO_2 in the soil air becomes too great, detrimental effects may result. This was demonstrated by Chang and Loomis (1945), who found that an excess of CO_2 reduced absorption of water and nutrients by wheat, maize, and rice as compared with aerated cultures of the same plants. Leonard and Princkard (1946) found that in nutrient solutions cotton root development was optimum when the concentration of CO_2 ranged from 0–15% and O_2 concentration was maintained at 21%. Both root and shoot growth were reduced with high concentration of CO_2.

Requirements for soil aeration differ widely among species. As was indicated by the work of Loehwing (1934), hydrophytes germinate and grow best under conditions quite unsuitable for the development of mesophytes and xerophytes. Effects of suboptimal aeration have been outlined by Daubenmire. Among morphologic effects are thin cell walls in the roots, suppression of root-hair formation, less complex root branching, shallow root system, and reduction of shoot and leaf areas. Physiologic effects include increase in anaerobic respiration of roots (with toxic by-product accumulation), decline in pH of plant sap, reduction of rate of absorption of water and nutrients, decrease in permeability of plasma membrane, reduction in transpiration rate, delay of reproductive process, and foliage discoloration.

AIR MOVEMENT AND WIND

While winds and air pressure variations, acting directly, are not of as great ecological importance as are moisture and temperature, they are highly important indirectly because they exert a great degree of control on the climate. Minor changes in pressure result in changes in velocity and direction of wind, and this may cause marked changes in temperature and precipitation.

Winds do two things: (1) transport heat from lower to higher latitudes, and (2) provide land masses with supplies of moisture for precipitation. Air moves from a region of high pressure to one of low pressure. Pressure differences are caused basically by unequal heating of the atmosphere, the equatorial regions receiving more heat than regions farther south and north. In general, this results in a movement of air from the poles (high pressure) toward the Equator (low pressure). Here the air rises and returns toward the poles. Modifications of this general pattern are caused by the action of the earth's rotation and by temperature differences caused by comparative sizes and positions of water and land masses. This general latitudinal pattern may be further subdivided into zonal belts, which are more evident in the Southern Hemisphere than in the Northern Hemisphere.

According to Trewartha (1954), the dominant features of the zonal pressure conditions are as follows:

(1) A series of high-pressure centers which form irregular belts of high pressure exists in each hemisphere at approximately 30° n and s. These are known as subtropical highs.

(2) Equatorward from these subtropical high-pressure ridges, pressure declines until the equatorial low-pressure trough is reached. This coincides with the region of highest annual temperature.

(3) From a subtropical high, pressure decreases toward the poles, reaching a rather low pressure at the latitude of the Arctic and Antarctic circles.

(4) Poleward, the pressure tends to increase again.

Three generalized patterns of surface winds are easily recognized. From the subtropical highs located at about 30° n and s, surface winds flow toward low-pressure areas, being turned into easterly winds by the Coriolis force. North of the Equator these are known as the northeast trade winds; south of the Equator they tend to be southeast winds. A second group of winds results from a flow poleward from the subtropical highs. This results in the middle-latitude westerlies. In the Northern Hemisphere, the prevailing direction is from the southwest, whereas in the Southern Hemisphere it is from the northwest.

A third type of wind includes those known as the polar easterlies, which are not as well defined nor characterized as the first two types. An idealized representation of these three types of winds is given in Figure 10-2.

In general, there is a predominance of easterly surface winds in the tropics, and a prevalence of westerly winds in the middle latitudes (Trewartha, 1954). In the high latitudes, easterly winds probably prevail, although the evidence is rather meager.

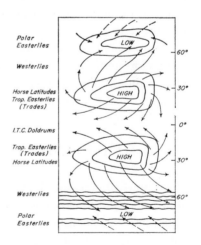

FIGURE 10-2.

Highly idealized diagram of the earth's principal patterns of surface winds. [After Finch, Trewartha, Robinson, and Hammond, Elements of Geography. N. Y.: McGraw-Hill, 1957.]

These idealized and highly simplified statements on surface winds are, of course, subject to great modification if actual conditions are to be represented. During World War II, observations in the low latitudes showed that there were many nonperiodic types of weather disturbance which tended to dispel the older concept of uniform periodic diurnal and seasonal character of the surface wind pattern and tropical weather (Trewartha, 1954). Apparently, the typical steady trade winds attributed to low latitudes are confined to restricted areas within the tropics.

The westerlies of the middle latitudes are particularly erratic. They are distinctive in that they are composed of extremes. As Trewartha has pointed out, spells of weather are a distinguishing characteristic. Moderate-to-strong winds are frequent, but the westerlies vary from winds of gale force to mild breezes. It is to be noted also that in the latitudes of the westerlies the most frequent winds blow from the west, but winds do come from all directions.

Surface winds are important from the ecological viewpoint, especially because of their effects on surface air temperatures. However, from the broader viewpoint, a treatment of winds as a basis for explaining climatic conditions in general must include consideration of winds in the free atmosphere aloft. Trewartha has noted that the circulation pattern of the free atmosphere is predominantly zonal. The basic reason for an atmospheric circulation is the fact that more solar energy is received in the low latitudes near the Equator and less in the high latitudes near the poles. Winds tend to correct this imbalance of solar energy and thus prevent a cumulative excess of energy in the tropics and a deficit poleward. A complete and satisfactory outline of the circulation of the earth's atmosphere is not available at the present time (Trewartha, 1954), and a more detailed discussion of this subject would appear to be beyond the scope of this chapter.

WIND MEASUREMENT

Wind speed is measured by an **anemometer.** The United States Weather Bureau has used one known as the cup anemometer. It consists of three or four conical or hemispherical cups, each attached to horizontal arms which rotate on a vertical axis. This drives a gear system which operates dials on an indicator. The units are expressed in miles per hour, or other units of time. Where a permanent installation is not feasible, a portable anemometer may be used. Another device, useful in microclimatology, is the hot-wire anemometer (Parr, 1947).

Winds are named by the direction from which they blow. A weather vane points toward the source of the wind. The term **windward** refers to the direction from which the wind comes, and **leeward** refers to the direction toward which the wind blows.

The velocity of a wind usually varies considerably with distance from the surface of the ground. Most winds are not uniform and steady air currents, but rather a succession of gusts and lulls. Near the surface this gustiness may be the result of eddies caused by irregularities of the earth's surface. At higher levels, convectional currents cause irregularities. To describe wind force, a scale giving a descriptive term, the general effect on the land, and the velocity in miles per hour, has been developed. This is known as the Beaufort Scale, and is reproduced in Table 10-1.

The rate of evaporation from plane surfaces increases with the square root of the velocity of the wind. This fact, that the influence of wind is not proportional to its velocity, helps explain the action of a **sling psychrometer** used for measuring relative humidity. This instrument is usually rotated at approximately ten miles per hour, and evaporation from the wet bulb is

TABLE 10-1. THE BEAUFORT SCALE OF WIND FORCE WITH VELOCITY EQUIVALENTS*

Beaufort Number	Beaufort Descriptive Term	Land Criteria	Velocity, miles per hour
0	Calm	Calm, smoke rises vertically	Less than 1
1	Light air	Direction shown by smoke drift, not by wind vanes	1 to 3
2	Light breeze	Wind felt on face; leaves rustle; ordinary vane moved by wind	4 to 7
3	Gentle breeze	Leaves and small twigs in motion; wind extends light flag	8 to 12
4	Moderate breeze	Raises dust and loose paper; small branches moved	13 to 18
5	Fresh breeze	Small trees in leaf begin to sway. Crested wavelets form on inland waters	19 to 24
6	Strong breeze	Large branches in motion; whistling in telegraph wires; umbrellas used with difficulty	25 to 31
7	Moderate gale	Whole trees in motion; some difficulty walking against wind	32 to 38
8	Fresh gale	Breaks twigs off trees; progress generally impeded	39 to 46
9	Strong gale	Slight structural damage occurs (chimney pots and slate removed)	47 to 54
10	Whole gale	Trees uprooted; considerable structural damage occurs; seldom experienced inland	55 to 63
11	Storm	Very rarely experienced; accompanied by widespread damage	64 to 75
12	Hurricane		Above 75

* From Trewartha. *An Introduction to Climate.* McGraw-Hill, N. Y., 1954.

affected but little by wind velocities of more than five miles per hour. This means that when the psychrometer is rotated rapidly, wet-bulb depression is determined mainly by the relative humidity.

EFFECTS OF AIR MOVEMENT ON PLANTS

Wind has a powerful effect on the humidity of the atmosphere. Layers of humid air adjacent to plant leaf surfaces are removed by wind and become mixed with dry air above. This tends to keep relative humidity low and to increase transpiration rate. During cold weather, winds greatly increase the evaporative power of the air. The velocity of wind increases with height, so trees may suffer more from drying effects than do herbaceous plants (Mitchell, 1936). In some mountainous regions, notably on the eastern slopes of the northern Rocky Mountains, warm **chinook** winds may cause the snow to melt and actually make winter grazing possible. However, Henson (1952) has shown that these warm, dry winds, which may occur suddenly in late winter, may raise the evaporative power of the air too much while soil temperatures are still very low. Consequently, many woody plants are unable to maintain a good internal water balance, and conditions of winter drought exist.

Even in environments where soils are warm and moist, consistent winds have been known to damage citrus trees extensively by killing leaves and twigs and causing fruit drop (Reed and Bartholomew, 1930).

Windswept coasts and high mountains subject plants to excessive water losses. Trees may present a stunted, gnarled appearance, caused in part by severe water losses and also by mechanical effects of the wind on the growth pattern and shape.

Ecological effects of wind on vegetation in exposed areas have been reported by Whitehead (1954). On Mount Maiella, Italy, at the permanent snow line, wind was shown to have a marked effect on both the number and the growth forms of plant species. At this elevation there is an exposed, fairly level site where strong winds are the rule. Observations were made in four local areas, varying from Site "A," with full exposure to the wind, to Site "D," a rock-sheltered site. In Site "A" were found the fewest species and also the fewest growth forms of those species present; in Site "D" were found the greatest number of species and the most growth forms.

Wind tunnel studies by Whitehead (1957) with crop plants, particularly with a variety of maize known as Nodak 301, gave the following results (Table 10-2) in a comparison of continuous wind vs air movement for ventilation only.

TABLE 10-2. GROWTH OF MAIZE NODAK 301 WITH AND WITHOUT WIND

Attributes	Control Plants Exposed to Ventilating Air Currents Only	Plants Subjected for 40 Days to 30-mph Wind
Width of leaf	5.75 cm	6.75 cm
Thickness of leaf	0.164 cm	0.433 cm
Leaf margin–number of rows of sclerenchyma	2	12
Number of secondary veins	51	72
Maximum diameter of phloem in main vein	38μ	70.4μ
Number of fibers in bundle sheath	59	144
Number of stomata per mm²	77	110
Size of stomata	32.19μ	28.49μ

Whitehead emphasized the general effect of wind in increasing the water deficit in leaves, even though the plant roots may be supplied with adequate moisture. Wind tunnel studies with *Senecio lividus* and other species have shown that an increase in wind speed is associated with an increase in saturation deficit in the leaves. After exposure of three hours to a 40-mph wind, little or no assimilation can take place. If exposure is continued for several more hours the plant will die. The lethal effect of wind, therefore, depends upon a wind-speed/time-tolerance factor which reaches a critical value resulting in permanent wilting and death. This critical point may be influenced by other environmental factors. A sudden increase in leaf temperature reduces the time required to reach wilting. The growth form of the plant and soil moisture conditions are also important modifying factors.

If moisture available to plants is abundant, winds of moderate speed may not affect growth rate. In an experiment designed to determine the effect of wind on the growth rate of rape, barley, and peas growing in water cultures, Wadsworth (1960) exposed young plants of these species to wind speeds of 0.3, 0.7, 1.7, and 4.0 meters per second. Wind speed apparently did not affect growth rate, the plants did not tend to dry out, and the water supplied to the roots was abundant. However, it should be noted that these plants were not subjected to the degree of stress imposed on the plants in the wind tunnel experiment reported by Whitehead.

Much damage to crops is caused by hot dry winds at or near the time of flowering. The internal water balance is upset, resulting in poor seed setting. Another form of damage noted by Taylor (1923) was blossom injury caused by evaporation of secretions from the stigmas. Moist winds tend to have the opposite effect. They may actually permit the growth of mesophytic vegetation in an otherwise arid environment.

Strong winds, blowing rather consistently from one direction, also exert direct effects on the appearance of vegetation. Dwarfing and deformation of trees are common expressions of these wind effects often found on sea coasts, exposed ridges, and at timberlines (Lawrence, 1939). Another wind effect, reported by Jacobs (1954), is the greater diameter of the lower trunk of trees in thin exposed stands, as compared with solid or closed stands in the same general environment.

Smith (1920) pointed out the importance of mechanical and erosive effects of wind. At sea level a wind velocity of 10 miles per hour exerts a pressure of $\frac{1}{3}$-pound per square foot; at 30 miles per hour, a pressure of 2.5 pounds per square foot; and at 60 miles per hour, a pressure of 9 pounds per square foot. It is easy to understand, therefore, that winds of velocities greater than 30 to 40 miles per hour often cause great physical damage to vegetation. Especially when high winds are accompanied by rain, hail, or sleet, destruction of crops and trees may be serious indeed. Along the Gulf Coast, and northward along the Atlantic Coast, storms of the hurricane type are most destructive. In the interior of the United States, from Texas northward to Michigan, storms of the tornado variety cause great damage every year.

WIND TRANSPORT

In addition to the important role of transporting water vapor inland from large bodies of water, wind performs important ecological functions in transporting pollen and in seed dissemination.

Most plants produce pollen in great abundance. An individual pollen grain may have little chance of survival but, because of the millions produced, the success of some pollen grains may be assured. Erdtman (1943) has given figures of pollen production for several common herbaceous and tree species. Almost unbelievable numbers of pollen grains are produced, particularly by coniferous trees.

Most pollen is light and may be carried long distances by wind, in some instances from several miles to several hundred miles.

Wind is an important factor in dissemination of seeds, fruits, spores, parts of plants, and even whole plants. One of the most striking examples of importance to crop production is the spread of cereal rusts from the Gulf Coast, or Mexico, northward into the midwest by means of windborne spores.

The spread of seeds, fruits, and plant parts by wind is facilitated by their gross morphological nature. Light, winglike structures and feathery extensions increase the likelihood of wind transport. Entire plants, such as the tumbleweed, *Salsola* and *Cycloloma* species, when broken off at the ground level may roll for miles with a little help from the wind. If the plants are mature, seeds may be scattered over a wide range of territory.

WIND AND SOIL EROSION

Fine particles of soil are easily transported by wind. In dry regions, or areas subjected to extended periods of drought, serious wind erosion has resulted in much drifting of soil and has caused the "dust bowl" conditions found in the Southwest during the 1930's.

Over longer periods of time, the quantities of material transported may be great indeed. This is amply shown by the deposits of **loess** (wind-transported soil) in various parts of the world. Many thousands of acres of rich farm land in the Mississippi Valley are of loessial origin, some dating back to glacial periods when soil and dust particles were taken up by the wind from the flood plains of glacial rivers, and transported to other areas where they accumulated to a considerable depth over many centuries.

References

1. Absolom, H. W. L., Wilkins, E. T., and Oswald, N. C. 1954. Smog. *Roy. Meteor. Soc. Quart. Jour.* 80: 261–278.
2. Baver, L. D. 1956. *Soil Physics.* Wiley, New York.
3. Chang, H. F. and Loomis, W. E. 1945. Effect of carbon dioxide on absorption of water and nutrients by roots. *Plant Phys.* 20: 221–232.
4. Chapman, H. W., Gleason, L. S., and Loomis, W. E. 1954. The carbon dioxide content of field air. *Plant Phys.* 29: 500–503.
5. Coile, T. S. 1940. Soil changes associated with loblolly pine successions on abandoned agricultural land of the Piedmont Plateau. Duke Univ. School For. Bull. 5.
6. Daubenmire, R. F. 1959. *Plants and Environment.* Wiley, New York.
7. Drinker, P. *Harben Lectures* (1957). Air pollution and public health. *Jour. Roy. Inst. Publ. Health and Hyg.* (July, Aug., Sept. 1957).
8. Erdtman, G. 1943. *An introduction to pollen analysis.* Chronica Botanica, Waltham, Mass.
9. Faith, W. L. 1959. *Air Pollution Control.* Wiley, New York.
10. Haagen-Smit, A. J. 1958. Air conservation. *Sci.* 128: 869–878.
11. Henson, W. R. 1952. Chinook winds and red belt injury to lodgepole pine in Rocky Mountain Parks area of Canada. *For. Chron.* 28: 62-64.
12. Hoover, W. H., Johnson, E. S., and Brackett, F. S. 1933. Carbon dioxide assimilation in a higher plant. Smithsonian Inst., Misc. Coll. Vol. 87, No. 16.
13. Hull, H. M. and Went, F. W. 1952. Life processes of plants as affected by air pollution. Proc. Natl. Air Poll. Symposium. 2nd Symposium, Pasadena, Calif. pp. 122–128.
14. Jacobs, M. R. 1954. The effect of wind sway on the form and development of *Pinus radiata. Austr. Jour. Bot.* 2: 35–51.

15. Lawrence, D. B. 1939. Some features of the vegetation of the Columbia River gorge with special reference to asymmetry in forest trees. *Ecol. Monog.* 9: 217–257.

16. Lemon, E. R. 1959. An aerodynamic method for determining the turbulent CO_2 exchange between the atmosphere and a corn field. *Agron. Abs.* p. 72. Amer. Soc. Agron., Madison, Wis.

17. Leonard, O. A. and Princkard, J. A. 1946. Effect of various oxygen and carbon dioxide concentrations on cotton root development. *Plant Phys.* 21: 18–36.

18. Loehwing, W. F. 1934. Physiological aspects of the effect of continuous soil aeration on plant growth. *Plant Phys.* 9: 567–584.

19. ———. 1953. Air pollution injury to crops. *Calif. Agr.* 7: 11–12.

20. Middleton, J. T., Kendrick, J. B., and Darley, E. F. 1955. Airborne oxidants as plant damaging agents. Proc. Natl. Air Poll. Symposium. 3rd Symposium, Pasadena, Calif. pp. 191–198.

21. Mitchell, H. L. 1936. The effect of varied solar radiation upon the growth, development and nutrient content of white pine seedlings grown under nursery conditions. Black Rock Forest Papers 1: 16–22. Cornwall-on-the-Hudson, New York.

22. Neiburger, M. 1957. Weather modification and smog. *Sci.* 126: 637–645.

23. Newell, Homer E. 1960. The space environment. *Sci.* 131: 385–390.

24. Nicholson, Arnold, 1959. Los Angeles battles the murk. Sat. Even. Post 231: 17–19, 90–93.

25. Page, J. B. and Bodman, G. B. 1951. The effect of soil physical properties on nutrient availability. In E. Truog (Ed.) *Mineral Nutrition of Plants.* pp. 133–166. Univ. Wis. Press, Madison.

26. Parr, R. G. 1947. A hot-wire anemometer for low wind speeds. *Jour. Sci. Instr.* 24: 317–319.

27. Reed, H. S. and Bartholomew, E. T. 1930. The effects of desiccating winds on citrus trees. *Calif. Agr. Exp. Sta. Bull.* 484.

28. Schuster, C. E. and Stephenson, R. E. 1940. Soil moisture, root distribution and aeration as factors in nut production in western Oregon. *Ore. Agr. Exp. Sta. Bul.* 372.

29. Smith, J. W. 1920. *Agricultural Meteorology.* Macmillan, New York.

30. Stanford Research Institute. 1949. Proc. First Natl. Air Pollution Symposium, Los Angeles, Calif.

31. Taylor, N. 1923. The vegetation of Long Island. *Brooklyn Bot. Gard. Mem.* 2: 1–107.

32. Thomas, M. D. 1951. Gas damage to plants. *Ann. Rev. Pl. Phys.* 2: 293–322.

33. Todd, Glen W., Middleton, John T., and Brewer, Robert F. 1956. Effect of air pollutants. *Calif. Agr.* 10: 7, 8, 14.

34. Trewartha, Glenn T. 1954. *An Introduction to Climate.* McGraw-Hill, New York.

35. Turpin, H. W. 1920. The carbon dioxide of the soil air. N. Y. (Cornell) *Agr. Exp. Sta. Mem.* 32: 319–362.

36. Wadsworth, R. M. 1960. The effect of artificial wind on the growth rate of plants in water culture. *Ann. Bot.* 24 (94).

37. Wallis, G. W. and Wilde, S. A. 1957. Rapid method for determination of carbon dioxide evolved from forest soils. *Ecol.* 38: 359–361.

38. Whitehead, F. H. 1954. Relation between growth form and exposure on Monte Maiella, Italy. *Jour. Ecol.* 42: 180–186.

39. ———. 1957. Wind as a factor in plant growth. In *Control of the Plant Environment*, edited by J. P. Hudson. Academic, New York.

40. Woodbury, A. M. 1954. *Principles of General Ecology.* Blakiston, New York.

Physiographic and Edaphic Factors

PHYSIOGRAPHIC FACTORS

Physiographic factors are those introduced by the structure and behavior of the earth's surface, that is by topographic features of elevation and slope, by processes of silting and erosion, and consequently by local geology (Polunin, 1960). Physiographic changes include the blowing of sand or dust, which has at times assumed vast proportions.

Topographic relief produces a marked effect on local climates, summits having climates different from those of slopes and narrow valleys having climates different from those of broad open plains. High altitudes mean lower soil and air temperatures, and usually greater windiness and exposure. Atmospheric pressure declines and heat radiation increases with altitude. In arid climates, physiographic effects may be especially important, as noted by Polunin. Although there may be unproductive plains near sea level, we may find fertile slopes and forests on mountain sides. Again, at very high altitudes, we may reach another unproductive zone of very low humidity and extreme exposure.

Topography may have a marked effect on climatic conditions at some distance. For example, mountain ranges such as the Sierras and Rockies may cause considerable local rainfall, but much drier conditions far in their lee.

Aspect is another physiographic effect, for in the northern hemisphere slopes facing north tend to be more moist than slopes facing south at the same latitude. In mountainous regions, vegetation on the two sides of a deep valley or a steep mountain may be quite different because of micro-climatic differences. Western slopes are often noticeably warmer and drier than eastern slopes, owing to the warmth of the sun in the afternoon. Slope direction is an important consideration in the location of sites for deciduous fruit orchards because of its influence on temperature rise in the spring.

Slope is, of course, a primary determiner of degree of erosion. Oosting (1956) has noted that normal or geologic erosion is a universal phenome-non. With any slope at all, material moves downward. If the movement is very slow, there may be no great damaging effect and no marked changes in the microenvironment. However, accelerated erosion which exceeds that of profile maintenance is highly destructive. The degree of slope, the nature of the underlying rock, the soil type, and the kind and frequency of hard rains (and winds) will determine the amount of erosion. Man has played a major role in increasing erosion by denuding forests, cropping steep slopes, and so managing irregular topography as to encourage soil losses.

Where topography is relatively level, a uniform type of vegetation may be expected. This is usually a distinct advantage in crop production, for mecha-nized equipment can be used to best advantage on level areas. Much of the world's grain production is obtained on the great, relatively level expanses of plains and flood plains. Such areas include the plains of the Mississippi Valley, the Argentine pampas, the plains extending across France and east-ward into northern U.S.S.R., the Hungarian plains, the southern Russian plains, the delta plain of the lower Nile River, and the delta flood plains of India and China.

Level areas also have disadvantages: in regions of somewhat immature topography, drainage may be poor and slight depressions contain ponds or lakes. As pointed out by Oosting, even with more mature topography where depressions contain streams which facilitate drainage, the streams usually are bordered by flood plains which support vegetation requiring favorable moisture conditions and which are not always suitable for cultivation of all crops. When the humid, tall-grass prairies of Illinois and Iowa and Min-nesota were first settled, much of the land was too wet for profitable use in agriculture. It was not until drainage was made possible that much of the humid prairie became desirable crop land.

On flat lands, water may leach materials down into deeper layers, where they often form a hardpan which is sometimes nearly impervious to plant roots, small animals, and water. Under very unfavorable drainage condi-tions, such as in bogs, decomposition is slow and humus accumulates be-cause of poor aeration. Lack of oxygen and accumulation of carbon dioxide and other toxic substances serve as limiting factors for plant growth. With good drainage, however, the muck and peat soils of the Florida Everglades and many smaller areas in Michigan, Wisconsin, and other states have become highly productive of a variety of crops.

EDAPHIC FACTORS

The plant is dependent on the soil for anchorage, water, and nutrients. In extent, the root system may be as great as, or even greater than, the top growth. The surface contact between the soil and the plant roots is great indeed, making the soil truly an intimate part of the plant's environment.

The soil may be of greater importance to the plant under natural conditions than it is under cultivation, because changes occasioned by the addition of fertilizer or by practices such as drainage or irrigation are made possible only by man. Warming (1909) recognized the importance of soil in the natural distribution of plants by attempting to classify them into specific groups based on the kind of soil substratum where they occurred. The soil itself may be considered a paramount factor in the level of productivity of an area, at least until man has changed the picture.

Soil Origin and Development

For ecological purposes, the soil may be considered the unconsolidated superficial material of the earth's crust, lying below areal vegetation and undecomposed litter, and extending down to the point where it no longer affects the plants growing about its surface (Polunin, 1960). Soil is the connecting link between the rock core of the earth and the living things at its surface (Simonson, 1957). Although it is composed mainly of material derived from the parent rock, the soil has developed largely through interaction of this substratum with climate and living organisms. The soil is composed, therefore, of a parent material (the underlying geologic or mineral substrate) and organic matter in which organisms and their products are intermingled with finely divided particles of the modified parent material (Odum, 1959).

Some effects of climate on soil formation were reported by Jenny (1941). In a study of the effect of moisture over large areas of reasonable uniformity in topography, vegetation, and geologic strata, he found that where moisture tended to be limiting for plant growth, the nitrogen and organic matter of surface soils increased as moisture increased. Also, with increasing moisture, clay and base saturation capacity tended to be higher, whereas con-

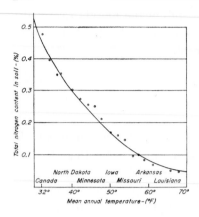

FIGURE 11-1.

Decline in nitrogen content of the soil with rise in mean annual temperature (Fahrenheit) in the semihumid region of the United States. [After Jenny, Factors of Soil Formation. N. Y.: McGraw-Hill, 1941.]

centration of soluble salts decreased. These relationships did not hold as well in forested, humid sections in the eastern part of the United States.

In considering temperature as a soil-forming factor, it must be remembered that chemical reaction rates increase exponentially with rising temperature. In the Mississippi Valley, Jenny (1941) found that within relatively uniform moisture belts, nitrogen and organic matter in the soil decreased as the annual temperature rose (Figure 11-1). This proved to be not a universal relationship, however. Later investigations by Jenny (1950) indicated that some tropical forest soils are relatively high in nitrogen and organic matter. It was suggested that the predominance of legume trees, with the accompanying symbiotic nitrogen fixation, may have accounted for the high nitrogen content even under conditions of high average temperature.

Development of Soil Horizons

Simonson (1957) suggested that soil formation proceeds in two steps: (1) accumulation of soil parent materials and (2) differentiation of horizons in the soil profile. The first step follows the gradual and continuous process of weathering of rocks. The second step, development of horizons, proceeds at rates which vary with conditions of climate and vegetation.

As soon as the soil begins to develop, plants become established. With the establishment of vegetation, many kinds of animals begin to live in the soil, to take advantage of the food provided by plants, or to prey on one another. Insects, millipedes, earthworms, gophers, and prairie dogs live interdependent lives in the soil. Burrowing operations stir the soil, mix it with fresh minerals, cause decay of plant roots, and hasten the process of humification. The soil thus becomes a community of activity, an ecosystem (Waksman, 1952; Norman, 1946; Russell and Russell, 1950.

As the surface layer begins to show differentiation from layers below, a faint A horizon becomes noticeable. The B horizon may make its appearance soon thereafter, although in some soils the two horizons develop together.

The *C* horizon (weathered parent material) is decreased in depth as the *A* and *B* horizons develop. Sometimes the *A* and *C* horizons are distinct long before there is evidence of a definite *B* horizon. Changes in color, structure, texture, porosity, and other properties, and the kinds and rates of these changes, are important in the differentiation of horizons. A schematic presentation of a soil profile is given in Figure 11-2.

The development of the soil profile is determined by the nature of the parent rock, the climate, and the vegetation. Over similar parent rock, similar climate, vegetation, and relief would be expected to produce similar kinds of soils. But, if the environment is different, different profiles will develop over the same kind of parent material. Thus the soil profile and relative thickness of the horizons tend to be characteristic for different climatic regions and for different physiographic conditions (Byers, *et al*, 1938). Grassland soils are different from forest soils because in them humification is rapid and mineralization is relatively slow. Grass plants are short-lived compared with trees and the entire plant decays rapidly, adding large amounts of organic matter to the soil. Forests, on the other hand, add much litter or duff to the surface but relatively little humus. Litter and tree roots decay slowly and mineralization is rapid. Daubenmire (1959) has noted that the humus content of a grassland soil may average 600 tons per acre, whereas that of forest soils may be but 50 tons per acre.

The ecologist is interested in several aspects of the *A* and *B* soil horizons from the standpoint of adaptation and distribution. The texture of the soil (percentage of sand, silt, and clay), the percentage of organic matter, and the exchange capacity are especially important.

Residual and Transported Soils

Soils which overlie the parent rock from which they were derived are known as residual soils. The results of weathering are most apparent in the surface horizons, with the soil showing more and more similarity to the parent rock at increasing depths. Where parent rock contains great quantities of minerals like quartz, sandy and gravelly soils are likely to develop, but where easily soluble rocks are prevalent, fine-textured soils develop.

In contrast to residual soils, transported soils are those which have been moved into present locations. Many of these are the **loess** soils, representing materials transported by wind. Such soils are found in parts of Iowa, Kansas, and Nebraska, where their depths range from a few to fifty feet. Other areas

Organic debris lodged on the soil, usually absent on soils developed from grasses.		A_{00}	Loose leaves and organic debris, largely undecomposed.
		A_0	Organic debris partially decomposed or matted.
		A_1	Dark-colored horizon with high content of organic matter mixed with mineral matter.
	Horizons of maximum biological activity, of removal of materials dissolved or suspended in water, or both.	A_2	Light-colored horizon of maximum eluviation. Prominent in Podzolic, but faintly developed or absent in Chernozemic soils.
THE SOLUM (The genetic soil developed by soil-forming processes)		A_3	Transitional to B, more like A than B. May be absent.
		B_1	Transitional to B, more like B than A.
	Horizons of accumulation of suspended material from A, or of maximum clay accumulation, or of blocky or prismatic structure or both.	B_2	Maximum accumulation of silicate clay minerals or of iron and organic matter; maximum development of blocky or prismatic structure, or both.
		B_3	Transitional to C.
The weathered parent material. May be absent in soil-building. Follows weathering such that no weathered material not included in solum is found between B and D.		G	Horizon G for intensely gleyed layers, as in hydromorphic soils.
	Cca		Horizons Cca and Ccs are layers of accumulated calcium carbonate and calcium sulfate found in some soils.
	Ccs		
Any stratum beneath the soil, such as hard rock or layers of clay or sand, that are not parent material but which may have significance to the overlying soil.		D	

FIGURE 11-2.

Hypothetical soil profile with all the principal horizons. Not all of these horizons are present in most profiles, but every profile has some of them. [After Simonson, What soils are. Yearbook of Agriculture, U.S.D.A., 1957.]

of great loessial deposits are found in Argentina, the Rhineland, and in north-central China.

Another group of transported soils is the alluvial group, which includes deposits by water in the form of flood plains, river terraces, deltas, and alluvial fans. These deposits show characteristic forms of strata based on size of particles, and a rounding and smoothing of particles themselves caused by action of water.

Glacial deposits make up still another form of transported materials from which soils have developed. Often such deposits include particles of all sizes, ranging from huge boulders to fine clay. Layers deposited by successive advances of glacial ice may exhibit characteristic differences.

In North America, extensive glacial till plains cover much of Canada, New England, and the northern part of the Mississippi Valley.

Zonal Soils

From the ecological viewpoint, soils may be considered in two groups: (1) zonal soils, or those which are controlled by the climate and vegetation of the region, and (2) intrazonal soils or those controlled largely by local conditions of extreme or unusual topography, water level, or parent material.

In regions which are geologically young, climate and vegetation may not have had sufficient time to develop a typical zonal pattern, and differences in biotic communities may be directly correlated with differences in soil types. As noted by Wolfanger (1930), 83% of the soils in Marshall County, Iowa, are considered mature, while only 15% of the soils in Bertie County, North Carolina, are mature.

In the eastern half of North America rainfall is usually abundant for vegetation. From Greenland to the West Indies precipitation exceeds evaporation and transpiration combined, resulting in a net downward movement of water in the soil. Under this continuous downward movement, soluble salts are leached out of surface layers and eventually lost through the drainage waters. Within humid regions, temperature has a marked effect on the kind of soil which develops (Carter and Pendleton, 1956).

Gleization

Near the Arctic Ocean, where it is always cold, a soil-forming process called **gleization** occurs. A sticky, compact, and structureless layer develops at the bottom of the solum. This glei layer is blue-gray in color because of the reduced iron compounds resulting from anaerobic conditions. Organic matter may accumulate at the surface. Where the subsoil is continually frozen, in arctic and subarctic regions, a belt of soils with a characteristic glei horizon may be found. These are the **tundra** soils, so named because of the vegetation common to them.

Podzolization

Extending southward from the polar regions are soils formed in cool, moist climates under forest vegetation. The litter from this vegetation undergoes decomposition, with a consequent production of acid which is carried down through the soil by the rain. The continuous down-drainage results in loss of soluble salts and adsorbed basic irons. This process, known as **podzolization**, results in distinctly acid soils and, if sufficiently vigorous, a considerably lower level of fertility as time goes on. There is an accumulation of iron and aluminum compounds in the B horizon, and a deflocculation of the soil colloids. Silica, which is relatively insoluble, is left in the A horizon and often makes up a large share of the mineral matter which remains in that layer.

According to Daubenmire, soils which have developed under coniferous forests, especially those dominated by the genera *Picea, Abies*, and *Tsuga*, are true podzols. These soils are low in fertility, and highly acid. The A_1 horizon is very thin, the A_2 horizon is an ashy-gray (podzol) siliceous sand, and the B horizon dark brown, owing to accumulation of iron oxides. Even in their virgin condition, these podzols are infertile. Satisfactory crop production requires adequate applications of calcium, phosphorus, and other fertilizers.

In climates slightly warmer, such as in much of the northeastern part of the United States, gray-brown podzolic soils develop. Forest trees include maple, beech, yellow pine, and, on the Pacific Coast, redwood. Under the somewhat higher temperatures, more bases are returned to the soil than in the true podzol region, decomposition processes result in a slower accumulation of acid, and the soil remains moderately fertile. These podzolic soils are suitable, with adequate fertilization practices, for a wide range of crop plants. Along with the true podzols, the podzolic soils are typical of the group of humid soils known as **pedalfers.** These soils are characterized by accumulations of the oxides of aluminum and iron which may give a discoloration to the B horizon. There is no visible deposition of calcium carbonate in their profiles.

Latosols or Laterites

In the humid tropics and subtropics, the weathering process is known as **latosolization.** Under the constantly high temperatures, bases are quickly released, with a resultant low acidity. Rapid decay of organic matter from plant residues releases more bases in organic combination. This results in the breakdown of silica and a loss of silicic acid into the drainage waters. The solubility of Fe, Al, and Mn sesquioxides tends to be retarded, with intense oxidation taking place if drainage is good. As weathering proceeds, red and yellow parent materials high in sesquioxides and low in silica accumulate in the surface layers. A peculiar granular condition may develop, which allows cultivation shortly after heavy rains. The dominant characteristics of latosols include the low silica-sesquioxide ratios of clay fractions, low base-exchange capacity, low content of soluble constituents, high degree of aggregate stability, and appearance of some red color (Kellogg, 1949).

Within the latosol group, true **laterites** may develop under certain conditions. A laterite implies an indurated, slag-like, iron-oxide-rich, alluvial horizon, not found in many tropical soils of the latosol group. Latosols include also the reddish-brown lateritic soils, yellowish-brown lateritic soils, red-yellow podzolic soils, and several kinds of latosols. They are strongly leached, relatively infertile, and require continuous and heavy fertilization for sustained crop production.

In the latosolic group are many of the soils found in southern United States, southern France, Spain, Italy, Central America, Mexico, Cuba, northern South America, India, Burma, Java, Hawaii, and other areas.

Prairie Soils

Along the western edge of the forested area of eastern North America, especially in the "prairie wedge" extending from Missouri north to Minnesota and eastward as far as Indiana, are some of the most fertile soils of the world. These soils developed under grassland, in the subhumid-moist region where a woodland climate now prevails. Centuries of grassland, however, resulted in the production of the deep, dark-colored prairie soils or "prairie earths." These soils are characteristic of much of the highly productive cornbelt land of the Grand Prairie of Illinois and the Iowa prairie which occupies large portions of Iowa and southern Minnesota.

Because of an annual rainfall which surpasses the combined evaporation and transpiration, many of these soils, particularly in the eastern part of the tall-grass prairie region, have undergone mild podzolization. They have dark-colored, deep A horizons, however, not characteristic of the podzolized soils of the forest regions. On the other hand, these prairie soils have no characteristic accumulation of lime, as do the Chernozems or black earths, farther west.

To the west of the humid prairie is found the rich, black Chernozem belt, extending from Canada to Mexico. Under grassland vegetation, in a climate where precipitation was less than evaporation and transpiration, a

permanent dry layer developed in the soil profile below the depth of penetration of water from rain and snow. Under these conditions, carbonates
accumulated because of the dry layer, instead of being leached out and
lost into the streams. This process is known as calcification, and the soils are
known as lime-accumulating soils (**pedocals**).

The zero line of Thornthwaite (1948) separates the subhumid-moist from
the subhumid-dry moisture province (roughly at 99° west longitude). It
also separates (roughly at least) the pedalfer soils of the humid region
from the pedocals of the dry region.

Typical Chernozem soils, such as are found in the Red River Valley of
North Dakota, Minnesota, and Manitoba, have a deep, dark *A* horizon (at
two to four feet) and a whitish accumulation of lines at the bottom of the
B horizon. Wheat has long been one of the important crops in the North
American Chernozem belt.

West of the Chernozems are the **chestnut** soils. The dark brown *A* horizon
is not as deep as that of the Chernozem (one and one-half to three feet)
and, because of uncertain precipitation, crops are grown with much risk
of possible failure. The chestnut soils occupy areas of slightly drier climate
than the Chernozems, including much of the Great Plains region, from
North Dakota to Texas.

Under more arid conditions to the west of the chestnut soils, there is a
belt of **brown** soils. These have a shallower *A* horizon and a lower average
rainfall. Irrigation is essential for crop production; under dry land conditions, cattle grazing probably is the best use of this land.

With still less rainfall, desert soils develop. Here the *A* horizon may be
quite shallow, and the lime accumulation (and other salts) close to or
actually on the surface. In the north, gray desert and sierozem soils (pale
grayish soils grading into calcareous material at a depth of one foot or less)
are found associated particularly with sage, *Artemisia tridentata*, from
Wyoming to Oregon. Farther south, the color of the soils becomes reddish,
the typical red desert soils occurring in parts of Arizona, California, and
adjacent Mexico (Richards, 1947).

Intrazonal Soils

Groups of soils which reflect the dominant influence of certain local conditions, such as relief, parent material, or age, in contrast to the influence
of climate in general, are called intrazonal soils. Several important intrazonal groups are the **planosols, wiesenboden,** and **bog** soils.

Planosols are soils with strongly leached surface horizons over claypans on nearly flat land in cool-to-warm, humid-to-subhumid regions, under grassland or forest vegetation.

Wiesenboden, or ground water podzols, are dark brown or black soils with poor drainage, developed under grasses in humid-to-subhumid regions.

Bog soils are dark-colored, poorly drained peat or muck soils, underlain with peat, found mostly in humid regions, under swamp or marsh vegetation.

Azonal Soils

Soils without well developed profile characteristics are known as azonal soils and include **lithosols,** composed largely of an imperfectly weathered mass of rock fragments, sands, and alluvial deposits, too recent to have developed profile characteristics.

Soil Classification

A further step in the classification of soils is the grouping into Great Soil Groups. This classification recognizes the influence of environmental conditions in the development of profile characteristics. It involves effects of topography and vegetation as well as those of climate. A classification of soils into Orders, Suborders, and Great Soil Groups is given in Table 11-1.

The Great Soil Groups may be divided further into soil types. A soil type is a more limited designation implying a restricted range of climatic conditions and a restricted area of distribution. The soil type is the basic unit of detailed soil mapping and land-use planning, a designation of great usefulness to the ecologist, agronomist, and farmer alike. Soil types alike in profile characteristics except in texture, that is, the proportions of sand, silt, and clay, are considered members of a soil series. Typical of a soil series found in one county in the Iowa Soil Survey are the soils illustrated diagrammatically in Figure 11-3.

Three Great Patterns of Climate, Soils, and Vegetation

That climates tend to remain relatively uniform over wide areas and that similar climates are repeated throughout the world on the land masses in characteristic latitudinal and continental locations are recognized generalizations. As Trewartha (1954) has pointed out, there is a definite and repeated world pattern of relatively few climates. These climates are likely

TABLE 11-1.   CLASSIFICATION OF THE GREAT SOIL GROUPS*

Order	Suborder	Great Soil Groups
Zonal soils	1. Soils of the cold zone	Tundra soils
	2. Light-colored soils of arid regions	Desert soils
		Red desert soils
		Sierozem
		Brown soils
		Reddish-brown soils
	3. Dark-colored soils of semiarid, subhumid, and humid grasslands	Chestnut soils
		Reddish chestnut soils
		Chernozem soils
		Prairie soils
		Reddish prairie soils
	4. Soils of the forest-grassland transition	Degraded Chernozem
		Non-calcic Brown or
		Shantung Brown soils
	5. Light-colored podzolized soils of timbered regions	Podzol soils
		Gray wooded or
		Gray Podzolic soils†
		Brown Podzolic soils
		Gray-brown Podzolic soils
		Red-yellow Podzolic soils†
	6. Lateritic soils of forested warm-temperate and tropical regions	Reddish brown lateritic soils†
		Yellowish brown lateritic soils
		Laterite soils†
Intrazonal soils	1. Halomorphic (saline and alkali) soils of imperfectly drained and arid regions and littoral deposits	Solonchak or
		Saline soils
		Solonetz soils
		Soloth soils
	2. Hydromorphic soils of marshes, swamps, seep areas and flats	Humic-gley soils† (includes *Wiesenboden*)
		Alpine meadow soils
		Bog soils
		Low humic-gley soils†
		Planosols
		Ground water Podzol soils
		Ground water Laterite soils
	3. Calcimorphic soils	Brown forest soils (*Braunerde*)
		Rendzina soils
Anzonal soils		Lithosols
		Regosols (includes dry sands)
		Alluvial soils

* From Thorp and Smith. *Soil Sci.* 67:118, 1949. Courtesy of Williams and Wilkins Co.
† New or recently modified great soil groups.

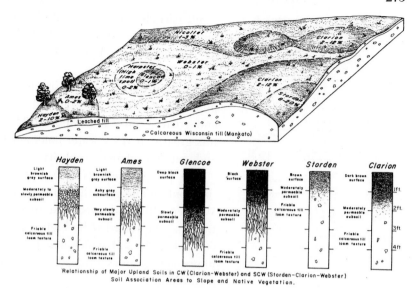

Relationship of Major Upland Soils in CW (Clarion-Webster) and SCW (Storden-Clarion-Webster)
Soil Association Areas to Slope and Native Vegetation.

FIGURE 11-3.

Relationship of major upland soils in the Clarion-Webster and Stor-
den-Clarion-Webster soil association areas of northcentral Iowa to
slope and native vegetation. [*From Simonson, Riecken, and Smith,*
Understanding Iowa Soils. *Dubuque, Iowa: Wm. C. Brown Co.,*
1952.]

to be associated with general and repeated patterns of native vegetation
and soils. Again, it appears that climatic factors overshadow the other two.
A schematic representation of the distribution of these world patterns of
climate, vegetation, and soils, is given in Figure 11-4. These relationships
are emphasized further in the maps showing world distribution of Great
Soil Groups, Figure 11-5, and world natural vegetation, Figure 11-6.

Soil Texture

"Soil texture" refers to relative fineness or coarseness, or the proportions
of different size groups of soil particles. According to the International System of Soil Particle Classification, coarse sands range in diameter from 2.00
to 0.20 mm, whereas clay particles are less than 0.002 mm in diameter.
Sand particles expose much less surface than do clay particles (23 square
cm per gram as compared with 11,342 square cm per gram). Sands are
relatively inactive and have a low nutrient capacity and a low cation absorption capacity. Sands tend to increase the size of pore spaces in soils,
which aids in movement of air and water.

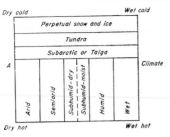

FIGURE 11-4.

The three great patterns of climate, native vegetation, and soils: (A) distribution of climatic types; (B) distribution of vegetation formations on a climatic base; (C) distribution of major zonal soil groups on a climatic base. [After Blumenstock and Thornthwaite, Climate and Man. Yearbook of Agriculture, U.S.D.A., 1941.]

Silt particles are somewhat like fine sand, but have greater surface and are more active chemically (Lyon, Buckman, and Brady, 1952).

The clay fraction of the soil is most important because of its colloidal properties and great surface area exposed. These factors greatly increase water-holding capacity and cation-exchange capacity of the soil.

The physical effects of soil texture on distribution and growth of plants are many. Weaver (1919) showed that root penetration may be retarded by high silt and clay content of the soil, which may be especially important in areas subject to long periods of drought.

Infiltration of water may be restricted by fine-textured soils. This may result in greater runoff and a lower rainfall effectiveness. Forest trees have extended their range farther into dry regions where surface soils were sufficiently coarse that infiltration of water was not impeded (Patton, 1930; Smith, 1949). Rate of water movement through the soil varies inversely with texture: the finer the particles the slower the rate. Texture of soil may affect crop quality, as was noted by Baver and Farnsworth (1940). They showed that sugar beets and other root crops often produced a poor quality of root on very fine-textured, heavy-clay soils. In general, fine-textured soils tend to hold much of their water in the upper soil layers, which may dry out quickly. They lose more moisture by runoff than do sands. They cause slow root penetration, tend to be poorly aerated below, which forces shallow rooting, and favor damping-off fungi (Hansen, *et al*, 1923; Daubenmire, 1959).

On the plus side, however, increased water-holding capacity of fine-textured soils may greatly improve crop production. Stewart (1927) observed that with the same rainfall a fine sandy loam soil sustained corn

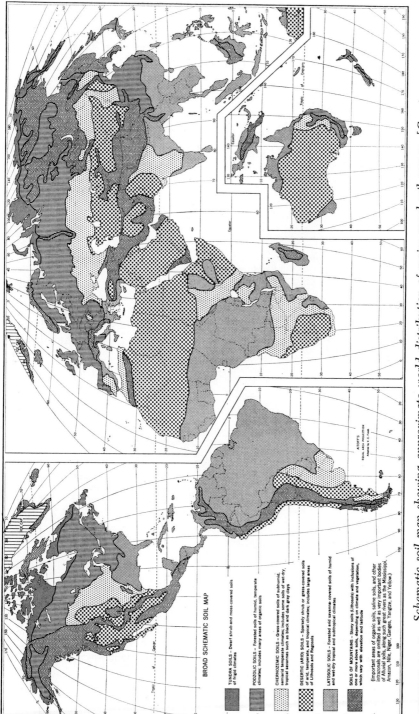

BROAD SCHEMATIC SOIL MAP

TUNDRA SOILS – Dwarf shrub and moss-covered soils of frigid climates

PODZOLIC SOILS – Forested soils of humid, temperate climates; includes many areas of organic soils

CHERNOZEMIC SOILS – Grass-covered soils of subhumid, semiarid temperate climates; includes some soils of wet-dry, tropical savannas such as black and dark gray clays

DESERTIC (ARID) SOILS – Sparsely shrub or grass-covered soils of arid, temperate, and tropical climates; includes large areas of Lithosols and Regosols

LATOSOLIC SOILS – Forested and savanna-covered soils of humid and wet-dry tropical and subtropical climates

SOILS OF MOUNTAINS – Stony soils (Lithosols) with inclusions of one or more above soils, depending on climate and vegetation, which vary with elevation and latitude

(Important areas of organic soils, saline soils, and other intrazonals are omitted as well as very important bodies of Alluvial soils, along such great rivers as the Mississippi, Amazon, Nile, Niger, Ganges, Yangtze, and Yellow.)

FIGURE 11-5. *Schematic soil map showing approximate world distribution of major zonal soil groups. [Courtesy U. S. Dept. of Agriculture, Soil Conservation Service.]*

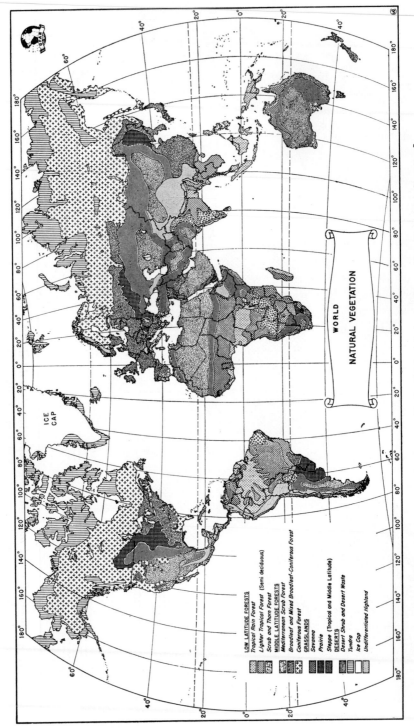

FIGURE 11-6. *World natural vegetation.* [*Courtesy U. S. Dept. of Agriculture, Foreign Agr. Service.*]

seedlings without wilting for 20 days, whereas on medium sands corn wilted in 12 days.

Soil Structure

"Structure" refers to the arrangement of soil particles. Primary soil particles usually exist in clusters or aggregations of compound particles. As the profile develops, a natural structural pattern is formed. Soil structure is modified by the action of climate as well as through cultivation by man. The nature of the root systems of forest trees and grasses, with the differential accumulation of organic matter and the type of its decay, exerts a marked influence in bringing about differences in soil structure of woodland and prairie soils. The degree of granulation and makeup of soil-particle aggregation affects the suitability of soils for certain crops, and determines the cultural practices necessary for their effective production (Carlson, 1925; Russell, 1949; Coile, 1952).

Aeration of soils is related to soil structure. In well-aggregated soils, or those moderately coarse in texture, the relatively large interstitial spaces allow ready diffusion of gases. In fine-textured, heavy soils, which are poorly aerated, a deficiency of oxygen and an excess of carbon dioxide may become limiting to normal growth of many plants. Coarse-textured soils, on the other hand, warm up rapidly and may become depleted of humus because of rapid oxidation processes. This may be an advantage in some instances, such as early spring when crops may be planted earlier than in heavier, colder soils.

Another aspect of soil structure is soil compaction and the effects of long-time tillage. Compaction in fine-textured soils may be a deterrent to normal root development. It was found by Veihmeyer and Hendrickson (1948) that there was a critical soil density beyond which normal soil roots were unable to penetrate.

Tillage, such as plowing and cultivation, loosens and aerates the soil, but in most instances only makes more noticeable the soil aggregation already attained (Ackerman and Meyers, 1943). Actually, tillage may destroy good soil structure by mechanical means. In many areas, often after a long time under cultivation, soils show a decrease in granulation owing to the disruptive effects of tillage on soil aggregates (Klute and Jacob, 1949).

Soil Organic Matter

The rate of incorporation of plant and animal residues into a mineral soil depends on both climate and vegetation. Plant residues in grassland climates decay rather rapidly and add to the humus layer. Grass roots, fine and fibrous, are short-lived and contribute great quantities of organic matter to grassland soils. However, this material is mineralized slowly and adds to the dark colored layer of the surface soil.

Organic matter added to forest soils undergoes a somewhat different process. Tree roots are long-lived and contribute relatively little as compared with surface litter from leaves and dead twigs and branches. Surface litter is converted to the humus stage rather slowly, but mineralization is rapid after that stage is reached. The humus content of forest soils is likely to be only a fraction, possibly one-tenth, of that present in many grassland soils.

Organic matter in the soil is important to plants because it is a source of nutrients, it is a source of food for microorganisms, it increases the water-holding capacity, it increases cation-exchange capacity, and it improves soil structure. As far as nutrients are concerned, organic matter contains 95% of the total nitrogen, 5% to 60% of the total phosphorus, and 10% to 80% of the total sulfur. A continuous cycle or turnover of these elements, as discussed in Chapter 6, takes place among soils, plants, animals, and sometimes atmosphere (Dean, 1957).

Chemical Properties and Soil Fertility

At the present time at least sixteen elements are considered essential for the growth of higher plants: carbon (C), hydrogen (H), oxygen (O), nitrogen (N), phosphorus (P), potassium (K), calcium (Ca), magnesium (Mg), sulfur (S), iron (Fe), copper (Cu), manganese (Mn), zinc (Zn), boron (B), molybdenum (Mo) and chlorine (Cl). For some of the lower forms of plants, cobalt (Co) and vanadium (V) also are considered necessary. These elements, or plant nutrients, often are classified on the basis of the relative amounts normally required by plants, that is, (1) macronutrients and (2) micronutrients. The first nine listed are considered macronutrients and the last seven, micronutrients. This arbitrary classification has limited usefulness and does not necessarily imply relative importance (Dean, 1957; Nicholas, 1961).

Plants obtain carbon, hydrogen and oxygen from the air and water, while the other nutrients are obtained from the soil itself. Chemical analyses indicate that the total amount of nutrients in most soils is high compared with the requirements of plants. However, much of this total amount may be tightly bound in forms relatively unavailable to crops.

The organic fraction of soils serves as a source of nitrogen, phosphorus and sulfur, made available to plants through biological processes. The inorganic fraction, derived from rocks and the products of their breakdown, supplies the other essential elements.

The composition and capacity to supply plant nutrients is largely dependent on soil texture. The minerals that make up the sand and silt fractions contain most of the essential elements, but these are relatively unavailable to plants until considerable mineral decomposition takes place. This decomposition goes on very slowly in the soil.

The clay fraction of soils is made up of secondary minerals and amorphous materials which differ markedly from the components of sand. Clays are products of weathering and are composed of clay minerals, including kaolinite, montmorillonite and illite, as well as the hydrous oxides, mainly those of iron and aluminum.

The cation-exchange properties of soils are found in the clay fraction and in the organic matter fraction. The clay particle is represented as consisting of (1) an insoluble core or micelle which is negatively charged, and (2) a loosely held swarm of cations including H^+, Ca^{++}, Mg^{++}, K^+ and Na^+ (Lyon, Buckman, and Brady, 1952). The degree of saturation of the colloidal micelles with basic ions is an important measure of soil fertility. In humid regions the cations of first importance on the clay particles are H^+ and Ca^{++}, so the system is called a calcium-hydrogen complex. In arid and desert regions, the ions of Ca^{++} and Mg^{++} are of first importance, and the cation swarm is known as a calcium-magnesium complex.

The geographic distribution of clay minerals is of considerable importance. Southern clays have been found to be predominantly kaolinite. The prairie soils of the American Midwest have rather high proportions of montmorillonite, whereas the desert soils are comprised mainly of montmorillonite and hydrous micas. In view of the fact that the cation-exchange capacity of kaolinite is relatively low, that of hydrous micas, intermediate, and that of montmorillonite, high, the ecological importance of the distribution of these minerals is obvious.

The three elements or plant nutrients used in large quantities which are likely to be deficient in many soils are nitrogen, phosphorus, and potassium. Typical effects of an abundance or deficiency of these elements are of great importance to ecology. Responses of plants suggest their specific adaptation to the local microenvironmental conditions involved, and are discussed at some length by Millar, Turk, and Foth (1958).

An abundance of nitrogen results in rapid growth of vegetative tissues and a dark green color. If plenty of nitrogen is available only early in the season, maturity of the plant may be hastened. However, if nitrogen is available in abundance throughout the growing season, later maturity results. Also, tissues may be soft and succulent, making the plant more susceptible to disease and mechanical injury. Of great importance in the world's nitrogen balance is biological nitrogen fixation, discussed in Chapter 12.

The total supply of phosphorus in soils is relatively small and often short for normal plant development. Phosphorus is a nuclear component of cells, is essential in cell division, essential for transformation of carbohydrates, essential for assimilation of fats, and increases the efficiency of chloroplastic mechanisms. Adequate phosphorus is necessary for quality in forage legumes, normal development of plump seeds, and as an aid in decreasing lodging.

Potassium is essential to the metabolic processes of cells, essential in the synthesis of carbohydrates and their translocation through the plant, essential to chlorophyll development. It aids in synthesis of proteins, fats, and oils and aids in forming rigid stalks, plump seeds, and high test-weight.

Soil Reaction

Changes in the reaction of soil solutions are caused mainly by the pressure of CO_2 (Lyon, Buckman, and Brady, 1952). In the presence of water this gas tends to form carbonic acid. In humid regions, where rainfall is sufficient to cause leaching, the soluble bicarbonates formed by the reaction of carbonic acid and bases are removed. The colloidal complexes continue to lose their adsorbed basic cations with the result that the H-ion concentration of the soil solution increases. This means that in the soils of the humid regions there is a continuous trend toward increasing acidity. Minor fluctuations in soil pH also occur because of wetting and drying, changes in temperature, root development of plants, and changes in biological activity in the soil. Drastic changes in pH over a short period of time, however, are prevented to a great extent by the buffering action of mixtures of weak acids and their salts present in the colloidal clay and humic complexes.

Tolerance of Crops to Acidity

Because of the many physiological factors involved, it is difficult to associate with any high degree of accuracy the optimum growth of crops with the pH of mineral soils. With alfalfa, for example, it is known that abundant calcium is essential, and if it is supplied the crop will grow well at a relatively low pH. Azaleas are known to be tolerant of low pH, but their apparent high requirement for iron, more abundantly available in highly acid soils, may be of equal or greater importance.

Most crops grow well on slightly to moderately acid soils. Small grains, corn, forage grasses, many legumes, and many vegetables are broadly tolerant, growing well within the range of pH 5.8 to 7 or slightly above. A diagram showing the relation of crop plants to soils of a wide range of pH is given in Figure 11-7.

In humid regions, leaching of soils results in increased soil acidity. In contrast, lack of rainfall in arid regions results in an accumulation of carbonates at some point in the soil profile. Most arid zonal soils are found where rainfall is 20 inches or less annually. Little leaching leaves these soils high in bases. A calcium carbonate layer will usually accumulate in the C horizon, but the position of this layer depends on extent of leaching. The drier the climate, the nearer the surface will be the high carbonate layer. Such arid soils may have alkaline subsoils and either alkaline or neutral surface layers. Where some leaching takes place, a mild acidity

FIGURE 11-7.

Tolerance of crop plants to physiological conditions in mineral soils of different reactions. Fertility level and balance of plant nutrients are highly important in determining tolerance.

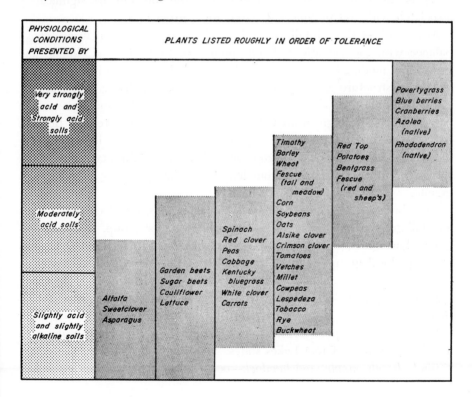

may develop in the surface soil, a situation which often occurs in Chernozems. But, if drainage is impeded and if evaporation at the surface is high, salts may accumulate in the A horizon, or actually on the surface. (See discussion under irrigation in arid regions in Chapter 7.)

Plants as Soil Indicators

It was suggested by Billings (1952) that since vegetation was the product of the interaction of the environment and the genetic tolerance limits of its component species, it should therefore be a good indicator of environmental conditions. He pointed out, however, that it is often dangerous to predict changes in an environment because of the vegetation present. Many species may not yet have occupied all of their potential environment, and it would be incorrect, therefore, to evaluate an environment on the basis of *absence* of a species.

Shantz (1938) has discussed the possibilities of using plant cover as an indicator of climatic conditions, of the soils on which it grew, and of the practices of grazing or other use to which it had been subjected. He noted that large plant communities (formations and associations) are relatively independent of the physical composition of the soil, but are significantly associated with soil provinces or large zonal groups.

As a result of the rainfall available, a plant cover develops in ecological balance with the climatic and soil conditions. Interaction of climate and vegetation modified the earth's surface materials, and this surface developed a structure and composition which we recognize as a soil profile.

Plant communities are often closely correlated with the soil series which has developed in a given area. In certain instances, as noted by Billings, parent material has exerted a dominant influence as evidenced by the fact that certain trees and shrubs have become established much more successfully on soils derived from limestones than on those derived from granite.

On a broad basis it might be said that coniferous and deciduous forests and tall-grass prairie occur on soils of the pedalfer group, whereas mid-grass, short grass, desert grasses, and shrubs tend to be limited to soils of the pedocal group. Shantz classified vegetation types and soil series as follows:

Spruce-fir forest—occurs on podzols or raw soils undergoing podzolization.

White- and *Jack-pine forest*—found on gray-brown podzolic soils, such as are found in the Great Lakes states, New England and the Alleghenies.

Birch, beech, maple, and *hemlock*—occur on gray-brown and red-yellow podzolic soils of the Lake states and in the eastern states as far south as Georgia.

Oak (southern hardwood) forest—found on gray-brown and red-yellow podzolic soils.

Oak-hickory (midwest) forest—occurs on gray-brown podzolic and on humid prairie soils.

Oak-pine (southern) forest—found on red and yellow podzolic soils.

Tall-grass prairie (Andropogon spp. etc.) grassland—occurs on deep, dark prairie soils developed under centuries of grassland.

Short-grass (Plains grassland)—occurs on Chernozem, chestnut, and brown soils.

Mesquite-desert grass savanna—occurs on chestnut, brown and desert soils.

Sagebrush (northern desert)—found on brown- and gray-desert soils, often with alkali present.

Creosote bush (southern desert)—occurs on red-desert soils, with alkali likely.

Greasewood (salt-desert shrub)—found on desert soils where alkali problem prevails.

In the Sonoran Desert of Arizona, Yang and Lowe (1956) found that major vegetation climaxes are highly correlated with soil characteristics. The lighter and more rocky soils of the higher slopes (3400–2000 feet elevation) were associated with the Paloverde–Sahuaro (*Cercidium–Cereus*) vegetation type. The finer soil of the lower slopes supported the creosote-bush-Bursage (*Larrea–Franseria*) association. These two vegetation groups represent the climax associations of the Sonoran Desert.

Soil Requirements for Crop Plants

Basic soil conditions required for crop production may be stated as follows:

1. Suitability for cultural implements required for efficient crop production.

2. Effective resistance to destructive erosion or deflation under the management involved in profitable farming.

3. Adequate moisture storage to meet normal requirements of the crop, under natural rainfall or irrigation.

4. Adequate aeration to a suitable depth to permit development of a favorable root system.

5. Availability of plant nutrients sufficient for profitable yields.

6. Freedom from adverse chemical conditions, such as harmful con-

centration of soluble constituents, and from other special conditions that favor the development of organisms parasitic to the crop.

The prevailing topography and relief associated with a given soil may determine its suitability for crops, with respect to both cultural operations and erosion hazard. This is of particular importance with the increased use of mechanized equipment in farming operations.

Undesirable physical properties of certain heavy clays make their profitable use rather difficult. Prevalence of boulders on the surface or just below the surface makes tillage difficult. Erodability of certain silt loams and fine sandy loams, such as some of the loessial deposits of the Mississippi basin, make the long-term use of these soils difficult indeed.

Moisture storage in the soil may be modified by irrigation, but this is not feasible in great areas of sandy soils, or in regions where water for irrigation is not available. The depth of the water table may be highly important. Adequate soil aeration may be precluded if the water table is high, or if subsoils are so heavy and impervious that they cannot be adequately drained.

Although an adequate supply of soil nutrients is essential, this can often be adjusted successfully by fertilizer application. It is still true, however, that basically fertile soils require a comparatively small investment of fertilizer for the growing of common field crops.

The last condition mentioned, freedom from adverse chemical conditions, is subject to a considerable degree of intelligent control. If adequate drainage can be supplied, and plenty of water is available, excessive harmful salts often can be leached out and alkalinity can be partially corrected by the application of gypsum (hydrated calcium sulfate) or sometimes by sulfur applications. Adverse conditions of soil acidity can be corrected by liming, a practice long advocated but still extremely important in most of the humid regions.

Direct Effects of Soil Type on Plants

An elaborate experiment was designed in the United Kingdom some years ago for the purpose of determining specific effects of different soil types on a number of attributes of growth and development of plants. Marsden-Jones and Turrill (1945) found marked effects caused by soil-type differences, in the following attributes:

1. Germination ability of seeds.
2. Size of plant and degree of erectness.
3. General vigor of vegetative parts.
4. Woodiness of the stem.

5. Depth of root system.
6. Pubescence on stems and leaves.
7. Susceptibility to drought, frost, and parasites.
8. Number of flowers, and date of flowering.

The Changing Places of Soils in Crop Production

In a thoughtful study, Simonson (1955) suggested that the changes in soils brought about over time through their use in agriculture tended to reduce differences between many good and poor soils. Chernozem soils are among the most fertile in the world. Through cultivation over a period of approximately 80 years, the North American Chernozems have lost fertility, deteriorated in structure, and lost about one-third of their original organic-matter content. Fertility depletion presumably was a sensible course of action for early settlers on these and other highly fertile soils. It seems impracticable to maintain the high level of native fertility of these soils, and a fertility level somewhat below the natural one becomes optimum under continued cultivation. In contrast, Simonson noted that soils of western Europe, closely related to the North American gray-brown podsolic group, have been improved substantially during the last 200 years of cultivation.

The level of technology in a society determines, to a great extent, the range in use-suitability of each type of soil. Many of the desert soils of southwestern United States are useful at the present time only for short-season grazing. The Chernozems of western Minnesota and eastern North Dakota can be used for small grains, corn, hay, or pasture. Even here the uses are limited, particularly by climatic factors. The red-yellow podsolic soils of the Cotton Belt are much less fertile naturally than the Chernozems, but they can produce a far greater variety of crops under present conditions. In the Chernozem region, the growing season is short and annual solar energy available is relatively low. In the southeastern part of the United States, climatic conditions are more favorable for potential crop production. It appears to be far easier to improve the podsolic soils of this area than to improve the climatic conditions of the northern Chernozem region.

The level of technology in a society may exert a more powerful effect on use-suitability of soils than do their natural characteristics. Sustained production over long periods has proven possible. Some Puerto Rican soils have been under cultivation, producing sugarcane mainly, for 400 years. Yields today are higher now than in the past. In Hawaii, some plantations have fields which have been growing sugarcane continuously for nearly

100 years, with yields today at the highest level attained. The production of lima beans, under dry land conditions in California, has been shown to maintain nearly a constant level through a period of 45 years of continuous cropping. Even in the Midwest, where rotations have been advocated since early settlement, there is a growing belief, with evidence to back this view, that many of the level, fertile Corn Belt areas can profitably be planted to corn more or less continuously so that land less suitable for corn can be used for production of other crops.

Agricultural production has increased greatly in the United States during the past two decades. This has been the result of the use of better crop varieties, better livestock, and a great advancement in the technology of production. The increase in production has not been uniform throughout the United States. In the South, the production increase from 1935 to 1950 has been 25%, whereas in the northern Great Plains, production increased approximately 14%. According to Simonson (1955), more than half of the increase for the United States as a whole has come from regions of naturally infertile soils, and perhaps one-tenth of it from the naturally fertile soils.

The conclusion reached from this study is that, on the whole, soil has less control over productivity now than it did prior to the growth of scientific knowledge and technology. The complex of management has become more important and the soil relatively less important to primary agricultural production. Conversely, the nature of the soil was and still is more important to the production of food and fiber in a primitive society than it is in a modern industrial society (Simonson, 1955).

References

1. Ackerman, F. G. and Meyers, H. E. 1943. Some factors influencing aggregation of clay-pan soils. *Soil Sci.* 55: 405–413.
2. Baver, L. D. and Farnsworth, R. B. 1940. Soil structure effects in the growth of sugar beets. *Soil Sci. Amer. Proc.* 5: 45–48.
3. Billings, W. D. 1952. The environmental complex in relation to plant growth and distribution. *Quart. Rev. Biol.* 27 (3): 251–265.
4. Blumenstock, D. I. and Thornthwaite, C. W. 1941. Climate and the world pattern. *Climate and Man.* U.S.D.A. Yearbook of Agriculture, 98–127.
5. Byers, M. G., Kellogg, C. E., Anderson, M. S. and Thorp, James. 1938. Formation of soil. *Soils and Men.* U.S.D.A. Yearbook of Agriculture, 948–978.
6. Carlson, F. A. 1925. Effect of soil structure on the character of alfalfa root systems. *Jour. Amer. Soc. Agron.* 17: 336–345.
7. Carter, G. F. and Pendleton, R. L. 1956. The humid soil: process and time. *Geog. Rev.* 46: 488–507.
8. Coile, T. S. 1952. Soil and the growth of forests. *Adv. in Agron.* 4: 329–398.

9. Daubenmire, R. F. 1959. *Plants and Environment*. Wiley, New York.
10. Dean, L. A. 1957. Plant nutrition and soil fertility. *Soil*. U.S.D.A. Yearbook of Agriculture, 80–85.
11. Hansen, T. S., Kenety, W. H., Wiggin, G. H., and Stakman, E. C. 1923. A study of damping-off disease of coniferous seedlings. *Minn. Agr. Exp. Sta. Tech. Bul.* 15.
12. Higbee, Edward. 1958. *American Agriculture: Geography, Resources, Conservation*. Wiley, New York.
13. ———. 1941. *Factors of Soil Formation*. McGraw-Hill, New York.
14. Jenny, Hans. 1950. Causes of the high nitrogen and organic matter content of certain tropical forest soils. *Soil Sci.* 69: 63–69.
15. Kellogg, C. E. 1949. Preliminary suggestions for classification of the Great Soil Groups in tropical and equatorial regions. Common. Bur. Soil Sci. Tech. Commun. No. 46: 79.
16. Klute, A. and Jacob, W. C. 1949. Physical properties of Sassafras silt loam as affected by long-time organic matter additions. *Proc. Soil Sci. Soc. Amer.* 14: 24–28.
17. Lyon, T. L., Buckman, H. O., and Brady, N. C. 1952. *The Nature and Properties of Soils*. 5th ed., Macmillan, New York.
18. Marsden-Jones, E. M. and Turrill, W. B. 1945. Sixth report of the transplant experiments of the British Ecological Society at Potterne, Wiltshire. *Jour. Ecol.* 33: 57–81.
19. Millar, C. E., Turk, L. M., and Foth, H. D. 1958. *Fundamentals of Soil Science*. 3rd ed. Wiley, New York.
20. Nicholas, D. J. D. 1961. Minor mineral nutrients. *Ann. Rev. Pl. Physiol.* 12: 63–90.
21. Norman, A. G. 1946. Recent advances in soil microbiology. *Proc. Soil Sci. Soc. Amer.* 11: 9–15.
22. Odum, Eugene P. 1959. *Fundamentals of Ecology*. 2nd. ed. Saunders, New York.
23. Oosting, H. J. 1956. *The Study of Plant Communities*. Freeman, San Francisco.
24. Patton, R. T. 1930. Factors controlling the distribution of trees in Victoria. *Roy. Soc. Victoria Proc.* 42: 154–210.
25. Polunin, N. 1960. *Introduction to Plant Geography*. McGraw-Hill, New York, Toronto, London.
26. Richards, L. A. 1947. Diagnosis and Improvement of Saline and Alkali Soils. U. S. Reg. Sal. Lab.
27. Russell, E. J. and Russell, E. W. 1950. *Soil Conditions and Plant Growth*. 8th ed. Longmans, Green, New York.
28. Russell, M. B. 1949. Methods of measuring soil structure and aeration. *Soil Sci.* 68: 25–35.
29. Scholtes, W. H., Smith, Guy D., and Riecken, F. F. 1954. Taylor County, Iowa, Soils. Govt. Print. Office, Washington, D. C.
30. Shantz, H. L. 1938. Plants as soil indicators. *Soils and Men*. U.S.D.A., Yearbook of Agriculture, 835–860.
31. Simonson, Roy W. 1955. Changing place of soils in agricultural production. *The Sci. Monthly* 81(4): 173–182.
32. ———. 1957. What soils are. *Soil*. U.S.D.A Yearbook of Agriculture, 17–31.
33. Smith, J. 1949. Distribution of tree species in the Sudan in relation to rainfall and soil texture. Sudan Ministry Agr. Bul. 4.
34. Stewart, H. W. 1927. On the effect of texture of sandy soils on the moisture supply for corn during seasons of favorable and unfavorable distribution of rainfall. *Soil Sci.* 24: 231–240.
35. Thornthwaite, C. W. 1948. An approach to a rational classification of climate. *Geog. Rev.* 38: 55–94.

36. Trewartha, G. T. 1954. *An Introduction to Climate.* McGraw-Hill, New York.
37. Veihmeyer, F. J. and Hendrickson, A. H. 1948. Soil density and root penetration. *Soil Sci.* 65: 487–493.
38. Waksman, S. A. 1952. *Soil Microbiology.* Wiley, New York.
39. Warming, E. 1909. *Oecology of Plants.* (Transl. by P. Groom and I. B. Balfour.) Clarendon, Oxford.
40. Weaver, J. E. 1919. The ecological relations of roots. Carnegie Inst. Wash. Publ. 292.
41. Wolfanger, L. A. 1930. *The Major Soil Divisions of the United States.* Wiley, New York.
42. Yang, Tien Wei and Lowe, Chas. H. J. 1956. Correlation of major vegetation climaxes with soil characteristics of the Sonoran Desert. Sci. 123: 342.

Biotic Factors

In a broad sense, the biotic factors of the plant's environment are those related directly or indirectly to living organisms. These range from soil microorganisms to man himself.

It is natural to consider the higher plants as independent, because they synthesize their own food, but we know that every plant is influenced to a degree by other organisms. The carbon dioxide used by green plants in photosynthesis is made available largely through the respiration of other organisms. The amount of heat, light, and nutrients available to a plant is determined in part by the proximity of other plants, and much of the nitrogen is made available in organic form. The environment of any organism, therefore, is in part biological and in part physical.

As was noted in Chapter 6, organisms associated together, having mutual relationships to each other and to their environment, constitute a biotic community. They make up the living part of an ecosystem. Plants, for example, are both a part of the community where they occur, and a part of the environment of other plants and animals. A dominant species often provides conditions favorable for survival of a lesser species, or it may eliminate other species. Both plants and animals serve as environmental factors which influence plant distribution and behavior. Man is, perhaps, the most important of all biological factors, because of his ability to influence or modify many factors of both his physical and biological environment.

BIOTIC POTENTIAL AND
ENVIRONMENTAL RESISTANCE

Every plant and animal species is capable of producing, over time, more offspring than can possibly survive. In ecological terms, the inherent ability of an organism to multiply may be considered the **breeding potential** or **biotic potential** (Woodbury, 1954). The biotic potential depends on mode of reproduction and fecundity (often expressed in different terms for different organisms). If all progeny do not survive there must be some preventive force or forces. Food, light, water, or even space may be insufficient for all to survive, and only those which do survive may become the parents of the succeeding generations. Forces which tend to limit the population of an organism are known collectively as **environmental resistance.** These include unfavorable factors of the physical environment and unfavorable biotic factors. If an individual, a race, or a species is able to cope with environmental resistance, it is said to have the quality of **persistence** in a given area.

Populations do not increase indefinitely. The introduction of a species

FIGURE 12-1.

Graph showing basic population growth curve and derivative curves showing opportunities for growth, rate of increase, environmental resistance, and intensity of struggle for existence. [Adapted from Struggle for Existence, *Gause, 1934, Williams and Wilkins, Baltimore.]*

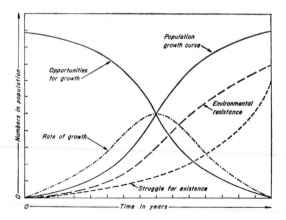

from one part of the world to another provides an opportunity for observing population growth. The cactus from North America and the jackrabbit from Europe were introduced into Australia, with the result that populations increased so rapidly that they became a serious threat to the forage resources. As noted by Woodbury, there was little environmental resistance at first. The populations grew rapidly until environmental resistance began to overtake breeding potential, and equilibrium populations were finally reached. Pearl and Reed (1920) suggested that this type of population growth follows a logistic curve. This curve and other curves showing growth rate, opportunities for growth, and curve of resistance are shown in Figure 12-1.

When a population growth curve reaches the upper limit, it means that the population has reached the maximum limit possible in a given environment. If the range is expanded, another increase may result in a still higher peak, but if the range is contracted, the population will stabilize at a lower level. In the total biotic community, populations of the several component species may fluctuate greatly, especially if conditions of the physical environment fluctuate, either irregularly or in a cyclical manner. As populations increase toward maximum limits, competitive factors brought about by the organisms themselves are of great importance.

COMPETITION, SUCCESSION, AND CLIMAX

When there is not enough of any particular requirement for survival—light, moisture, or temperature—for all demands in the same habitat, competition results. According to the principle of Gause (1934), two or more species with similar tolerances and similar ways of life cannot coexist indefinitely in the same habitat, because one of them will inevitably prove to be more efficient than the others and will crowd out or eliminate its competitors. Competition is one of the key factors in ecological succession, which may be defined as the sequence of plant communities which replace one another in a given area. Competitive factors among units of vegetation result in change in a particular direction. Typically, plant community development begins with pioneer stages which are replaced by a series of more mature stages until a relatively stable community develops which is in equilibrium with the local environment (Odum, 1959). Succession, according to Polunin (1960) often goes from less complex communities of small plants to more complex ones dominated by plants of higher life-form, or at least plants with a greater potential for competition.

The whole series of communities which develop in a given situation is known as a **sere,** and the mature, relatively stable community is called the **climax.**

Although ecologists are not in complete agreement on the nature of the forces and the consequent results of succession, it is generally agreed that succession is directional. Odum has noted that, although succession is directed by climate, climate is not its cause. Rather, succession results from the fact that action of the community itself on the habitat tends to make the area less favorable for itself and more favorable for other communities of organisms, until an equilibrium or climax stage is reached. Unidirectional succession is not necessarily inevitable, for, if the organisms of the community itself do not modify the environment, orderly succession cannot take place. As expressed by Polunin, the broad tendency of succession is from simplicity to complexity, from dominance of lower to dominance of higher life-forms which make more exacting demands on the habitat. However, retrogression to dominance of a lower life-form may occur when the habitat becomes less favorable, for example, with respect to moisture.

Secondary succession in the Piedmont region of the southeastern United States has been discussed by Odum. The principal plant dominants of the upland sere which follows the abandonment of crop land are indicated in Figure 12-2. Animals and birds usually play an important role in this succession through seed dispersal. The final stage, in relative equilibrium with the climate, is an oak-hickory forest.

Two schools of thought interpret the concept of climax somewhat differently. On one hand, the "monoclimax" idea suggests that any region has only one climax toward which all plant communities are developing.

FIGURE 12-2.

Secondary succession on the piedmont region of southeastern United States. [*Adapted from* Fundamentals of Ecology, *Odum, 2nd Ed., 1959, Saunders, Philadelphia*).

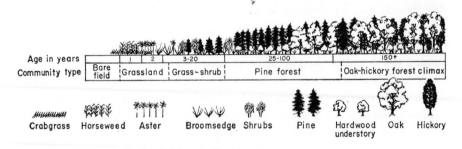

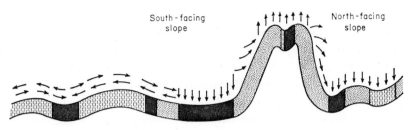

Habitat — Microclimate and Soil	Climax biotic Community	
Normal microclimate over moist soil	Maple – beech	} CLIMATIC CLIMAX
Normal microclimate over wet soil	Oak – **ash**	
Normal microclimate over dry soil	Oak – hickory	
Warmer microclimate over moist soil	Tulip – walnut	
Warmer microclimate over wet soil	Sycamore – tulip	} EDAPHIC CLIMAXES
Warmer microclimate over dry soil	Oak – chestnut	
Colder microclimate over moist soil	Elm – ash – oak	
Colder microclimate over wet soil	White spruce – balsam fir	
Colder microclimate over dry soil	Hemlock – yellow birch	

FIGURE 12-3.

Climatic climax and edaphic climaxes in southern Ontario. [Adapted from Hills, Res. Rept. 24, 1952, Ontario Dept. Lands, Ottawa, Canada.]

On the other, the "polyclimax" theory suggests that it is not realistic to assume that all communities in a given climatic region will reach the same climax when conditions of the physical habitat are variable. Odum has proposed that we may recognize a single theoretical climatic climax and a number of edaphic climaxes in a given climatic region. This concept is illustrated by an example from southern Ontario where the general climatic climax is the beech-maple community. Local conditions, including slope and soil moisture particularly, result in a series of edaphic climaxes associated with differences in microenvironment, as illustrated in Figure 12-3. It is not known whether these edaphic climaxes would eventually be replaced by the beech-maple climax, but it is known that under favorable conditions a beech-maple community may develop in 200 years or less, beginning with a plowed field (Odum, 1959).

A third concept of climax, the climax pattern hypothesis, has been discussed by Whittaker (1953). Both the mono- and polyclimax theories are rejected because they are too rigid and unrealistic. Instead, "climax is considered a steady-state of community productivity, structure, and populations, with the dynamic balance of its populations determined in relation to its site. The balance among populations shifts with changes in the environment, and climax vegetation is a pattern of populations which corresponds to the pattern of environmental gradients." This implies that climax vegetation may be more or less diverse, depending on the diversity of environments and the kinds of populations present. Whittaker notes further that there is no absolute climax for any area, and climax composition has meaning only relative to position along the environmental gradients, and to all factors of the mature ecosystem.

COMPETITION IN FIELD CROPS

Forage and Pasture Plants

Studies of competitive relationships of two or more species of forage plants have been numerous, but in most of these the roles of both intraspecific and interspecific competition have been difficult or impossible to assess. Recently, Black (1960) has attempted to evaluate the effects of plant density on yield of seedlings of red clover and alfalfa in pure stands and in associated mixed stands. Densities of 50 to 12,500 plants per square meter were chosen for pure stands. In mixtures, all combinations of 50, 250, 1250, and 6250 plants per square meter were used. Two harvests were made, at approximately 43 and 60 days after emergence, and the

effects of initial density on density and yield
at harvest were determined. It was found
that alfalfa reached a maximum yield at a
much lower density than did red clover.
Also, it was shown that at the lowest densities alfalfa outyielded red clover, but at
the high densities red clover yielded much
more than alfalfa. These results are shown
in Figure 12-4.

The relative growth rates of the two
species in pure stands were computed for
the period from emergence to harvest 1 and
for the period from harvest 1 to harvest 2. A
small increase in plant density at low plant
numbers resulted in a decrease in relative
growth rates; the rate of decrease in growth
rates declined, however, with greater increases in plant density. Black interpreted
this relationship as a function of the time at
which interplant competition reaches an in-
tensity sufficient to restrict growth of the individual plant.

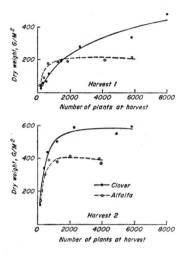

FIGURE 12-4.

*The effect of planting density
on dry weight of alfalfa and red
clover grown in pure stands.
[Adapted from Black, Okios
11:26–42, 1960.]*

It was found that in mixtures the growth of one species was depressed
when that species was present at high densities, and the other present at
low densities, and was increased when that species was present at low
densities and the other at high densities. Black concluded that the data
confirm the proposition of Clements, Weaver, and Hanson (1929) that
the most intense competition occurred among individual plants which
were the most similar.

A common example of interspecified competition is found in the use of
companion crops for establishing small-seeded legumes and grasses. For
generations it has been common farm practice to plant small grain, peas,
or flax with new seedings of alfalfa, clovers, or other forage crops. The
older term "nurse crop" implied that the small grain in some way protected
the new seeding or nursed it along in some way until it was strong enough
to shift for itself. This idea was erroneous, for the most part, because the
small grain served as a direct competitor for moisture, light, space, and
soil nutrients. There are instances in which some protection may be af-
forded the tiny legume seedlings in a new planting. On soils of rather fine
texture, a wind may blow soil and sand particles across the field just above
the surface. A growth of four inches of oats on this field would serve to
cut down on wind damage to young legume seedlings which might other-

wise be cut off at the ground level by the driving sand and soil. In the main, however, the effects are competitive rather than cooperative.

The comparative survival of two forage species planted at widely varying rates was studied by Eisele and Aikman (1933). Timothy and red clover were planted in various mixtures, and two years later it was found that there was a remarkable constancy in the number of plants surviving regardless of the species planted or the rates sown. For example, timothy planted at eight pounds per acre had approximately 2360 seeds per square meter available for possible establishment. Red clover at seven pounds per acre included 390 seeds per square meter. The surviving plants two years later, from such a seeding mixture, included 66 timothy plants and 67 red clover plants per square meter.

General relationships between stand and yield of forage legumes have been studied by Willard (1931). Over a period of seven years with 520 samples, the correlation in alfalfa between stand and yield of tops was $r = 0.28$; for sweetclover it was $r = 0.29$. A higher correlation was obtained for stand and yield of roots: $r = 0.55$ in alfalfa and $r = 0.45$ in sweetclover.

Under tropical conditions, Wilsie (1935) found a high correlation between plant population and yield of seed of blue lupine, within the range of from 2178 to 17,424 plants per acre. In pigeon pea (*Cajanus indicus*), however, there was little difference in seed yield from stands of 1100 plants per acre and 14,000 plants per acre. The intraspecific competitive effect in the latter case appeared to be mainly one of the suppression of branching in dense stands.

The ecological effects of competing ability have been demonstrated in the southern states through the introduction of Kudzu, *Pueraria lobata*. This legume, planted primarily for its value in controlling erosion, and secondarily for forage purposes, has spread so rapidly and is so competitive as to be considered undesirable in many locations (Oosting, 1958).

Cereal Crops

Some examples of competition in cereals were discussed under natural selection in Chapter 3. In plant breeding, the relative competitive ability of individual varieties, strains, or genotypes is highly important. The competitive ability of individual plants of rice as related to their chromosome numbers and degree of hybridity has been investigated by Sakai (1957) and Sakai and Utiyamada (1957).

Local strains of barley were evaluated for competitive ability by Gotoh (1956). Data on number of tillers, weight of heads, and weight of whole plants indicated that some barley strains were very competitive, giving higher yields and higher ratings in competition than when grown in pure stands.

Many studies of intraspecific competition in corn have been conducted in an attempt to show the relationship between plant population and yield. In general, on soils at high levels of fertility, grain yields tend to increase as plant populations are increased from 8000 to 16,000 or more plants per acre. In Illinois, Lang, Pendleton, and Dungan (1956) reported that nine hybrids, when grown at high levels of fertility, produced increased yields of grain with population increases from 4000 to 20,000 plants per acre. However, at low fertility levels, 12,000 plants per acre appeared to be optimum. In Iowa, Duncan (1954) found increases in grain yields of corn with population increases from 8000 to 24,000 plants per acre on highly fertile soils. In the southern states, data by Long (1953) and by Thomas (1956) have indicated optimum populations of 12,000 plants per acre with applications of about 90 pounds of nitrogen per acre.

Using the mutant "compact," which grows to a height approximately half that of normal corn, Sowell, Ohlrogge, and Nelson (1961) showed that cessation of vegetative growth in the "compact" strain occurs approximately at the time of flowering. When grown under a high population stress (52,000 plants per acre) in comparison with "Hy" normal inbred, the "compact" mutant is able to fruit because, following cessation of vegetative growth, the reproductive functions only are supported.

Computing Competition Effects

A mathematical model was developed by Odum (1959) to illustrate the effects of competition. The growth rate of each population is equal to the unlimited (specific) rate minus its own self-crowding effects (which increase as its population increases) minus the detrimental effect of other species, N_2 (which also increases as the numbers of both species N and N_2 increase):

$$\underset{\substack{\text{(growth} \\ \text{rate)}}}{\frac{\Delta N}{\Delta t}} = \underset{\substack{\text{(unlimited} \\ \text{rate)}}}{rN} - \underset{\substack{\text{(self-crowding} \\ \text{effects)}}}{\frac{r}{k}N^2} - \underset{\substack{\text{(detrimental effects} \\ \text{of other species)}}}{CN_2N}$$

As Odum has suggested, there may be several possible results. If "C" (competition effect) is small for both species so that the interspecific effects are less than the intraspecific effects, both species may be able to live together nicely. If "C" is large, however, the species exerting the greater effect will tend to eliminate its competitor or force it into another ecological niche. Thus, through the use of this model we can explain

the operation of *Gause's Principle* that species having the same environmental requirements cannot live together in exactly the same niche because of competition.

The self-crowding effects expressed in Odum's formula as $(r/k)N^2$
represent the intraspecific competition, the ecological importance of which
should not be overlooked. It cannot be emphasized too strongly that
studies of the effects of environmental factors on the growth and development of individual spaced plants may yield little information on the effects
of those factors on plant populations of various degrees of density. In
most problems of crop production it is not the yield of the single plant
in which we are most interested, but rather in the yield per acre of a
population of closely-spaced plants which are under stress of competition.
This interplant competition drastically affects the size and shape of the
plant, its physiology, and its final yield of seed or forage. It poses one of
the major problems facing breeders of forage plants because performance
of single plant selections and their progenies in spaced plantings usually
gives a poor indication of the performance of such progenies under sward
conditions.

Weeds, Universal Competitor

An almost universal example of competition is that of weeds, which
compete for space and nutrients and cause major nuisances by choking
waterways, destroying wild life habitats, and making large areas of land
practically useless. Associations of weeds and crops are usually complex,
and include many species of weeds and one crop species. The ecological
effects of weeds vary tremendously, depending on environmental conditions
and on man's management practices. To understand the nature of the
effect of weeds, the ecology of both the crop and the weeds concerned
must be understood (Robbins, Crafts, and Raynor, 1952; Staniforth, 1961).

Parasites

A plant parasite is dependent on its host for its existence; it is therefore
an environmental factor in the biotic community. Under conditions which
are near the optimum for the host plant, some parasitism can exist more
or less indefinitely without serious effects. Common examples of this
situation include parasitic fungi and bacteria which are nearly always
present. The biotic community may not appear to suffer greatly from their
presence unless the environment becomes extremely favorable for their

rapid increase. This could occur through a change in some factor of the physical environment, or through a change in populations of some of the other organisms of the community. Noteworthy examples are found in the rapid increase in little-known or minor races of rust fungi infecting wheat and oats when dominant races of the organism are practically eliminated through the introduction of disease-resistant varieties (Stakman, 1938; Stakman, *et al*, 1943; McCubbin, 1946; Stanton and Murphy, 1949; Stakman and Christensen, 1953; Johnson, 1961).

Chestnut blight disease has almost eliminated the chestnut tree in the eastern United States, with the result that oak has become the dominant tree (Anderson and Rankin, 1914). Another parasite, *Graphium ulmi*, responsible for the devastating Dutch Elm disease, has had a marked effect on the ecology and distribution of the American elm (Clinton and McCormick, 1936).

Losses from plant diseases are difficult to estimate, but it was suggested by Wood (1953) that an annual loss in the United States alone of three billion dollars might be somewhat realistic. Diseases which attack basic food crops, such as cereals, especially wheat, rice and corn, potatoes, and others, are of great national concern. Epidemics in important centers of production can cause scarcity, with serious national and possibly international consequences.

A parasitic viny plant which causes considerable damage in small grain, flax, red clover, and alfalfa is dodder, *Cuscuta* spp. Dodder is a small twining herb which climbs the upright stems of the host plant. Adventitious roots develop from the stem of the parasite and penetrate the stem of the host. Water is extracted from the host plant and the dodder eventually produces flowers and seeds. After contact with the host has been firmly established, the dodder plant loses its connection with the soil.

The mistletoes, *Loranthaceae* spp., are common parasites which grow rooted to branches of trees. Haustoria serve to connect the plant to the vascular tissue of the host. In mistletoe we do find an abundance of chlorophyll, and so should possibly consider it only partially parasitic in its habits (Daubenmire, 1959).

SYMBIOSIS

Nitrogen Fixation

One of the most important kinds of interaction between species is symbiosis or "living together." The symbiotic relationship between legumes and rhizobia, which results in nitrogen fixation, is of great significance to

agriculture. In considering the world's nitrogen balance, it has been estimated that annual losses of nitrogen amount to 24 million tons or more.
These losses come about through removal by harvested crops, erosion,
leaching, and removal by grazing animals. To replace these losses, gains
of 3.8 million tons annually may be added by fertilizers and manures,
3.5 million tons by rainfall and irrigation waters, 4.4 million tons by non-
symbiotic nitrogen fixation, and 5.5 million tons by symbiotic nitrogen
fixation. This still leaves an annual deficit of 6.8 million tons (Burris,
1955). These estimates suggest that nitrogen fixation, including both non-
symbiotic and symbiotic, is of paramount importance in helping to
maintain the world's nitrogen balance.

For more than 400 years, legumes have been known to bear nodules,
but it was not until the classical work of Hellriegel and Wilfarth (1888)
that the complexity of the symbiotic relationship began to be understood.

In a survey of nodulation among legumes, Allen and Allen (1947) reported that 887 species in 167 genera were nodulated, and that 77 species
in 17 genera appeared to lack nodules. One of the most noted of the
latter is the genus *Cassia*, which is found widely distributed in tropical and
subtropical areas.

Important contributions on the significance of symbiotic nitrogen fixation,
and the mechanism of the process, have been reported by Thornton (1930);
Wilson (1940); Virtanen (1945, 1947); Nutman (1948, 1949); Waksman
(1952); Harris (1953); and others.

In an effective association between legumes and rhizobia there are
characteristic patterns of nodule development. Annuals tend to large, pinkish,
fleshy nodules singly or in clusters about the tap roots or the first-formed
lateral roots. Biennials and perennials may have smaller root nodules, elon-
gated, clustered, and widely distributed.

Nutman has suggested these stages in normal symbiosis development:
(1) initial root hair infection, (2) proliferation of host cells and development of infection threads, (3) intracellular invasion of the host by bacteria
from infection threads, (4) multiplication of bacteria (rod form) within
the host cytoplasm, (5) hypertrophic growth of individual bacteria (bac-
teroid formation), (6) functional symbiosis, (7) senescence and degenera-
tion of nodule.

If healthy nodules are sliced longitudinally, a central area is exposed
which contains bright pink or scarlet tissue. This color is indicative of
the presence of a hemoprotein similar to hemoglobin of mammalian blood.
The identification of hemoglobin in nodules, through its characteristic
absorption band maxima of 575 mμ and 540 mμ, was made by Kubo
(1939), who compared it with hemoglobin of the horse. Nodule hemoglobin

appeared to have the typical hemoprotein characteristic of taking up and giving off oxygen. It was found to be present in nodules of 24 common legumes studied by Kubo.

Additional research by Keilin and Wang (1945), Virtanen (1945), and Little and Burris (1947), confirmed the identification of hemoglobin in nodules and indicated that it differed from blood hemoglobin mainly in a difference in its amino acid composition. Although the exact function of hemoglobin in nitrogen fixation is not completely understood, its role in storing and carrying oxygen appears to be basic. In nitrogen fixation the energy required is supplied by respiratory oxidation. Molecular nitrogen is reduced to the ammonia form, from which it changes rapidly to amino acids (Bonner and Galston, 1952).

Virtanen (1945, 1947) showed that there was a high degree of correlation between hemoglobin content of nodules and intensity of nitrogen fixation. *Rhizobium* cells alone cannot synthesize hemoglobin nor fix nitrogen, nor can the legume root tissue by itself. The nodules, however, which contain cells of *Rhizobium* species as well as root tissue, provide the essentials necessary for the synthesis of hemoglobin and the fixation of atmospheric nitrogen. It is believed that the *Rhizobium* cells induce growth and multiplication of the proliferating cells characteristic in nodule formation, and either directly or indirectly supply the factors necessary for synthesis of hemoglobin. It was observed by Virtanen (1947) that as nodules grew older, or were kept in darkness for several days, they changed from red to green in color. Under these conditions, active fixation of nitrogen practically ceased.

The effectiveness of fixation of gaseous nitrogen by rhizobia varies widely with the bacterial strain and the genotype of the legume. The genus *Rhizobium* has been divided into a number of groups, based in part on their specificity in effectively inoculating a legume species or group of species. The ordinary classification of rhizobia and legumes into cross-inoculation groups, however, has never been satisfactory. A new basis for classification was proposed by Norris (1956). He pointed out that both legumes and the associated bacteria originated in the tropics, and that even today two-thirds of all legumes are still confined to tropical regions. As the legumes became specialized through natural selection and migration, some spread to the temperate areas. Finally such genera as *Medicago* and *Trifolium* emerged, and their bacterial requirements were met only by a few highly specialized strains of *Rhizobium*. The original less-specialized legumes can be inoculated by a wide range of *Rhizobium* strains. On this basis, two groups may be recognized: (1) the ancestral type (a more or less universal type), and (2) the calicole type, which requires more than a trace of calcium for growth (a highly specialized type). Norris (1959) has shown evidence also that the growth of some of the specialized *Rhizobium* strains may be more dependent on magnesium than on calcium.

Plants benefit from symbiotic nitrogen fixation mainly through the use of nitrogen made available through the senescence and decay of nodules. Under some conditions of cool temperatures and long days, however, Virtanen, *et al* (1935, 1937) found evidence of nitrogen excretion from the legume before nodule decomposition had taken place.

Although the total amount of nitrogen fixed by a well-inoculated legume crop varies greatly, depending on the species of legume, the soil and other environmental conditions, as well as the management of the crop, some rough approximations may be given. Alfalfa has been shown to fix as much as 200 to 250 pounds of nitrogen per acre per year, and red clover, from 100 to 150 pounds (Collison, Beattie and Harlan, 1933; Lyon and Bizzell, 1934).

The amount of nitrogen fixed tends to increase with increased light intensity, increased O_2, increased partial pressure of CO_2, and an extraneous supply of carbohydrate. Nitrogen fixation may be decreased by the presence of a source of readily assimilable nitrogen. Under most field conditions, therefore, nitrogen fixation by legumes probably ranges from 50 pounds to 150 pounds per acre (and often less), rather than the higher amounts suggested.

Nitrogen fixation has been found in a number of nonleguminous plants, and some are believed to assimilate atmospheric nitrogen symbiotically. Nodules on the roots of these plants vary from what appears to be simply modified or dwarfed lateral roots to a more regular nodule formation. Waksman (1952) has noted that some of these nodules are perennial, branch in all directions, and finally develop into roundish aggregates of considerable size. In some cases, bacteria which closely resemble the *Rhizobium* group appear to be responsible for the symbiotic relationship and nitrogen fixation. Species known to fix nitrogen include silver berry (*Elaeagnus* spp.), alder (*Alnus glutinosa*), sweet gale (*Myrica gale*), and *Casuarina* species. (Humm, 1944; Ferguson and Bond, 1953; Shields, 1953; Bond and Scott, 1955). In studies with alder, Ferguson and Bond found that nodulated plants grew well in water cultures without combined nitrogen. Nodules formed over a pH range of 5.4 to 7.0, and after nodulation best growth was obtained at pH 4.2 to 5.4, considerably lower than the optimum pH for the bacteria concerned. The O_2 requirement of the nodules was high, and the nitrogen fixation per unit dry weight of nodular tissue was found to exceed that of most legumes under similar conditions.

Among lower plants, some of the blue-green algae, especially *Nostoc* species, are important in nitrogen fixation. In aquatic and wet-land culture, such as flooded rice, for example, nitrogen fixation by the blue-green algae probably is of great value (Waksman, 1952; Burris, 1955; Bond and Scott, 1955).

Mycorhizae

An association of plants found to be of great importance in forestry is the development of mycorhizae. These are compound structures developed through combination of fungal mycelia and roots, or other underground parts. Fungi taking part in this association usually are either basidiomycetes or phycomycetes.

Pine rootlets, according to Hatch (1937), are of two kinds morphologically: long roots (main axes) and short, lateral roots. In soils of high fertility the small roots are not mycorhizal. Root-hair zones of the long roots absorb most of the water and nutrients taken from the soil. In soils deficient in N, P, K, or Ca, however, the long roots appear to have insufficient absorptive powers. Under these conditions short roots invaded by fungi tend to take over absorption of water and nutrients. Because of the invasion by fungi, these short roots are stimulated to branch extensively. They thus become mycorhizae which have a high efficiency of absorption because of the extent of surface exposed. The relationship between tree and fungus seems to be obligatory. The pine takes water and nutrients from the fungal hyphae, and the fungus obtains food and growth substances from the tree roots (Levisohn, 1956; Melin, 1953). Pines introduced into areas where soils are not highly fertile and symbiotic fungi are absent are most likely to fail. Miller (1938) suggested that long-continued deforestation could result in the practical elimination of fungi favorable for mycorhizal development. This presents an important consideration in attempts at reforestation of such areas.

ANIMALS AS BIOTIC FACTORS

Soil Animals

The soil fauna, including protozoa, nematodes, rotifers, snails, earthworms, and insects constitute a highly important part of the environment for plant roots. All of these organisms contribute to organic decomposition and use a portion of the products for food (Fenton, 1947).

Earthworms are particularly influential in changing soil conditions. Burrowing facilitates aeration and drainage, and the ingestion of organic matter and mineral matter results in a constant mixing of these materials in the soil (Waksman, 1952). This probably tends to make for better plant growth.

Crop and Forest Insects

Many insects present in plant communities remain in a relatively stable balance without serious damage to plants. They contribute substantially to the maintenance of organic matter in the soil, since their feeding and burrowing in the soil tends to facilitate decomposition and distribution of organic matter.

Occasionally, when environmental conditions favor rapid increases in populations, insects cause great destruction to field, garden, and orchard crops. Haeussler (1952) reported estimates of losses from specific insects in the United States. Crop losses by grasshopper damage are believed to average 20 million dollars each year, by the European corn borer (*Pyrausta nubilalis*) 75 to 100 million dollars per year, and by the small grain greenbug (*Toxoptera graminum*), 75 million per year. Cotton insects have been especially damaging. The National Cotton Council estimates a 900-million-dollar loss in cotton lint and seed in 1950.

In the United States Forest Service, damage by insects yearly has been estimated to be as great as that from losses by fire. The spruce bud worm, Engleman spruce beetle, Douglas fir beetle, and southern pine beetle have been particularly destructive to our forest resources.

Beneficial Insects

Many crop plants, including fruits, legumes, buckwheat, crucifers, and cucurbits, are pollinated, primarily by insects. Bees and wasps are probably the pollinators of greatest importance, but flies, beetles, moths, and butterflies do considerable pollination. Several species of bees are valuable assets to the horticulturist and the producer of legume seed. Both red clover and alfalfa are pollinated effectively by several of the bumblebees, *Bombus* spp. Some of the solitary bees, especially the alkali bee, *Nomia* spp., and the leaf cutters, *Megachile* spp., are highly effective in pollinating alfalfa. Two or three decades ago, the abundance of wild bees in certain new production areas, especially in Utah, Idaho, Washington, and parts of western Canada, made these areas highly favored for alfalfa and other legume seed production. With intensification of cultivation and destruction of the natural habitats of wild bees, seed production began to decline. Coupled with this loss of effective pollinators, the prevalence of destructive insects, especially *Lygus* species, resulted in a drastic drop in seed yields in many locations. More recently, with satisfactory control of *Lygus* bugs and greater attention toward restoration of nesting sites for wild bees, seed yields have improved. Today, in some of the irrigated valleys of central and eastern Washington where wild bee populations are high, seed yields of alfalfa as high as 1000 to 1200 pounds per acre are not at all uncommon.

Honeybees are effective pollinators of certain fruit crops, but are rather inefficient in pollinating alfalfa and red clover. Nectar is often obtained from legume flowers without effecting pollination, and only if the bees are collecting pollen do they become efficient in pollination. An exception to this generalization appears to be the relative effectiveness of honeybees in increasing the production of alfalfa seed in the Central Valley of California. With weather conditions sunny and warm, populations of wild bees low, and few other plants competing for the attention of the bees, the addition of honeybee colonies to alfalfa seed fields has proven profitable.

Small Animals

Many small animals, including rabbits, prairie dogs, ground squirrels, gophers, and field mice constitute an important ecological factor. They effect changes in the environment by consuming green plants, burrowing, soil mixing, and other operations. Losses to forage on range lands, particularly in semiarid or arid regions, may be indeed serious. Taylor (1935) estimated that jackrabbits in southern Arizona often consumed from 25% to 55% of the forage present on the range. In Australia, Stead (1935) reported that rabbits, which were introduced originally for sporting purposes, had multiplied so rapidly that they constituted a serious menace to forage resources.

Small rodents such as mice often cause extensive damage to field and garden crops. In the midwest, field mice often become sufficiently numerous to cause substantial losses to red clover and alfalfa which are covered by snow. The extent of this kind of damage fluctuates with the build-up of populations, which may become rapid when foxes, skunks, and other predators are too few to keep the populations of mice in reasonable ecological balance.

A remarkable ecological change is often caused by animals, such as beavers, operating in a different manner. Through the felling of trees, watercourses are dammed, ponds or marshy valleys turned into lakes, and the general aspects of ecosystems altered greatly.

Large Animals

The ecological consequences of biotic factors as related to our forage resources are recognized best in the development of the practices used in range management. Under natural conditions, the composition of vegetation of the range was determined largely by the climatic conditions of the region. Thus, a tallgrass prairie species such as big bluestem, *Andropogon gerardi*, was dominant in portions of Illinois and Iowa; little bluestem, *Andropogon scoparius*, was prevalent in western Iowa and eastern Nebraska and Kansas; the grama grasses, *Bouteloua* species, were dominant where annual rainfall was 16 inches or less; and finally sagebrush, *Artemisia* species, short-lived grasses, and desert shrubs predominated in the arid regions.

Plants vary as to the season of the year when grazing can be practiced to best advantage, and vary in the degree and frequency of grazing they can withstand and still recover. Big bluestem, for example, is a late-starting, warm-weather producer, and may easily be ruined by continuous and close grazing, especially if grazing is started early.

Grazing and browsing animals vary, too, particularly as to their eating habits. Cattle and horses usually prefer grass, sheep often prefer forbs in preference to grasses, and goats and deer do a great deal of browsing on leaves and twigs of broad-leaved woody plants.

Odum (1959) has stressed that no phase of applied ecology is of more importance to the west and to the United States as a whole than the management of the range. The problem, which is not easy to solve, is to determine a system of management that maintains a good ecological balance and continued maximum productivity. This has been emphasized by Sampson and Malmsten (1926), McIlvain and Savage (1954), Stoddart and Smith (1955), Harlan (1956), and others. Overgrazing is one of the more serious aspects of range management, for it causes stand depletion, changes in botanical composition (usually from desirable to less desirable species), and an increase in hazards of erosion.

Moderate grazing, on the other hand, is beneficial to the range. If the ecology of shifts in plant population is well known, management can be intelligently applied to maintain approximate botanical composition. Harlan has indicated that maximum sustained production is usually obtained at some stage below a grassland climax. Frequent range surveys to indicate any marked changes in the range condition should be most useful. The practice of deferred grazing is used widely if some of the important dominant species are unduly injured when grazed at certain critical periods of the year. Areas deferred are rotated in a systematic manner, a popular system in some areas being to defer one-third of the range for two consecutive years, then another third for two years, etc. (Harlan, 1956).

Grazing pressure may be used deliberately to control certain less desirable species. Weedy, short-lived grasses such as *Bromus secalinus*, *B. tectorum*, *B. commutatus*, *Hordeum murinum*, and *H. jubatum* may be overgrazed heavily to permit the reestablishment of greater numbers of the more desirable grasses.

Within a given season, continuous or rotational grazing is a controversial issue. Livestock gains often have been as high or higher under continuous grazing, but there are many indications of improvement in botanical composition over long periods of time through rotational grazing (Rogler, 1951; McIlvain and Savage, 1951; Harlan, 1956).

Perennials suffer the least damage from grazing if new growth is not removed until the plant has had sufficient time to restore at least part of the underground reserves which may have become depleted in building new photosynthetic leaf area. This is an important reason for the consideration of a system of deferred rotational grazing.

References

1. Allen, O. N. and Allen, E. K. 1947. A survey of nodulation among leguminous plants. *Soil Sci. Soc. Amer. Proc.* 12: 203–208.
2. Anderson, P. J. and Rankin, W. H. 1914. Endothia canker of chestnut. Cornell Univ. Agr. Exp. Sta. Bul. 347.
3. Black, J. N. 1960. An assessment of the role of planting density in competition between red clover and lucerne in the early vegetative stage. *Okios* 11(1): 26–42.
4. Bond, G. and Scott, D. D. 1955. An examination of some symbiotic systems for fixation of nitrogen. *Ann. Bot.* 19: 66–77.
5. Bonner, James and Galston, Arthur W. 1952. *Principles of Plant Physiology.*
6. Burris, R. H. 1955. Nitrogen fixation. Lecture at Ames, Iowa, Nov. 14.
7. Clements, F. E., Weaver, J. E., and Hanson, H. C. 1929. *Plant Competition.* Carnegie Institution, Washington.
8. Clinton, G. P. and McCormick, F. A. 1936. Dutch elm disease, *Graphium ulnii.* Conn. Agr. Exp. Sta. Bul. 389.
9. Collison, R. C., Beattie, H. C. and Harlan, J. D. 1933. Mineral and water relations and final nitrogen balance in leguminous and non-leguminous crop rotations for a period of 16 years. N. Y. (State) Agr. Exp. Sta. Bul. 212.
10. Daubenmire, R. F. 1959. *Plants and Environment.* 2nd ed. Wiley, New York.
11. Duncan, E. R. 1954. Influences of varying plant population, soil fertility, and hybrid on corn yields. *Soil Sci. Soc. Amer. Proc.* 18: 437–440.
12. Eisele, H. F. and Aikman, J. M. 1933. Development and survival of species and varieties in planted species. *Ecol.* 14: 123–135.
13. Fenton, G. R. 1947. The soil fauna. *Jour. Ecol.* 16: 76–93.

14. Ferguson, T. P. and Bond, G. 1953. Observations on the formation and function of the root nodules of *Alnus glutinosa* (L.) Gaertn. *Ann. Bot.* 17: 175–188.

15. Gause, G. F. 1934. *The Struggle for Existence.* Williams and Wilkins, Baltimore.

16. Gotoh, K. 1956. Competitive ability of local strains of the barley variety, Hosogara No. 2. *Jap. Jour. Gen.* 31: 1–8.

17. Haeussler, G. J. 1952. Losses caused by insects. *Yearbook of Agriculture, Insects.* U. S. Dept. Agr., Washington, D. C.

18. Harlan, Jack. 1956. *Theory and Dynamics of Grassland Agriculture.* Van Nostrand, New York.

19. Harris, J. R. 1953. The significance of symbiotic nitrogen fixation. In *Legumes in Agriculture,* F.A.O. of United Nations, Rome.

20. Hatch, A. B. 1937. The physical basis of mycotrophy in *Pinus. Black Rock For. Bul.* 6.

21. Hellriegel, H. and Wilfarth, H. 1888. Untersuchungen über die Stickstoffnahrung der Gramineen und Leguminosen. Zeit. des Vereins f. d. Rübensucher-Industrie.

22. Hills, G. A. 1952. The classification and evaluation of site for forestry. Res. Rept. 24, Ontario Dept. Lands and Forests, Ottawa, Canada.

23. Humm, H. J. 1944. Bacterial leaf nodules. *Jour. N. Y. Bot. Gard.* 45: 193–199.

24. Johnson, T. 1961. Man-guided evolution in plant rusts. *Sci.* 133: 357–362.

25. Keilin, D. and Wang, Y. L. 1945. Haemoglobin in the root nodules of leguminous plants. *Nature* 155: 227–229.

26. Kubo, Heido. 1939. Über hämprotein ans den Wurzelknöllchen von Leguminosen. *Acta Phytochim.* 11: 195–200.

27. Lang, A. L., Pendleton, J. W., and Dungan, G. H. 1956. Influence of population and nitrogen levels on yield and protein content of nine corn hybrids. *Agron. Jour.* 48: 284–289.

28. Levisohn, I. 1956. Growth stimulation of forest tree seedlings by the activity of free-living mycorrhizal mycelia. *Forestry* 29: 53–59.

29. Little, H. N. and Burris, R. H. 1947. Activity of the red pigment from leguminous root nodules. *Jour. Amer. Chem. Soc.* 69: 838–841.

30. Long, O. H. 1953. Nitrogen and spacing experiments with corn. Tenn. Agr. Exp. Sta. Bul. 232.

31. Lyon, T. L. and Bizzell, J. A. 1934. A comparison of several legumes with respect to nitrogen accretion. *Jour. Amer. Soc. Agron.* 26: 651–656.

32. McCubbin, W. A. 1946. Preventing plant disease introduction. *Bot. Rev.* 12: 101–139.

33. ———. 1951. Eight-year comparisons of continuous and rotational grazing in the Southern Plains Experimental Range. *Jour. Range Mgt.* 4: 42–47.

34. McIlvain, E. H. and Savage, D. A. 1954. Progress in range improvement. *Adv. in Agron.* 6: 1–65.

35. Melin, E. 1953. Physiology of mycorrhizal relations in plants. *Ann. Rev. Pl. Physiol.* 4: 325–346.

36. Miller, F. H. 1938. The influence of mycorrhizae on the growth of shortleaf pine seedlings. *Jour. For.* 36: 526–527.

37. Norris, D. O. 1956. Legumes and rhizobia symbiosis. *Emp. Jour. Exp. Agr.* 24: 247–270.

38. ———. 1959. The role of calcium and magnesium in the nutrition of Rhizobia. *Austr. Jour. Agr. Res.* 10: 651–698.

39. Nutman, P. S. 1948. Physiological studies of nodule formation. I. The relation between nodulation and lateral root formation in red clover. *Ann. Bot.* 12: 81–96.

40. ———. 1949. Nuclear and cytoplasmic inheritance of resistance to infection by nodule bacteria in red clover. *Heredity* 3: 263–291.

41. Odum, Eugene P. 1959. *Fundamentals of Ecology.* Saunders, Philadelphia.

42. Oosting, Henry J. 1958. *The Study of Plant Communities*. Freeman, San Francisco.

43. Pearl, R. and Reed, L. J. 1920. On the rate of growth of the population of the United States since 1790 and its mathematical representation. Proc. Natl. Acad. Sci. U. S. 6: 275.

44. Polunin, N. 1960. *Introduction to Plant Geography*. McGraw-Hill, New York.

45. Robbins, W. W., Crafts, A. S., and Raynor, R. N. 1952. *Weed Control: A Textbook and Manual*. McGraw-Hill, New York.

46. Rogler, G. A. 1951. A 25-year comparison of continuous and rotational grazing in the Northern Plains. *Jour. Range Mgt.* 4: 35–41.

47. Sakai, K. 1957. Effect on competition of a varying number of competing and non-competing individuals. *Jour. Gen.* 55: 227–234.

48. ——— and Utiyamada, H. 1957. Chromosome number, hybridity and competitive ability in *Oryza sativa* L. *Jour. Gen.* 55: 235–240.

49. Sampson, A. W. and Malmsten, H. E. 1926. Grazing periods and forage production in the national forests. U.S.D.A. Bul. 1405.

50. Shields, Lora M. 1953. Nitrogen sources of seed plants and environmental influences affecting the nitrogen cycle. *Bot. Rev.* 19: 321–376.

51. Sowell, W. F., Ohlrogge, A. J., and Nelson, O. E., Jr. 1961. Growth and fruiting of compact and Hy normal corn types under a high population stress. *Agron. Jour.* 53: 25–28.

52. Stakman, E. C. 1938. Plant disease fungi constantly evolving new types. *Sci.* 88: 438–439.

53. ———, Loegering, W. Q., Cassell, R. C., and Hines, L. 1943. Population trends of physiologic races of *Puccinia tritici* in the United States for the period 1930–1941. *Phytopath.* 33: 884–898.

54. Stakman, E. C. and Christensen, J. J. 1953. Problems of variability in fungi. *Plant Disease, The Yearbook of Agriculture*. U. S. Dept. Agr., Washington, D. C.

55. Staniforth, D. 1961. Crop-weed ecology in relation to weed control research. Paper presented at 14th Sou. Weed Conference, St. Petersburg, Fla. Jan. 18.

56. Stanton, T. R. and Murphy, H. C. 1949. New oat varieties make good in '48. What's New in Crops and Soils 1(5): 5–9.

57. Stead, D. G. 1935. *The Rabbit in Australia*. Winn and Co., Sydney.

58. Stoddart, L. A. and Smith, A. D. 1955. *Range Management*. 2nd ed. McGraw-Hill, New York.

59. Taylor, W. P. 1935. The relation of jack rabbits to grazing in southern Arizona. *Jour. For.* 33: 490–498.

60. Thomas, Winfred. 1956. Effect of plant population and rates of fertilizer nitrogen on average weight of ears and yield of corn in the South. *Agron. Jour.* 48: 228–230.

61. Thornton, H. G. 1930. Early development of the root nodule of lucerne (*Medicago sativa*, L.). *Ann. Bot.* 44: 385–392.

62. Virtanen, A. I. and von Hausen, S. 1935. Effect of air content of the medium on the function of the nodule and on the excretion of nitrogen. *Jour. Agr. Sci.* 25: 278–296.

63. ———, and Laine, T. 1937. Excretion of nitrogen in associated cultures of legumes and non-legumes. *Jour. Agr. Sci.* 27: 584–610.

64. Virtanen, A. I. 1945. Symbiotic nitrogen fixation. *Nature* 155: 747–748.

65. ———. 1947. On the relation between nitrogen fixation and leghaemoglobin content of leguminous root nodules. *Acta Chim. Scand.* 1: 90–111.

66. Waksman, S. A. 1952. *Soil Microbiology*. Wiley, New York.

67. Whittaker, R. H. 1953. A consideration of climax theory: the climax as a population and a pattern. *Ecol. Monogr.* 23: 41–78.
68. Willard, C. J. 1931. The correlation between stand and yield in alfalfa and sweetclover. *Jour. Agr. Res.* 43:461–464.
69. Wilsie, C. P. 1935. Seed production studies with legumes in Hawaii. *Jour. Amer. Soc. Agron.* 27: 784–790.
70. Wilson, P. W. 1940. *The Biochemistry of Symbiotic Nitrogen Fixation.* Univ. Wis. Press.
71. Wood, Jessie I. 1953. Three billion dollars a year. In *Plant Diseases—The Yearbook of Agriculture.* U. S. Govt. Print. Office, Washington, D. C.
72. Woodbury, A. M. 1954. *Principles of General Ecology.* Blakiston, New York.

Classification of
Climates

INTRODUCTION

The importance of climatic factors in the distribution of plants has been emphasized. The principal elements of weather and climate—temperature, precipitation, humidity, winds, and air pressure—have been given major consideration in Part II of this book. Climate as a whole, however, is made up of a composite or generalization of the variety of day-to-day weather conditions. In this sense, climate has been mentioned but not described in any detail. Climate is not just average weather, for variations from the mean are just as important as the mean itself. As was pointed out by Kendrew (1949), "no picture of climate is at all true unless it is painted in all the colors of the constant variation of weather and the changes of season which are the really prominent features."

The variation in weather from day to day, place to place, and season to season is caused by a number of climatic controls (Trewartha, 1954). These include latitude or sun, distribution of land and water, semipermanent low- and high-pressure cells, winds, altitude, mountain barriers, ocean currents, and storms of various kinds. Variations in amount, intensity, and seasonal distribution of temperature, precipitation and humidity, air pressure, and winds, as they are determined by the climatic controls, furnish the basis for the existence of a variety of climates.

By classification—recognizing similarities between individual types, and then grouping individuals into classes—some degree of simplicity and order may be brought out of a large number of individual and slightly different climates. A simple and reliable classification of climates is highly useful to the student of crop ecology. It furnishes a basis for relating the specific environmental requirements and tolerances of crop plants to their actual distribution and potential possibilities throughout the world.

Trewartha (1954) has defined a **climatic region** as any portion of the earth's surface over which the climatic elements, and therefore the broad climatic characteristics, are similar. Areas with similar climates may be found in widely separated parts of the earth, but most likely in corresponding latitudinal and continental locations. Because there appears to be some order and system in the origin and distribution of climatic elements, it is possible to classify numerous climatic regions into a few principal **climatic types.** Because the greatest controls of climate are found in the distribution

FIGURE 13-1.

Arrangement of the principal types of climate on a hypothetical continent of relatively low and uniform elevation. [*Adapted by permission from* Elements of Geography, *Finch, Trewartha, Robinson and Hammond, 1957, McGraw-Hill, New York.*]

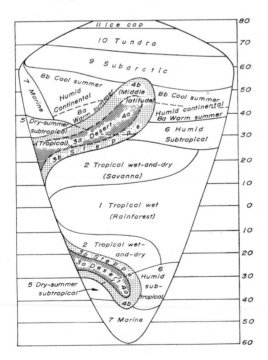

of solar energy and the general circulation of the atmosphere, there is a world pattern of recognizable latitudinal and continental arrangements of climatic regions and types. Figure 13-1 is an illustration of the general features of world distribution of climates, as the arrangement might appear on a hypothetical continent of relatively low and uniform elevation.

It is obvious that there are many modifications of, and deviations from, any such idealized scheme of climatic distribution. For our purpose, however, explanations for departures from normal world patterns will not be attempted. Instead, emphasis will be given to general climatic types and their world distribution.

Although the need for a simple world classification of climates is recognized, Trewartha has pointed out many of the difficulties involved. A regional climatic picture might be presented by (1) an analysis of the individual climatic elements from data observed using meteorological instruments, and (2) an analysis of the prevailing weather types revealed through a study of the daily weather map. Both of these approaches appear to be essential, as are supplementary data concerning frequency and characteristics of cyclonic storms.

Two of the better known classifications of climate today, especially to American workers, are Köppen's and Thornthwaite's. These are quantitative systems which use numerical values for defining boundaries of climatic groups and types.

KÖPPEN'S CLASSIFICATION

Devised by Wladimir Köppen of Austria and first published in 1918, this classification is based on annual and monthly means of temperature and precipitation (Köppen-Geiger, 1936). Native vegetation is considered the best expression of the over-all effect of climate. Effectiveness of rainfall is determined by combining precipitation and temperature. A certain amount of rainfall in a hot climate is less effective than the same amount in a cool climate. This method, however, is not entirely satisfactory for determining precipitation effectiveness (see Chapter 7). The set of symbols which represent climatic types makes the system relatively simple and readily workable. Each type of climate is described by a formula of letters, each of which has a specific meaning. For example, *Af* is translated as follows: A = constantly hot, average temperature of the coldest month above 64.4°F; f = constantly wet, no month having on the average less than 2.4 inches of precipitation.

Köppen's classification has been criticized on the basis of its broad generalizations, its failure to discriminate between climates which are not alike, and its even greater discrepancies at higher altitudes. However, as Trewartha has pointed out, in spite of its limitations, it offers a simple, workable scheme by which the world pattern of climates may be taught.

THORNTHWAITE'S CLASSIFICATION

Thornthwaite (1931, 1948) published two classifications of climate. In the first one, the plant was assumed to be, in a sense, a measure of all the integrated elements of the climate. Moisture provinces were delineated by measures of precipitation effectiveness. A weakness of the system, however, was that data on evaporation were available at but few weather recording stations, making accurate mapping of moisture effectiveness difficult.

In the 1948 classification, the concept of **potential evapotranspiration** was brought into the picture. Climatic boundaries were determined by comparing precipitation with potential evapotranspiration, both wholly meteorological measurements. Thus, vegetation was no longer the criterion of determination; boundaries were determined by climatic data alone. For many years, lack of adequate data on evapotranspiration retarded acceptance and use of this system, but in recent years much progress has been made toward a greatly extended use (Thornthwaite and Mather, 1955). Complete world maps of climates based on this system have not been available, however, so the system is hardly satisfactory for relating climatic types to world crop distribution.

TREWARTHA'S MODIFIED KÖPPEN SYSTEM

A modified system of classification based upon that of Köppen will be used in this book for the purpose of relating climates to crop adaptation and distribution (Trewartha, 1954).

Five great groups of climates are recognized. In the equatorial lowlatitudes, there is a winterless region of constantly high temperatures with adequate rainfall, designated (A). Within this group (humid tropics), based on rainfall differences, are the constantly wet type (Af) and the tropical savanna type, with summer rains and a low-sun dry season (Aw).

Extending poleward through the tropics and far into the middle latitudes are the dry climates (B). This group is subdivided into an arid, or desert, type (BW) and a semiarid, or steppe, type (BS). A further subdivision separates the hot tropical and subtropical deserts and steppes (BWh, BSh) from the cold middle-latitude deserts and steppes (*BWk, BSk*). The *h/k* boundary is the 32°F isotherm for the coldest month.

The humid middle latitudes are divided into two climatic groups, the mesothermal in which the winters are mild and short (*C*), and the microthermal in which they are severe and long (*D*). Within the *C* group, three types are recognized: subhumid dry-summer subtropical (*Cs*), humid subtropical with hot summers (*Ca*), and middle-latitude marine with cool summers (*Cb*). These subdivisions in the *C* group differ somewhat from those of Köppen's system. The *Cs* group with its winter rainfall and summer drought is influenced by middle-latitude westerlies and their cyclonic storms in winter, and by subtropical highs in summer. The *Ca* type, also subtropical, is affected by the unstable western margin of the subtropical anticyclone in summer, and by the westerlies and their cyclonic storms in winter. The *Cb* type, poleward of the subtropics and usually on the windward side of the continent, is affected by the cyclonic westerlies the year round.

The microthermal group of climates is characterized by temperature contrasts. It is associated with large land masses in relatively high middle latitudes, and so receives the effects of the westerlies in summer and the polar winds in winter. The humid continental types (*Da* and *Db*) are differentiated on the basis of summer temperatures, *Da* having warm summers (warmest month over 71.6°F) and *Db* cool summers (warm month under 71.6°F). The subarctic type (*Dc, Dd*) has very short cool summers and long severe winters (*c* = fewer than four months over 50°F; *d* = coldest month below −36.4°F).

In the higher latitudes are found the summerless polar climates (*E*). These are dominated by polar winds throughout the year. Two subdivisions are recognized, *ET*, or tundra, where the warmest month is above 32°F but below 50°F, and *EF*, or ice cap, where all months are below 32°F.

The Trewartha-modified Köppen classification of climates is presented in Table 13-1 in outline form.

MODIFICATIONS FROM THE KÖPPEN SYSTEM

Trewartha elaborated on the departures in his modified classification from Köppen's earlier one as follows:

(1) In the *B* climates the 32°F isotherm for the coldest month has been substituted for the mean annual isotherm of 64.4°F as a boundary between the hot-dry and cold-dry climates.

(2) Köppen used the coldest month isotherm of 26.6°F, which has been replaced by 32°F as the boundary between *C* and *D* climates.

TABLE 13-1. TYPES OF CLIMATE*

Groups	Types

A. Tropical humid climates	I. Low latitudes (the tropics)
	  1. Tropical wet (Af, constantly wet)
	                  (Am, monsoon type)
	  2. Tropical wet-and-dry (Aw, savanna)
	  3. Low-latitude dry climates
	    a. Low-latitude desert (BWh, arid)
	    b. Low-latitude steppe (BSh, semiarid)

B. Dry climates	II. Middle latitudes (intermediate zones)
	  4. Middle-latitude dry climates
	    a. Middle-latitude desert (BWk, arid)
	    b. Middle-latitude steppe (BSk, semiarid)

C. Humid mesothermal climates	5. Dry-summer subtropical (Cs, Mediterranean)
	  6. Humid subtropical (Ca)
	  7. Marine (Cb, Cc)

D. Humid microthermal climates	8. Humid continental climates
	    a. Humid continental, warm summer (Da)
	    b. Humid continental, cool summer (Db)
	  9. Subarctic (Dc, Db)

E. Polar climates	III. High latitudes (polar caps) or high altitudes
	  10. Tundra (ET)
	  11. Ice Cap (EF)

H. Undifferentiated highlands	

A = temperature of coolest month over 18°C (64.4°F)
B = evaporation exceeds precipitation
C = coldest month between 18°C (64.4°F) and 0°C (32°F)
D = temperature of coldest month under 0°C (32°F); warmest month over 10°C (50°F)
E = temperature of warmest month under 10°C (50°F)
a = warmest month over 22°C (71.6°F)
b = warmest month below 22°C (71.6°F)
c = warmest month below 22°C (71.6°F); less than four months above 10°C (50°F)
d = coldest month below −3°C (−36.4°F)
With A climates:
f = no dry season; driest month over 6 cm. (2.4 in.)
s = dry period at high sun or summer; rare in A climates
w = dry period at low sun or winter; driest month under 6 cm. (2.4 in.)
With C and D climates:
f = no dry season; difference between rainiest and driest months less than in s and w; driest
    month of summer over 3 cm. (1.2 in.)
s = summer dry; at least 3 times as much rain in wettest month of winter as in driest month
    of summer; driest month less than 3 cm. (1.2 in.)
w = winter dry; at least 10 times as much rain in wettest month of summer as in driest month
    of winter.

  * From Finch, Trewartha, Robinson, and Hammond. *Elements of Geography*. McGraw-Hill,
N. Y., 1957.

(3) Köppen differentiates three principal climatic types in the *C* group on the basis of seasonal distribution: *Cs*, summer dry; *Cw*, winter dry; and *Cf*, no dry season. In the present system it is only in *Cs* climates that seasonal rainfall is a critical factor of differentiation. The second and third divisions of the *C* group are *Ca(f, w)* and *Cb(f, w)*, one having warm summers such as the cotton belt of southeastern United States, and the other cool summers such as western Europe.

(4) In the humid microthermal group (*D*) Köppen again differentiates the principal types on the basis of seasonal distribution of rainfall: *Dw*, winter-dry; *Df*, no dry season. *Dw* occurs only in eastern Asia where a strong monsoon wind system prevails; but most of the *D* regions have a pronounced summer maximum, even though they cannot qualify as *Dw*. It was Trewartha's belief that the *Dw* and *Df* climates in Asia do not differ so fundamentally in vegetation, soils, and culture as do *Da*, *Db*, and *Dc* climates, where summer temperature is used as the element of differentiation. In the present classification, therefore, the subdivisions of the *D* group are based primarily on summer temperatures.

(5) Attempts to differentiate highland areas using the same criteria as used for lowlands have not been satisfactory. Few data are available from highland areas and no differentiation has been attempted in this classification. It is recognized, however, that there is a great complexity in mountain climates and, although elevation is a paramount factor, many other features of the region must be taken into consideration.

The limitations of any classification of climates must be emphasized. In order for the system to be workable, the number of classes should be kept to a minimum. If this is adhered to, however, it is obvious that areas somewhat dissimilar in certain climatic aspects are lumped together into one type of climate. It appears to be obvious also that boundaries between climatic types must be considered not as specific lines as drawn on the map, but only as approximations based on average values. The variability from year to year is great in some climates and small in others. The boundary separating the humid area from the dry area in the United States, for example, is known to vary over a distance (east and west) of as much as 300 miles, based on conditions in individual years.

A map of world climates based on the classification of Köppen, as modified by Trewartha, is given in Figure 13-2.

THE TROPICAL RAINY CLIMATES (A)

The humid tropics occupy a belt of varying width around the world. This belt extends out from the equator to approximately 20° latitude both north

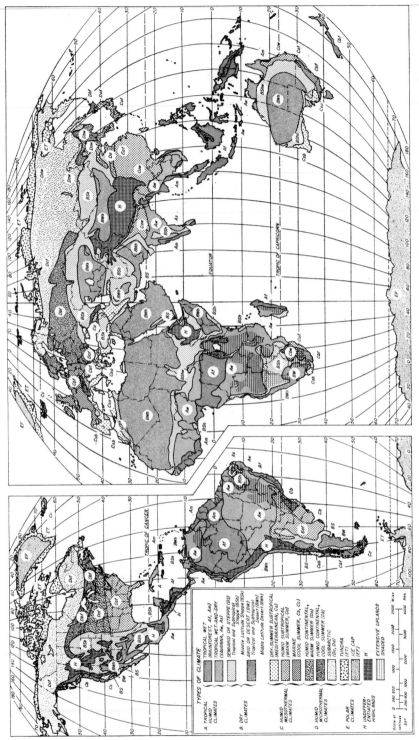

FIGURE 13-2. *Climates of the earth. [By permission from Elements of Geography, Finch, Trewartha, Robinson and Hammond, 4th Ed., 1957, McGraw-Hill, New York.]*

and south. The feature which distinguishes this region from other humid regions is that it is constantly warm (except at high altitudes). It is truly a winterless region where the diurnal range in temperature exceeds the difference between the warmest and coolest months of the year. Within this climatic group no month has an average temperature of less than 64°F. Near the equator the *A* climates extend up to elevations of approximately 3000 feet or more.

The *A* climates are more widespread than any other group, occupying nearly 36% of the earth's surface. Trewartha has noted that tropical rainy climates have their greatest latitudinal range in the eastern parts of continents, which is explained on the basis of certain features of the atmospheric circulation. Within the *A* group are included two types, *Af*, tropical rainforest, and *Aw*, tropical savanna (or tropical wet and dry). Still further modifications may be made, especially within the savanna type.

Tropical Rainforest Climate (*Af*)

This climate is found typically near the equator, extending out 5° or 10° on both sides. Along windward margins of continents, the latitude spread may increase to 20° or 25°. Temperatures in the *Af* climate are uniformly high, annual means ranging from 77° to 80°+F, with little seasonal variation. The uniformity and monotony of the constant high temperatures, rather than excessively high temperatures, characterizes the tropical rainforest climate.

The daily range of temperature is usually 10° to 25°F, several times greater than the annual monthly range. At Belém, Brazil, the average of the daily maxima is 91° and the average of the daily minima 68°F. Daytime temperatures are not excessively high compared with those reached in most American cities in July and August, but the constant heat, slight air movement, high humidity, and consequent low cooling power of the air, make the *Af* climate sultry and oppressive.

Rainfall is both heavy and well distributed, with no distinctly dry season. Much of the *Af* region receives as much as 100 inches of rainfall annually, with maximum amounts usually falling during the warmer hours of the day. Heavy showers and thunderstorms are frequent: there are from 75 to 150 such storms each year. The weather pattern strongly reflects sun control and is therefore mainly a diurnal phenomenon. Average monthly temperatures and rainfall for a station in a typical tropical rainforest region are shown in Figure 13-3.

The Amazon Valley in South America and the Congo Basin in Africa are the largest individual areas with a tropical wet climate. Indonesia, the

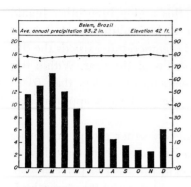

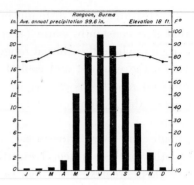

FIGURE 13-3.

Average monthly temperatures and rainfall for a tropical wet (Af) climate.

FIGURE 13-4.

Average monthly temperatures and rainfall for a tropical wet, monsoon (Am) climate.

Philippines, and some of the coastal lands of tropical Asia also have tropical wet climates. Small, somewhat isolated areas having *Af* climate include Central America, parts of the West Indies, western Colombia, the lowland coast of eastern Brazil, and the Guianas, eastern Madagascar, and parts of the Guinea coast of Africa. Crops such as rubber, bananas, and cacao, which have a very narrow range of tolerance for temperature, are grown in the *Af* climate. A modification of this climatic type is the monsoon *Am* climate characterized by heavy annual rainfall, but having a short dry season (Figure 13-4).

The Tropical Savanna Climate (Aw)

The tropical savanna extends mainly from 5° to 15° on both sides of the equator. The *Aw* climate differs from the *Af* in two respects: (1) it usually has less precipitation, and (2) rainfall is unevenly distributed throughout the year, with a distinctly wet and a distinctly dry season. It may be considered intermediate between dry climates on the poleward side and wet climates on the equatorward side. This implies considerable variation within the *Aw* climates.

Extensive areas of tropical savanna are found in South America, one to the north of the *Af* climate in Venezuela, Colombia, and the Guianas, the other in south-central Brazil and adjacent parts of Bolivia and Paraguay. In Africa, *Aw* climates are found in the Sudan to the north of the equator and in the extensive veld area south of the equator. Areas in northern Aus-

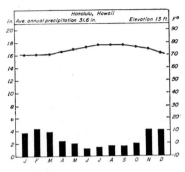

FIGURE 13-5.

Average monthly temperatures and rainfall for a tropical savanna (Aw) climate.

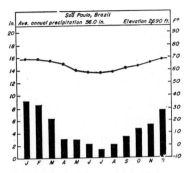

FIGURE 13-6.

Average monthly temperatures and rainfall for a tropical highland (Aw-Cw) climate.

tralia, India, Burma, Thailand, and Indo-China also have a rather typical *Aw* climate. Less typical but still within the general climatic type are areas of eastern and southern Africa and southeastern Brazil. Some insular and peninsular areas in the Caribbean region have an *Aw* climate.

Three temperature periods are often recognized in the *Aw* climate: (1) a cooler dry season, (2) a hotter dry season just preceding the rains, and (3) a hot wet season during the rains. Trewartha has observed that during the rainy season the weather of the *Aw* climate resembles that of the *Af* climate at its worst. Figure 13-5 shows temperature and rainfall conditions of the tropical suvanna (*Aw*) climate.

A modified form of the tropical wet-and-dry climate is the upland type characterized by somewhat lower temperatures. The Brazilian plateau of the Saõ Paulo and Paraná areas is an example of the upland *Cw* climate. A chart showing average monthly temperatures and rainfall in an upland *Aw-Cw* climate is given in Figure 13-6.

Typical crops of the tropical savanna climate are coffee, sugarcane, millet, cotton, legumes, rice (if irrigation water is available), and grasses for cattle grazing.

THE DRY CLIMATES (B)

The dry climates are those in which the potential loss of water from the soil surface plus the loss from the transpiration of vegetation exceeds the annual precipitation. In such a climate a water deficiency prevails, variability in precipitation is usually high, and production of crops entails considerable risk.

As has been emphasized earlier, the boundaries of dry climates are difficult to define. Water deficiency will depend on the quantity of precipitation which falls and the rate at which it is lost through evaporation and transpiration. Also, the distribution of precipitation in dry regions may be quite nonuniform, with a few heavy downpours accompanied by a high percentage of runoff making up a large proportion of the total. Thornthwaite's contributions to this problem, through his potential evapotranspiration concept and his water balance theory, have aided greatly in characterizing the essential differences between the humid and dry climates.

Two subdivisions of the B climates usually are recognized: (1) the arid or desert type, and (2) the semiarid or steppe type. Trewartha has noted that the steppe is a transitional type separating the desert from the humid climate. Although the boundary between arid and semiarid climates is arbitrary, Köppen suggested that it is approximately one-half the amount of rainfall separating the semiarid and humid climates. Thus, if 19–20 inches marks the outer boundary of semiarid climates, $9\frac{1}{2}$–10 inches may be considered the boundary between desert and steppe.

Dry climates are very extensive, occupying 26% of the continental land area of the world. Of this total, 14% is steppe and about 12% desert.

Tropical and subtropical desert climates (*BWh*) range in position from 15° to 30° latitude, both north and south. Some of the more important deserts include the Sahara in North Africa, the Kalahari in South Africa, the Atacama-Peruvian in western South America, the total Australian desert, the Thar in India, and the Sonora in southwestern United States and north-

FIGURE 13-7.

Average monthly temperatures and rainfall for a low-latitude desert (Bw) climate.

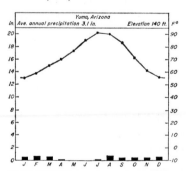

FIGURE 13-8.

Average monthly temperatures and rainfall for a low-latitude steppe (BSh) climate.

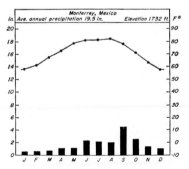

western Mexico. Annual rainfall ranges from less than 1 to 5 inches. Figure 13-7 shows a climatic chart for Yuma, Arizona which has a *BW* climate.

Temperature ranges, both annual and diurnal, are great, 25° to 30°F not being uncommon.

Middle-latitude deserts (*BWk*) tend to be somewhat less completely rainless than the tropical deserts. They occupy basin-like or depressed areas, usually in continental interiors. The Tarim and Turkistan deserts of Asia lie within highland rims, and the principal desert region of the United States coincides with the Great Basin. Characteristically, high temperatures, approaching those of the tropical deserts, prevail in summer, whereas relatively low temperatures are common in winter.

Low-latitude steppes (*BSh*) usually surround the low-latitude deserts, excepting that in several instances mountains make up their western boundaries. In Africa a steppe region of this type borders the Sahara in the north. Other tropical steppes surrounding deserts are located in Arabia, Mesopotamia, southern Iran, southern Australia, northwestern Mexico, and adjacent southwestern United States. A climatic chart for a subtropical steppe (*BSh*) climate is presented in Figure 13-8.

Steppe climates which lie between the *BW* and *Aw* types include an area equatorward from the Sahara, dry southwestern Africa, northwestern India, and two belts in Australia, one poleward, the other equatorward from the central Australian desert.

Middle-latitude steppes (*BSk*) occupy transitional regions between deserts and humid climates in the middle latitudes. These continental steppes offer better conditions for human occupation than do the deserts, but the unreliable nature of the rainfall makes them economically hazardous for agricultural use. Commercial grazing offers the best possible long-run use of many of these lands. Dry farming, however, is a highly important enterprise on many of the world's middle-latitude steppes. In the Great Plains region of North America, as well as on the vast Russian steppes of southwest Asia, a considerable portion of the world's production of wheat is grown. Other important crops are barley, millet, and grain sorghum. Average monthly temperatures and rainfall for a station having a middle-latitude steppe (*BSk*) climate are shown in Figure 13-9.

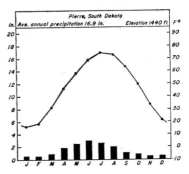

FIGURE 13-9.

Average monthly temperatures and precipitation for a middle-latitude steppe (BSk) climate.

THE HUMID MESOTHERMAL CLIMATES (C)

These intermediate climates are characterized by a seasonal rhythm in temperature, the range being greatest at the northern limits of the climatic type. Weather conditions are likely to be changeable because of the conflict between contrasting air masses from polar and tropical sources.

In the humid middle latitudes, two climatic groups are recognized: (1) the C climates, and (2) the D climates. The boundary, by Trewartha's modification, is the cold-month isotherm of 32°F.

Within the mesothermal group three climatic types are found: (1) the Mediterranean, (Cs); (2) humid subtropical, (Ca); and (3) marine, (Cb).

The most extensive area of Mediterranean climate is that of the coastal areas bordering the Mediterranean Sea. In other parts of the world, this climate is usually found along west sides of continents, between latitudes of 30° and 40°. These Mediterranean regions include central and southern California, middle Chile, southern Africa, southwestern tip of Australia, and the Murray-Darling region of southern Australia. The Cs climate forms a transition between the desert climates equatorward and the humid climates poleward. In middle Chile and in California, mountain barriers on the east restrict the cooling effect of the Pacific ocean to a relatively narrow strip of land near the coast.

The Cs climate is characterized by its relatively low rainfall, which is highly variable in amount and falls mainly in the cool season. The warm season, usually from April to October (in the northern hemisphere), is without rain of any consequence.

The vegetation of Mediterranean climates shows the effect of the mild climate and hot dry summers. Rainfall is too scanty to support luxuriant forests, but brush and scrub forest is typical, such as the chaparral of California, consisting of live oak, scrub oak, hollyleaf cherry, manzanita, and sumac.

Agriculture is diverse and yet highly specialized. Cereal grains under natural rainfall occupy a high proportion of the crop land in Italy, Algeria, and Greece. Tree and fruit crops like olives, citrus, figs, dates, and grapes are also grown without additional water in some areas, but become much more productive under irrigation. Cotton, corn, barley, specialized seed crops, and vegetables produce exceptionally high yields with plenty of water. Irrigation becomes one of the highly expensive items in production costs. Finally, in the Mediterranean climate livestock and grazing are important enterprises.

Two subdivisions of the *Cs* climate are known: (1) *Csa*, with warm to hot summers, and (2) *Csb*, with cool summers. Coastal areas on the western sides of continents, especially between latitudes 30° and 40°, have typical *Csb* climates, whereas the more interior areas, such as California's coastal valleys and the Sacramento Valley and many of the borderlands of the Mediterranean Sea in southern Europe, northern Africa, and western Asia, have *Csa* climates. Climatic charts typical of the subtropical dry-summer (hot) and dry-summer (cool) climates are illustrated in Figures 13-10 and 13-11.

A second type of mesothermal humid climate is the humid subtropical, (*Ca*). This type is widely distributed throughout the world. In Asia, large portions of China, India, Japan, Thailand, Indo-China, and a bit of Pakistan are included. In Europe there are only a few *Ca* climates. These include much of the Po Valley of Italy, portions of Yugoslavia, and small areas east and west of the Black Sea belonging to Bulgaria and the U.S.S.R. In South America, portions of Brazil and much of Argentina, Uruguay, and Paraguay are included. In Africa the *Ca* climate is represented by a small part of South Africa. It is found also in portions of eastern Australia. In North America, most of the southeastern part of the United States has a humid subtropical climate.

The *Ca* climate is transitional between the tropical savanna or rainforest on the equatorward boundary and the humid continental on the poleward side. Summer drought is absent in the typical humid subtropical climate, although there are fairly extensive areas in southeastern United States where summer drought is common (see Chapter 7). If there is no regular period

FIGURE 13-10.

Average monthly temperatures and rainfall for a dry-summer hot subtropical, or Mediterranean (Csa) climate.

FIGURE 13-11.

Average monthly temperatures and rainfall for a dry-summer (cool) subtropical, or Mediterranean (Csb) climate.

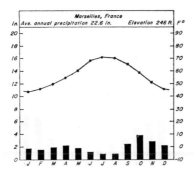

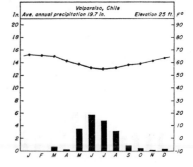

of drought, the designation is *Caf* (Figure 13-12); winter drought areas are designated *Caw*.

Summers are warm to hot, especially in North America and Asia. July temperatures at Charleston, South Carolina, and Montgomery, Alabama, average 82°F; at Shanghai, China, 81°F; at Durban, South Africa, 77°F; at Buenos Aires, Argentina, 74°F. Relative humidity is usually high, making for sultry conditions with low cooling power. Average daily maxima for July and August in much of the American Cotton Belt lie between 90° and 100°F, with night temperatures somewhat higher than is characteristic of the *Cs* climate.

Important crops in humid subtropical climates include cotton, rice, tobacco, corn, citrus fruit, peanuts, and pasture grasses and legumes.

A modification of the *C* climate, which is really quite different from the humid subtropical, is the west-coast marine type (*Cb*). Marine climates are found on western or windward sides of middle-latitude continents, poleward from 40°, where westerlies give them cool summers as well as mild winters.

In North America the west-coast marine climates include the coastal regions of northern California, Oregon, Washington, British Columbia, and southern Alaska. In South America, much of southern Chile and a little of Argentina are included. In Australia this type includes the southeastern coastal area, Tasmania, and the Eastern Highlands as far north as Queensland. All of New Zealand has the *Cb* climate. In Europe it includes the British Isles, northern Spain, most of France, Belgium, the Netherlands, Denmark, much of northwest Germany, and the southwest coast of Norway.

Summers of west-coast marine climates are cooler than for continental

FIGURE 13-12.

Average monthly temperatures and rainfall for a humid subtropical (Caf) climate.

FIGURE 13-13.

Average monthly temperatures and rainfall for a West Coast Marine (Cb) climate.

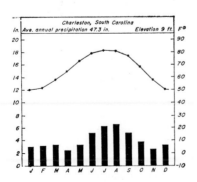

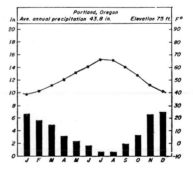

climates at similar latitudes. Rainfall patterns are somewhat like those of Mediterranean climates but in magnitude usually much greater. Precipitation comes mainly from cyclonic storms. Figure 13-13 shows a climatic chart for a west-coast marine (*Cb*) climate.

Forests are numerous and often luxuriant in the west-coast marine climate. When forests are removed, forage crops, cereal grains, sugar beets, and other root crops thrive, with yields particularly high in western Europe. A highly developed livestock industry exists in many of the *Cb* climates, especially in New Zealand, the United States, the United Kingdom, and western Europe.

THE HUMID MICROTHERMAL CLIMATES (*D*)

These climates are characterized by a real winter, usually with snow which may stay on the ground for several weeks, and a genuine summer. Fall and spring are often short, seemingly mere transitions. In general, microthermal climates lie poleward from the *Cs* and *Ca* climates and occupy more interior and leeward locations on great land masses than does the marine type *Cb*. These climates (*D*) are land-controlled and, because they are found in the higher latitudes, they are confined to the Northern Hemisphere. In latitude they range from 40° to 60° or 65° north. Characteristically, summers are warm for that latitude, but it is the winter cold that is distinctive. Variability is likely to be great from year to year, often with wide deviations from average conditions.

In North America, the *Da* and *Db* climates, humid continental, lie poleward of 35° latitude and extend into the subtropical *Ca* type to the south. Asia is similar, but in Europe the *Cs* climate is found on the southern border of the *Da* climate.

Cold winters and warm to hot summers are typical of the continental *D* climates. The severity of the climate tends to increase from south to north and from coasts toward the interior. Westerly winds tend to carry continental air masses down to the eastern littorals, but onshore winds of cyclonic origin do act to give east coasts a modified continental climate. New York, for example, has an average July temperature of 73.9°F and a January mean of 30.9°F. In contrast, Omaha, Nebraska, has a July mean of 76.8°F and a January mean of 21.8°F.

These land-controlled climates usually have more precipitation in summer than in winter. In North America this tendency is more pronounced as one goes inland from the Atlantic coast. In New York, for example, the winter months average about three inches of precipitation, and the summer months a little more than four inches. At Omaha, Nebraska, however, the January precipitation averages 0.7 inch and the June average is 4.7 inches.

The Humid Continental, Warm Summer, Daf and Daw

The boundary between the *Da* and *Db* climates is 71.6°F for the warmest month. The warm-summer humid continental climate (*Da*) is the mildest and most equable of the microthermal group. In the United States it extends from central Kansas and Nebraska in the west to the Atlantic seaboard, and includes Iowa, northern and central Missouri, Illinois, Indiana, Ohio, parts of Pennsylvania, Maryland, New Jersey, and Connecticut (Figure 13-14).

In Europe the *Da* type occurs mainly in the southern portion—the Danube and Balkan States, and the upper Po Valley in Italy. A third principal region in eastern Asia includes much of North China and Korea.

Summer precipitation is usually greater than that of winter. If no regular season of drought occurs, the designation *Daf* is used. This is the climate of eastern United States, from the corn belt to the east coast. In North China there is a characteristic winter drought. This climate is designated *Daw*.

Forest vegetation in the more humid portion and tall-grass prairie in the more interior subhumid region is characteristic for the *Da* and *Db* climates.

Soils vary widely, from the typical podsols of the coniferous forest to the dark-colored deep prairie soils near the western boundary of this climatic type.

FIGURE 13-14.

Average monthly temperatures and precipitation for a humid continental, warm summer (Daf) climate.

FIGURE 13-15.

Average monthly temperatures and precipitation for a humid continental, cool summer (Dbf) climate.

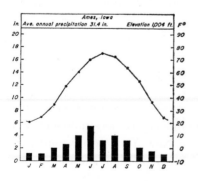

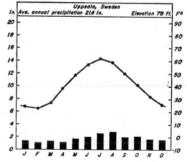

Some of the more important crops of the *D* climates in North America are corn, oats, soybeans, alfalfa, and clover. Fruits—apples, cherries, peaches, and grapes—are important in some areas, especially in Michigan and in other locations on leeward sides of the Great Lakes.

In Eurasia, including eastern Germany, Poland, Czechoslovakia, Yugoslavia, parts of Greece and Bulgaria, Hungary, Rumania, southern Sweden, and a large portion of Russia east of the Ural mountains, the natural vegetation ranges from heavy forests to tall grassland. Summers are cooler than in the *D* climates of the United States (Figure 13-15). Important crops are rye, barley, wheat, sugar beets, potatoes, and corn. Hemp and flax for fiber also are grown.

In northern Honshu and all of Hokkaido, Japan, the *D* climate has a marine influence. Potatoes, apples, oats, barley, buckwheat, and hay are important crops.

In Manchuria and on the North China plain, sorghum, millet, soybeans, and wheat are grown widely and furnish the main sources of food for the people of these regions.

Subarctic Climates (Dc, Dd)

These climates are found in the Northern Hemisphere, roughly north of 55°. On the poleward side they contact the tundra, one of the polar climates. This boundary is the isotherm of 50°F for the warmest month, which coincides with the northern limit of tree growth. To the south, the subarctic extends to the cool-summer humid continental *Db* type, or possibly to middle-latitude steppes and deserts. The Eurasian subarctic (taiga) climate extends from Sweden and Finland across the whole continent to the coast of Siberia. In North America the *Dc* climate extends from Alaska across Canada to Labrador and Newfoundland.

Long, bitter winters and short summers characterize the subarctic climate. The July mean temperature may be from 59° to 66°F, but the growing season is short. In the Mackenzie Valley, Canada, the growing season is 50 to 75 days, but severe frosts may be expected in July and August in at least half the years.

Rainfall tends to be meager in the subarctic, the total annual precipitation in much of subarctic Canada being less than 20 inches. At Point Barrow, Alaska, annual precipitation averages less than six inches and temperatures average below 0°F for five months (Figure 13-16).

The native vegetation of subarctic regions of North America and Eurasia is the softwood forest known as taiga. Although taiga consists predominantly

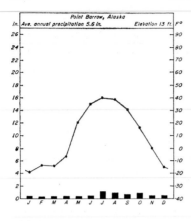

FIGURE 13-16.

Average monthly temperature and precipitation for a Tiaga, or tundra (ET) climate.

of conifers, especially spruce and fir, deciduous trees such as birch, poplar, and willow are often present.

Soils are mainly podsols, gray or ash-colored, low in humus, poor in structure, and rather infertile. Heavy applications of lime and fertilizer are required to make them moderately productive.

Agriculture is not a dominant factor in the subarctic climate. In Alaska much effort has been expended by the experiment stations at Palmer and Fairbanks to encourage farming, but the total acreage under cultivation is very small indeed. It is possible, however, to produce potatoes, turnips, beets, and other root crops, some small fruits, vegetables, and hardy, early maturing varieties of spring-sown cereals, particularly barley, oats, and rye. Winterhardy grasses have been grown for livestock feed, but legumes such as alfalfa (excepting the yellow-flowered *falcata* species) do not have sufficient winterhardiness to survive successfully.

In the vast Russian taiga region, subsistence farming is combined with hunting, fishing, and lumbering. Root crops, hardy cereals, and wild fruits make up most of the local produce. Small cattle are grown, probably descended from European wild cattle, and characterized by long shaggy hair and ability to live on small amounts of feed. According to Mirov (1951) reindeer are used by the Tungus people and there have been some efforts to domesticate the moose.

All things considered, it appears unlikely that the subarctic will be a factor of much importance in the near future as far as food production is concerned. Not many people are willing to suffer the privations of life in this climate in attempts to develop successful farming enterprises.

THE POLAR CLIMATES (*E*)

Polar climates lack a period of warm temperatures. The continued cold, with but a few days (perhaps) of temperatures favorable to plant growth, gives this type of climate an overwhelming handicap.

Two climatic types are recognized, the tundra (*ET*), and ice-cap (*EF*). The isotherm of 50°F for the warmest month marks the boundary between the tundra, *ET*, climate and the subarctic (intermediate) climate. Since this is practically the northern limit for forest growth, tundra vegetation consists chiefly of mosses, lichens, sedges, and some dwarfed birches, willows, and aspen. The dominant characteristic is the carpet of lichens and mosses, which gives the tundra its name.

Tundra soils have undergone the process of gleization, resulting in a very thin, highly leached layer (under raw peat or humus) underlain with a structureless, grayish-blue, sticky layer known as glei.

Tundra climate over land areas is confined mainly to the Northern Hemisphere. The most extensive tundra areas are the Arctic Sea margins of North America and Eurasia. The coastal fringe of Greenland and much of the Arctic archipelago are included. In the Antarctic, only the northern fringes of the Antarctic continent and some small islands have sufficient warmth in summer to be included in the tundra climate.

The warmest months of the tundra possibly resemble March and April in the latitude of southern Wisconsin (Trewartha, 1954) and are like January in the American cotton belt. There may be two to four months with average temperatures above freezing, but killing frost may occur at any time. Growing conditions are too limited for crop production of any consequence in the *ET* climate.

The poleward boundary between the tundra, *ET*, and the ice-cap, *EF*, climates is the 32°F isotherm for the warmest month. Typical of ice-cap climates are the great permanent continental ice sheets of Antarctica, Greenland, and the perpetually frozen ocean in the vicinity of the North Pole. Practically no plant life of any importance is found in the *EF* climate.

THE MICROCLIMATE

Data from meteorological instruments located in standard weather shelters are used to characterize climatic conditions. For example, temperature readings, taken at a standard height of five feet above the ground, may be of great significance to man and are representative of what may be called macroclimatic conditions. Most plants, however, are more greatly affected by the environment closer to the ground, which may deviate considerably from that a few feet above. This "ground air-layer" has been designated a "plant climate," or a microclimate (Geiger, 1957). The basic difference between the macroclimate and the microclimate lies in the proximity of the earth's surface.

The microclimate is of such great importance to plants, animals, and man that meteorologists, ecologists, and others have been stimulated to learn as much as possible about the actual environmental conditions near the ground. This interest is exemplified by the comprehensive treatments of this subject by Sutton (1953) and Geiger (1957). A few specific aspects of micro-climate will be considered briefly, with appropriate examples to illustrate their importance to the adaptation and distribution of crops. Temperature, humidity, and wind aspects of microclimate will be considered.

Temperature Near the Ground

The temperature conditions of the air-layer near the ground are determined by the immense amount of heat which the surface of the ground absorbs (Geiger, 1957). The earth's surface itself is extremely important in the heat economy, both by day and by night. The highest temperature at about midday is at the boundary between ground and air, and from this boundary the temperature decreases upward and downward. The temperature distribution at 1 P.M. at Tucson, Arizona, as plotted by Sinclair (1922), is shown in Figure 13-17.

The surface of the soil has the highest temperature (not indicated here), probably far above 71.5° recorded at a depth of 4 mm in the soil. The temperature decreases rapidly (with depth) in the first 10 cm into the soil, and less rapidly upward in the air above the ground surface.

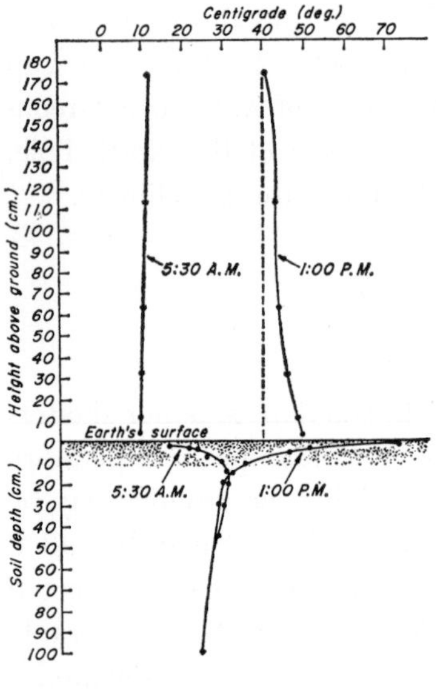

From incoming radiation, illustrated by a hot day at noon, we may go to the opposite situation, outgoing radiation on a cold winter night. The heat exchange now is dependent on radiation from the earth's surface and the outgoing radiation decreases with decreasing temperature. The earth's surface again plays an important role, similar to that of the heat exchange at noon. The boundary between the earth and air shows the lowest temperature at night; the temperature increases upward into the air layer and downward into the soil. A picture of vertical distribution of temperature would be the opposite of that shown in Figure 13-17 for the incoming radiation type. Lower temperatures normally occur with increasing altitude, so the nocturnal in-

FIGURE 13-17.

Graphic representation of diurnal changes in soil and air temperatures near the earth's surface at Tuscon, Arizona. [*Adapted from Sinclair, Mon. Wea. Rev. 50:144, 1922.*]

crease in temperature above the ground
is known as temperature inversion, an important climatic phenomenon (see Chapter 8).

Odum (1959) has given an illustration
of the effect of snow on microclimatic variation in a tundra climate (Figure 13-18).
During cold weather, with a snow cover
of approximately two feet, the minimum
air temperature at the surface of the snow
was —68°F. At a point one foot above the
ground level, the temperature reached
—40°F, and at the ground level it was
20°F.

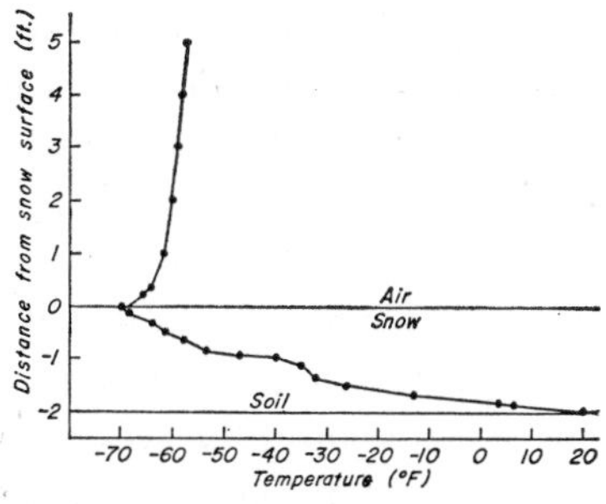

From the ecological standpoint, a number of organisms occupying the same general habitat may actually be living in

FIGURE 13-18.

Vertical temperature distribution near the snow and soil lines indicate marked microclimatic differences. [Adapted from Johnson in Odum, Fundamentals of Ecology. *2nd Ed., 1959, Saunders, Philadelphia.]*

markedly different environments. Animals like the caribou and the arctic
fox can live above the snow level under severe temperature conditions.
Small animals living near the ground surface are really living in a considerably warmer climate.

Snow cover may be an important factor in determining the amount of
winter injury to plants. The insulating effect of one to several feet of snow
may allow the plant to escape the otherwise normal temperature conditions
which would prevail without the snow. Pelletier (1958) observed that with
a snow cover of several feet each winter, birdsfoot trefoil, red clover, and
ladino clover survived satisfactorily at Ste. Anne de la Pocatiere, Quebec,
which is several degrees of latitude farther north than is normally considered within the area of adaptation of these crops.

Microclimates in crops of potatoes and sugar beets were studied by
Broadbent (1950) and Monteith (1960). In sunny weather, the temperature directly above a potato crop was 6°F above the true temperature for
that area. Over a five-week period, the daily range was 8°F greater within
the crop itself than it was in a standard Stevenson temperature screen. A
vertical gradient was produced, the highest temperature at 10 cm in an
open crop and at 30 cm in a dense stand. Under dry soil conditions, the
coolest point was 60 cm from the ground, whereas under wet soil conditions it was coolest at 10 cm above the ground. In a sugar beet field on a
July day, the temperature within the crop was 77°F, and just above the
crop, 72°F. At a nearby weather station air temperature was 68°F.

The temperature climate in the air layer over a Kentucky bluegrass sod,
below a height of four feet, was found by Sprague, *et al.* (1954) to be

much more rigorous than the macroclimate above. Whereas average daily and monthly temperatures at heights varying from three inches to eight feet were practically the same, greater extremes were found at lower levels, where temperatures were usually higher in the daytime and lower at night. Both daily and monthly temperature ranges were greater near the ground than at levels farther above it. Cloudiness and winds tended to reduce extreme microclimatic effects, and these effects were found to be more marked in the warm than in the cold seasons.

Microclimate on a somewhat larger scale was observed by Wolfe, Wareham, and Scofield (1949) in a small cliff-bordered, cove-headed valley in Ohio. Here, a number of sites were observed including frost-pockets, slopes facing different directions, cliff tops, ledges, and grottoes weathered out of cliff faces and located at the cove of the valley. Sites showing greatest differences in microclimate were compared with a weather bureau station not far away. Some observations are given in Table 13-2.

TABLE 13-2.   MICROCLIMATE AND MACROCLIMATE
OF NEOTOMA VALLEY, OHIO

Weather Attribute	Grotto	Frost Pocket	Weather Bureau
Frost-free period (days)	276	124	160
Maximum temperature (°F)	75	93	102
Minimum temperature (°F)	+14	−25	−18
Last spring frost	3/9	5/25	4/22
First fall frost	11/29	9/25	9/25

Aikman (1931) studied the microclimatic effects of slope direction on *Zea mays*. The west slope had the highest average air and soil temperatures, the highest maximum soil temperature at two inches, the longest frost-free season, the most evaporation, the greatest wind movement. The west slope was also the driest and suffered more heat injury than the others, followed in order by south, east, and north slopes. Cold injury, on the other hand, was greatest on the east-facing slope, followed in order by those facing south, north, and west.

Troll and Wien (1935) compared temperatures under tropical conditions, in a young coffee plantation, established where the forest had been cleared, and found that daily fluctuation in air temperature in the open was 11°C, at the ground level in the young coffee, 20°C, and in the nearby forest, only 8°C.

Relative Humidity of the Microclimate

The water vapor of the air-layer near the ground is highly important to the water balance of the atmosphere. As noted by Geiger, this water comes from the ground and, except for that condensed as dew, tends to go upward into the atmosphere above. In contrast to temperature, with its daily maximum and minimum every 24 hours, the water vapor tends to decrease steadily with height above the ground. The relative humidity at ground level normally follows that of the macroclimate rather closely, except that it drops below that of the macroclimate during the warm part of the day. In very dry climates, the relative humidity at the ground remains below that of the macroclimate, and is much lower at midday. In wet climates, by contrast, the relative humidity near the ground, especially at midday, is considerably higher than at a level two meters above the ground.

Stocker (1923) found that, on a calm summer day when the air temperature above a meadow was 29°C, the relative humidity in the open air at a height of 100 cm was 57%, at 13 cm between clover leaves it was 78%, and at 2 cm above the ground (in the grass) it was 96%.

The daily rhythm of relative humidity in the microclimate of a grass meadow was observed by Martini and Teubner (1933), as shown in Table 13-3.

TABLE 13-3.   DAILY RHYTHM OF RELATIVE HUMIDITY AT DIFFERENT HEIGHTS IN A GRASS MEADOW

Location	9 A.M.	12 Noon	3 P.M.	6 P.M.
In open air	88%	56%	48%	78%
In grass at ht of 50 cm	89	68	49	80
In grass at ht of 20 cm	98	85	78	80
In grass at ht of 10 cm	98	90	88	88

In forest vegetation, vertical stratification of environmental factors is especially important. When we refer to the environment of a tree do we mean the conditions at the ground level, 5 feet from the ground, or 50 feet or more in the air?

The opening of clearings in a forest raises many practical problems related to reestablishment of the same or other forest species. Larsen (1922) reported that the opening of clearings so changed the environment, especially as to daily rate of evaporation and soil temperature, that such open sites were unsuitable for reestablishment of forest trees. He noted further that, if grasses became established in the clearings, in ten years they often became too dense for natural reestablishment of trees.

Wind Velocity and Microclimate

Air movement is influenced greatly by proximity to the earth's surface. The daily wind pattern for the ground air-layer is for a maximum velocity at midday and a calm at night. Hellman (1915) showed that this pattern is similar below a level of two meters from the surface, but that the length of the calm period increases as the earth's surface is approached. Higher wind velocities mean increased convection and therefore decreased temperature gradients, resulting in lower temperature at the ground level by day and higher by night (Geiger, 1957). This phenomenon is most important because of the effect of wind on frost prevention on cold late summer or autumn nights. Over a three-day period in winter, McAdie (1912) found that on two nights with no wind the temperature dropped to freezing, but on one night a brisk wind kept the temperature to a minimum of 10°C. The over-all microclimatic effect of increased wind velocity is to reduce the normal (quiet air) differences between the macroclimate and the microclimate.

Other Factors Affecting Microclimate

Other factors of importance in determining microclimatic conditions include the nature of the ground surface, the soil type, the vegetative cover, and the topography of the area. Over generations, man has done much to destroy original microclimates through cutting down forests, plowing arid lands, burning undergrowth, replacing mixed forest with cultivated forest, and replacing forest with pasture or crop land. At the same time these practices have resulted in new microclimates. In addition, one notable factor in creating new microclimates is the erection of buildings. As pointed out by Geiger (1957) every new building tends to create a series of new microclimates where one existed before. Where buildings become numerous and close together, a city climate is eventually developed, which brings many special problems calling for man's ingenuity in their solution.

References

1. Aikman, J. M. 1931. The microclimate of *Zea mays* in central Iowa. *Iowa Acad. Sci. Proc.* 38:73–83.
2. Broadbent, L. 1950. The Microclimate of a potato crop. *Quart. Jour. Roy. Meteor. Soc. (London)* 76: 439–454.
3. Finch, V. C., Trewartha, G. T., Robinson, A. H. and Hammond, E. H. 1957. *Elements of Geography.* McGraw-Hill, New York.
4. Geiger, Rudolf. 1957. *The Climate Near the Ground.* (2nd. ed.) Harvard Univ. Press, Cambridge.
5. Hellman, G. 1915. Über d. Bewegung d. Luft in d. untersten Schichten d. Atm. *Met. Zeit.* 32:1–16.
6. Kendrew, W. G. 1949. *Climatology.* Oxford Univ. Press, Oxford.

7. Köppen-Geiger 1936. *Handbuch der Klimatologie,* Vol. 1, Part C, Gebrüder Borntraeger. Berlin.

8. Larsen, J. A. 1922. Effect of removal of virgin white pine stand on physical factors of the site. *Ecol.* 3: 302–305.

9. McAdie, A. G. 1912. Studies in frost protection—effect of mixing the air. *Mo. Wea. Rev.* 40: 122–123.

10. Martini, E. and Teubner, E. 1933. Ü.d. Verhalten v. Stechmücken by verschied. Temp. und Luftfeucht. Beih. z. Archiv. für Schiffs und Tropenhyg. 37, Beiheft 1.

11. Mirov, N. T. 1951. *Geography of Russia.* Wiley, New York.

12. Monteith, J. L. 1960. Micrometeorology in relation to plant and animal life. *Proc. Linn. Soc. London,* 171 (1): 71–82.

13. Odum, E. P. 1959. *Fundamentals of Ecology.* 2nd Ed. Saunders, New York.

14. Pelletier, J. R. 1958. Exp. Farm, Ste. Anne de la Pocatiere, Quebec. Progress Rept., Exp. Farm Service, Ottawa.

15. Shaw, E. B. 1955. *World Economic Geography.* Wiley, New York.

16. Sinclair, J. G. 1922. Temperature of the soil and air in a desert. *Mo. Wea. Rev.* 50: 142.

17. Sprague, V. G., Neuberger, H., Orgell, W. H., and Dodd, A. V. 1954. Air temperature distribution in the microclimatic layer. *Agron. Jour.* 46: 105–108.

18. Stocker, O. 1923. Klimamess. Auf kleinstem Raum an Wiesen-, Wald- und Heidepflanzen. *Ber. D. Bot. G.* 41: 145–150.

19. Sutton, O. G. 1953. *Micrometeorology.* McGraw-Hill, New York.

20. Thornthwaite, C. W. 1931. The climates of North America according to a new classification. *Geog. Rev.* 21: 633–655.

21. ———. 1948. An approach toward a rational classification of climate. *Geog. Rev.* 38: 55–94.

22. ——— and Mather, J. R. 1955. The water balance. Drexel Inst. Tech. Public. in Climatology 8 (1).

23. Trewartha, G. T. 1954. *An Introduction to Climate.* McGraw-Hill, New York.

24. Troll, C. and Wien, K. 1935. Oldeani-Ngorongoro. Wiss. Veröff. d. Mus. für Landerk. z. Leipzig, N.F. 3: 95–116.

25. Wolfe, J. N., Wareham, R. T., and Scofield, H. T. 1949. Microclimates and macroclimates of Neotoma Valley. *Ohio Biol. Survey* 8: 1–267.

CROP DISTRIBUTION ON A
CLIMATIC BASIS

Crops of the Tropics

The importance of climate as the dominant factor in determining the distribution of the world's crops has been emphasized. In the next few chapters, certain crops will be discussed, with reference particularly to their adaptation to one or more of the important climatic types which occur throughout the world.

It is not within the scope of this volume to consider all of the important world crops. Instead, a few examples will be chosen to illustrate the patterns of their distribution as related to the nature of the climatic controls characteristic of the regions where these crops are produced. The patterns of distribution, it is recognized, are based in part on principles of adaptation, and in part on historical, social, and economic considerations.

Latitude is the most important general climatic control of the tropical rainy climates, for the high noonday sun and approximately 12 hours of daylight which occur day after day throughout the year result in high temperatures. Rising air masses, resulting from high temperatures, tend to foster abundant rainfall. Lateritic soils are typical of many level areas, and poor drainage is common, with many waterlogged soils.

To illustrate crop adaptation and distribution in the tropics, four crops important in plantation farming will be considered: cacao, banana, sugarcane, and coffee. The tolerance limits of cacao are rather clearly defined by the tropical rainforest, *Af*, climate. The banana is also adapted to the rainforest climate, but is grown commercially in the tropical savanna, *Aw*, climate, especially where water for irrigation is available. Sugarcane is well adapted to the tropical savanna climates, and has a somewhat wider tolerance for temperature than either cacao or bananas. Coffee is grown in the tropical savanna climates, particularly in the tropical highlands where temperatures are somewhat cooler than in lowland areas.

CACAO

Cacao is indigenous to tropical America and is produced entirely within the tropics, mainly at relatively low elevations. Its culture spread to the Eastern Hemisphere where, in the African region of the Gold Coast, in Nigeria, and in other Gulf of Guinea countries, the greatest single production area is located.

The cacao bean of commerce is obtained from the fruit of the evergreen tree *Theobroma cacao*. The fruit, a pod which is melon or cucumber shaped, six to ten inches long and three to five inches in diameter, contains 20 or more beans. The pods containing these beans form from small clusters of flowers on the trunk and limbs of the tree, rather than on small branches or twigs. Cacao trees begin to produce when five or six years of age, but full production comes from trees much older. Trees grow to a height of from 25 to 40 feet and, if given proper care, may bear fruit for 40 to 50 years.

The cacao bean is used primarily for the production of cocoa and chocolate. When the roasted beans are ground and much of the fat pressed out, the product is cocoa. If the fat is not removed, the ground material has a darker color and is called chocolate. Cacao competes to some extent with coffee and tea as a beverage crop, is used also for food in candy, sodas, cakes, etc., and may be made into cocoa butter, an ingredient of soaps, cosmetics, perfumes, and ointments (Shaw, 1955).

Adaptation

Cacao is adapted to the tropical rainforest, *Af*, climate. The temperature requirements for the cacao tree are an average annual temperature between 75° and 80°F, with a mean minimum for the coolest month of not less than 60°F. High temperatures will not limit growth, providing shade is made available. Successful production, in fact, requires shading. Trees cannot withstand full tropical sunlight, although plant breeders have been working to develop varieties which can be grown without shade.

Rainfall must be abundant: 80 inches per year, rather well distributed, is needed for good production. An important limiting factor is wind, which tends to increase transpiration and cause the heavy pods to drop from the trees. In tradewind regions, protected valleys may afford good locations for cacao, but both fruit and trees suffer great damage in many exposed island areas.

In the Gold Coast region of Africa, low-lying, fairly well-drained lands extending inland for hundreds of miles provide an excellent site and climate for cacao. Here, the rainfall of approximately 80 inches is rather well distributed through the wet season, which is followed by a short but fairly dry season. These conditions promote high yields and facilitate harvest operations when the crop is mature.

In addition to the principal harvest season, which comes in the dry season on the Gold Coast (from September to February), there is a minor harvest season from May to July. Pods are cut from the trees, split open, and the seeds removed, subjected to a process of fermentation, dried, and shipped. Later, in preparation for commercial use, the beans are cleaned, dried, and roasted.

In Brazil, much of the cacao comes from the rainy coastal area of Bahia. Here, in a strip 300 miles long, there are more than half a million acres of cacao in a typical tropical rainforest, *Af*, climate with 80 inches of rainfall. Ecuador formerly produced an abundance of high quality cacao, but with the onset of devastating diseases, especially Monilia disease and witches'-broom disease, production dwindled to a low level (Jonasson (1951), Jones and Darkenwald, 1954).

World Production Centers

According to Shaw (1955), three widely separated areas of the world produce most of the cacao which enters world trade. These include the rainy coast of Bahia, Brazil; the Gulf of Guinea Coast of Africa; and the Atlantic Coast of Central America, Mexico, and the West Indies. Of the world's production, approximately two-thirds comes from the Gold Coast, Nigeria, and other Gulf of Guinea countries. One-third comes from Latin American countries. Much of the commercial production from Africa comes from small plantings on hundreds of farms. Cacao is a money crop supplementing what is otherwise likely to be subsistence farming. In the Latin American countries, much of the cacao is grown on large plantations specializing in the production of this crop.

Two principal types of cacao are grown, the Criollo and the Forastero. The Criollo type, grown principally in the American region, furnishes a superior grade of product but yields rather poorly and is susceptible to witches'-broom and other diseases. The bulk of the export crop is of the Forastero type. This type is hardy, yields well, but lacks the superior aroma of the Criollo. Selection from hybrids of these two types has also been prac-

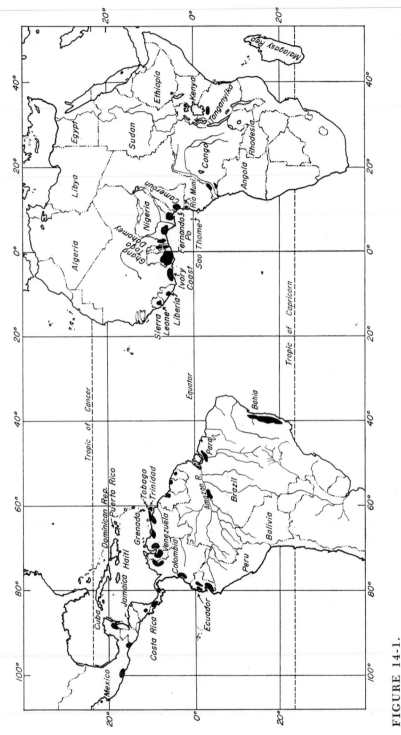

FIGURE 14-1.

Cacao: major producing regions of the world. [Adapted from Van Royen, Atlas of the World's Resources, Vol. 1, The Agricultural Resources of the World, (C), 1954, Prentice-Hall, Englewood Cliffs, N. J. and Foreign Agricultural Service, U.S.D.A.]

ticed and a number of new varieties have been produced in Trinidad and Indonesia (Ochse, *et al.*, 1961).

World production of cacao is shown in Table 14-1 and principal producing regions are indicated on the map in Figure 14-1.

TABLE 14-1. WORLD PRODUCTION OF CACAO BEANS *

| | Production in Millions of Pounds | | |
Area and Country	1951–1960 Average	1959–1960	1960–1961 †
Africa			
Ghana	550	705	700
Nigeria	254	340	325
Ivory Coast	133	128	133
Cameroun	127	137	140
Fernando Po and Rio Muni	44	50	50
Sao Thome and Principe	18	20	20
Togo	11	18	17
South America			
Brazil	325	397	370
Ecuador	65	78	83
Colombia	30	31	33
Venezuela	36	28	28
Caribbean Area			
Dominican Republic	73	85	80
Mexico	25	34	35
Costa Rica	16	23	22
Trinidad and Tobago	19	17	18
Asia and Oceana	25	44	50
World	1743	2210	2178

* Commodity Yearbook, 1960 and U.S.D.A. Foreign Agric. Service.
† Final estimate before harvest, Jan., 1961.

Production of cacao has been increasing steadily during the past 50 years. This has been caused in part by population increase, in part by the extension of cultivation in Africa, and in part by new uses for the product.

BANANA (*Musa sapientum*)

The banana is a staple food of the people of the humid tropics. In the United States, we are accustomed mainly to one type, the sweet banana; actually there are hundreds of varieties, which differ in size, color, flavor, and uses. The principal variety in world trade is the *Gros Michel* (bluefield), which has large fruit of good flavor and stands shipping rather well. Some shipments of Cavendish (Chinese), Jamaica Red, and others are occasionally found in the world market. In the tropics, varieties of the starchy type are used extensively; they may be baked or cooked by other methods.

Bananas and plantains are believed to have originated in southeastern Asia. Wild relatives of these species are indigenous in forests from northeastern India down through the Malay Peninsula and Archipelago to the South Sea islands (Cheesman, 1939). These wild relatives have fruits full of hard seeds and little edible pulp, but the seedless species seem clearly to have developed from them. Seedless kinds probably developed in several independent areas, including India, the Indo-Malayan Peninsula, and farther east in the Pacific islands. New-world varieties appear to have developed from the Malayan group, and were brought to the American tropics by 1516.

The banana plant, an herbaceous perennial which will grow to a height of 30 feet, has been described by Pope (1926). The true stem of the plant is a tuberous rhizome, wherein is stored starchy plant foods essential for the growth of the central bud, the roots, and the sucker-producing tissues. The trunk consists of a cylinder of concentric layers, each of which is the base of a leafstalk. These layers, combined, protect the younger leaves and the flowering stalk. The roots are of two kinds: horizontal, radiating from the tuberous rhizome, and vertical, extending downward from the base. Nutrients are taken in from the soil by both types of roots.

The leaves, consisting of leafstalk and blade, vary in number from eight to twenty or more. Normally they are eight to twelve feet in length and two feet or more in width. Under intense perpendicular rays of the sun the leaf blade may collapse, the under surfaces containing the stomata coming together and thus protecting the plant against excessive water loss (Pope, 1926).

The inflorescence is unique and of great importance. The flowering stalk grows up through the center of the trunk, appearing at the top in the form of a large bud when the trunk is about nine months of age. The flower bud develops rapidly and, because of its weight, hangs pendant from the plant. Flowers are monoecious, being pistillate, staminate, or neutral. The pistillate flowers, especially the ovaries, are most important for they eventually become the fruit. Neutral flowers bear undeveloped stamens and pistils, usually with no fertile pollen present. The staminate flowers occur in clusters near the end of the flowering stalk and usually bear little viable pollen. However, in some varieties good pollen is present and successful cross-pollination has been the basis of breeding improved varieties. Like some other fruits, the seedless banana is parthenocarpic and does not require the stimulus of pollination to insure the setting of fruit.

The banana fruit is borne in a bunch consisting of clusters of "hands," a further development of the floral panicle. The hands bear from 50 to 20 bananas arranged in two rows, commonly called "fingers." These grow separately in spiral arrangement on the axis of the rachis. The bunch is the commercial unit, and ranges in size from six to nine hands. Large bunches often weigh 100 pounds or more at harvest.

Propagation is by asexual methods, using: (1) large suckers four to six months old having well-developed basal rhizomes, (2) small suckers a few weeks old, and (3) old stumps of plants that have fruited.

A period of 14 to 18 months after planting is necessary for the first crop to attain maturity (Bengston and Van Royen, 1950). Even then the root systems may not have developed sufficiently to produce full-sized bunches of large, plump fruit. While the plant is maturing its fruit, young sprouts, or suckers, begin to develop.

Fruit is harvested when plump, but not at the stage where it will ripen and spoil before reaching the consumer. This is a matter of experience based on detailed knowledge of the ripening process as well as on the distance from market and speed of shipping facilities.

After the bunches of fruit are harvested, the main stem is cut off, because only one bunch or stem of fruit is borne. Suckers are removed from the inner side of the basal stem, leaving only a limited number at the outer edge to develop for the production of the next crop.

Adaptation

The banana is adapted to low elevation, well-drained lands in the tropics where no frost occurs. Uniformly high temperatures with maximum sunshine are essential to high yields of fruit. Optimum temperatures range from 75° to 85°F, with a minimum tolerance of 45° to 48°F. The crop is grown commercially in the tropical rainforest, *Af*, climate, with some production in the tropical savanna, *Aw*, climate. Large quantities of water are required for successful production, preferably 75 to 100 inches so distributed that there is no drought. Where dry seasons occur, as in northern Honduras, southern Jamaica, certain areas in Colombia, and western Central America, supplemental irrigation is used (Jones and Darkenwald, 1954).

Soils should be fertile, friable, and have good aggregation characteristics. The topsoil is particularly important because the banana plant has a shallow root system. To prevent waterlogging around the roots, clay content should be less than 40%. Good drainage is absolutely necessary for the production of high quality fruit, especially where irrigation is practiced. According to Pope (1926), more harm may be done to the banana crop by having too much water than by having too little water.

The banana plant is best adapted to locations having little or no wind. The normal trade winds of the tropics are usually not injurious, but high winds whip the young leaves into ribbons and retard normal development. When the fruit is maturing, wind damage may be disastrous. Plants may be blown down and much of the crop lost. Windbreaks of rapidly growing trees, such as bamboos for plantations and the legume, *Leucaena glauca*, for small areas, have been used successfully in some areas for reducing the wind hazard (Ochse, *et al*, 1961).

TABLE 14-2. WORLD PRODUCTION OF EXPORT BANANAS*

Area and Country	Thousands of Bunches, or Stems			
	1951–1955 Average	1957	1958	1959
American tropics				
Ecuador	19,109	33,500	38,052	44,838
Honduras	14,290	17,775	21,534	19,235
Costa Rica	15,644	13,681	13,297	10,255
Brazil	8,775	9,634	11,969	12,000
Panama	8,611	12,787	11,780	10,720
Guatemala	7,091	8,559	7,617	8,832
Colombia	6,968	8,625	8,505	9,892
Jamaica	5,251	6,367	5,581	5,819
Guadeloupe	3,126	3,502	4,147	5,136
Martinique	2,435	4,258	4,160	5,795
Mexico	2,078	1,565	1,111	1,262
Dominican Republic	1,779	2,283	3,280	4,000
Windward Islands	677	2,343	2,686	4,364
Africa				
Nigeria and Cameroun	6,984	7,243	7,086	5,570
French Guinea and Ivory Coast	4,249	4,754	4,900	4,894
Somaliland	1,595	1,877	1,984	2,034
Republic of Congo	990	1,581	1,252	1,371
Asia				
Taiwan	1,460	1,105	1,825	1,993
Lebanon	154	478	694	600
Oceana	692	1,014	1,440	1,409
World	121,068	151,769	160,882	168,287

* Data from U.S.D.A. Foreign Agric. Service.

World Centers of Production

Major centers of banana production for export trade include Ecuador,
Costa Rica, Panama, Honduras, Colombia, Guatemala, Jamaica, Brazil,
and equatorial Africa (Table 14-2 and Figure 14-2). In the Central American area, the production picture has changed drastically during recent
years because of the prevalence of Panama disease, caused by the fungus
Fusarium oxysporum cubense. Acreage has been shifted from Atlantic and

FIGURE 14-2.

*Banana production in the Caribbean and Ecuadorean areas. In recent years
there has been a shift to Pacific lowlands in Mexico, Guatemala, Costa Rica,
Panama and Ecuador.* [*Based on data from Jones and Morrison,* Econ. Geog.
28:1–19, 1952, and Parsons, Econ. Geog. *33:201–216, 1957.*]

Gulf lowlands to Pacific lowlands of Costa Rica and Ecuador (Jones and Morrison, 1952; Parsons, 1957; May and Plaza, 1958). Some areas have been completely abandoned. In others, through the practice of continuous flooding for several months, and the use of a control spray of copper sulfate and lime, production has been continued. Varieties resistant to Panama disease are being developed. Another major disease, prevalent in all Caribbean areas, is the Sigatoka leaf spot, caused by *Cercospora musae*. Maximum production of high quality fruit is cut, but the disease does not kill the plant. Control can be achieved by frequent spraying with Bordeaux mixture, but this adds greatly to the cost of production.

In international trade, the United States consumes about 63% of total banana imports. France, the United Kingdom, Argentina, and Spain also import substantial quantities. With the relatively small acreage suited to banana production and export marketing and the rapidly increasing world population, the demand for this crop will probably require some expansion of production in the near future.

SUGARCANE

Sugar is a commodity of great importance in world trade. It is an essential food, and every nation is vitally interested in having a continuous supply. In the production of sugar we find an example of both the importance of climatic adaptation and the restrictions on distribution and production imposed by man. Of the world's production of sugar, approximately 60% comes from sugarcane and 40% from sugar beets.

Species and Varieties

Sugarcane is a tropical perennial grass, characterized by the high sucrose content of its mature stalks.

It was cultivated as a crop in India and Indonesia before the dawn of history (Mangelsdorf, 1950). Five species are known:

1. *Saccharum officinarum*—large stalked, soft, juicy, and sweet. The early Dutch sugar breeders in Java called these varieties "noble" canes. The chromosome number is 2n = 80.

2. *S. sinense*—hardy, slender, with low sucrose content. These are also called Chinese or Uba canes. The 2n chromosome number = 118.

3. *S. barberi*—slender stalks, of Indian origin. The chromosome number varies: 2n = 82, 90, 92, 107, 116, and 124.

4. *S. spontaneum*—widely diverse forms which develop rhizomes. These are found in tropical Africa, Asia, Taiwan, Japan, New Guinea, and

Oceania. The chromosome number varies: 2n = 48, 50, 72, 80, 96, 112, 120, and 128.

5. *S. robustum*—wild type found in New Guinea, New Britain, and New Hibrides. Stalks are large and woody. Chromosome number varies: 2n = 60, 70, 80, 90, 100, . . . , 144.

Present day leading varieties are complex hybrids synthesized by bringing together a diversity of genotypes, from both cultivated and wild forms (Mangelsdorf, 1950). These varieties are characterized by their high tonnage, high sucrose content, rapid regrowth of ratoon crops, and resistance to diseases and insect pests.

The sugarcane plant is propagated vegetatively, so that once an improved hybrid seedling is selected, it is a relatively simple matter to increase it for commercial production. In Hawaii, practically all of the commercial varieties grown today trace to hybrid seedlings first selected in the period from 1930 to 1940 (or later). A major principle in cane-breeding philosophy has been to place emphasis on genetic diversity (Warner, 1954).

It seems to be the history of improved varieties that eventually they show some weakness and suffer a yield decline. This has puzzled geneticists for years but there is still no good explanation for this decline. Various aspects of this decline were considered at the 10th World Congress of the International Society of Sugarcane Technologists. It is believed that fungi, viruses, and nematodes all may be contributing factors. Crop damage becomes more important as a promising clone is propagated extensively over a wide range of plantation conditions. The best genetic approach would appear to be an active breeding program with decentralized testing of all promising hybrid seedlings, and the maintenance of a high degree of diversity in the breeding material (Mangelsdorf, 1959).

In most sugarcane production areas, no rotation with other crops is practiced. Large quantities of plant refuse have been incorporated into the soil over the years, and commercial fertilizers have been applied in liberal quantities. As a result, yields have been maintained and in many instances even increased over what they were 50 years ago (Pemberton, 1957). In 1953, on the island of Oahu, four plantations reported average sugar yields of 13.6 tons per acre (18–24 months) from 103.7 tons of cane per acre.

Adaptation

Sugarcane grows best in frost-free climates, *Af* and *Aw*, with plenty of warm to hot sunny weather. Such conditions are found in Cuba, Puerto Rico and Hawaii, where the monthly mean temperatures range from 70°

to 80°F throughout the year. The so-called "noble" canes, originating in Java, are known especially for their narrow tolerance or sensitivity to environment. These canes are characterized by their thick, relatively soft stalks and their high sugar content. In Hawaii, Burr *et al.* (1957) reported that a root temperature of 80°F is optimum for growth of cane and for nutrient absorption. Below 70°F, root growth is retarded and at 50°F no growth takes place. Full sunshine is important, yields being reduced practically one-half by cutting the light to one-half full sunshine. Cool nights are harmful, an air temperature of 53°F being about the lowest temperature tolerated without some harmful effect on the plants.

In the subtropics, sugarcane is grown commercially at latitudes of approximately 30° in Louisiana, Egypt, Australia, Argentina, Natal and other areas. Growth and yields are limited by winter temperatures, however, which often go as low as 32° or 34°F on many winter nights (Ochse, *et al*, 1961).

Stalk length growth varies directly with temperature. At low elevations in Hawaii, a crop comes to full maturity in two years or less. At 3000 feet, maturity will be reached a year later. In some places at the Equator, cane may be grown at elevations as high as 5000 feet.

The general crop cycle for sugarcane in Hawaii is about eight years. The plant crop comes to maturity in 20 to 24 months. Then three ratoon crops usually follow, each of which has a similar growth period. A growth in stalk length of 12 feet per year is expected, varying from .53 feet in February (mean temperature, 70°F) to 2.14 feet in July (mean temperature 77.8°F).

Without irrigation, a rainfall of 45 inches or more is desirable. In the tropical savanna, *Aw*, climate, harvesting and hauling is done in the dry season. Topography should be level to only slightly rolling, in order that heavy machinery for planting and harvesting may be used.

Because of the heavy production of dry matter, sugarcane depletes soil fertility. Nitrogen is required in practically all fields, and most soils require phosphorus and potassium as well. In Hawaii, calcium and magnesium are deficient in some areas. Cane leaves and parts of stalks may be incorporated into the soil, adding a good deal of organic matter over a period of years.

World Production of Sugarcane

Cuba, endowed with a nearly ideal climate and favorable soil, has been the world's leading producer of cane sugar. Other important production centers include Brazil, India, Puerto Rico, Hawaii, Australia, Continental United States, Peru, Argentina, and Java (Figure 14-3). Estimated world

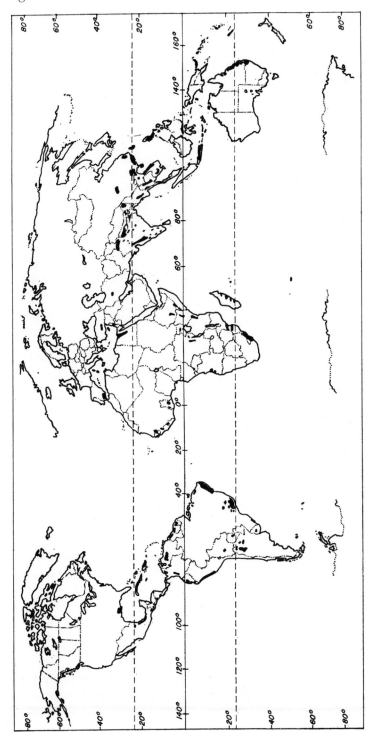

FIGURE 14-3.

Sugarcane: major producing areas of the world. [Courtesy United Nations, F.A.O., and U. S. Dept. Agriculture, Foreign Agricultural Service.]

production of sugar, including the distribution of production in the major cane areas is given in Table 14-3.

TABLE 14-3. DISTRIBUTION OF WORLD PRODUCTION OF SUGAR FROM SUGARCANE (with Comparative Summary of Production from Sugar Beets)*

Country	Production in Thousands of Short Tons			
	1950–1959 average	1958	1959	1960
Cuba	6,090	6,625	6,460	5,800
Brazil	2,611	3,770	3,562	3,877
India	2,158	2,642	3,308	3,595
United States				
Mainland	578	578	615	670
Hawaii	1,032	975	930	1,100
Philippines	1,277	1,522	1,530	1,562
Australia	1,256	1,525	1,543	1,401
Puerto Rico	1,155	1,067	1,019	1,150
Union of S. Africa	760	1,135	1,062	1,007
Indonesia	743	854	942	795
Argentina	773	1,184	1,041	760
Dominican Republic	718	994	880	1,175
Peru	645	794	870	880
Jamaica	364	421	480	500
World cane	26,463	31,333	31,808	32,158
World beet	17,984	23,032	21,731	25,564
World sugar total	44,447	54,365	53,539	57,722

* Data from U.S.D.A. Foreign Agric. Service.

In the future, mechanization is bound to increase. Organized labor and high costs of production have forced this trend in Hawaii in recent years. Most of the crop in Louisiana has been harvested mechanically for some time. As labor problems increase, production will undoubtedly become more and more mechanized. To be justified, however, machines must increase productivity sufficiently to offset the cost. Equally important to the success of the sugar industry of the future is improved human relations (Leffingwell, 1957).

COFFEE

The production of coffee is an established export industry in many tropical countries. Tropical America, however, and Brazil in particular, is the primary source of the world's supply. The coffee-producing region in Brazil is located mainly on a great plateau where modern agronomic methods are practiced. This is in contrast to many other countries where coffee is grown on rough, hilly lands unsuitable to extensive production methods. In some of these countries, however, coffees of exceptional flavor and quality are grown. These are highly desirable for blending with Brazilian coffee and, even though they are produced at higher costs, they occupy an important place in the coffee markets of the world.

Coffee is indigenous to Africa. Of the many species of *Coffea*, only three have been found useful for coffee production, *Coffea arabica*, *C. robusta* and *C. liberica*. The *arabica* species is believed to have originated in Abyssinia, and the other two are probably native to the Congo basin and Liberia. Of the three species, *Coffea arabica* is by far the most important.

Adaptation

Although coffee is grown widely throughout the tropics and warmer subtropics, the crop is better adapted to the savanna, *Aw*, and particularly to the tropical highland, *Aw-Cw*, climates than to the rainforest, *Af*, climates.

Altitude

Coffee is grown from sea level to 7000 feet. In Kenya, the plantings are all at high elevations, 4000 to 7000 feet; in Malay, 2000 to 4000 feet; in Colombia and Costa Rica, 3000 to 6000 feet; in Hawaii, 800 to 2000 feet. Plantings in Brazil range from 1800 to 3000 feet in the Saõ Paulo region to elevations as low as 800 feet in the Rio de Janeiro section. Altitude is important chiefly in its effect on temperature, rainfall, and humidity, but it is believed also that the lower atmospheric pressures at higher altitudes also may have a stimulating effect. *Coffea arabica* is best adapted to higher altitudes, whereas *C. robusta* and *C. liberica* are better adapted to low elevations (Ripperton, Goto, and Pahau, 1935; Bengston and Van Royen, 1950; Drew, 1956).

Temperature

The range of coffee production is limited (approximately) by the 55°F isotherm for the coldest month and near the equator by the annual mean maximum of 77°F. In most coffee-growing regions, the mean annual temperature is approximately 70°F, or slightly higher. However, much of the world's crop today is produced near the coldward limit of adaptation in the Saõ Paulo and Paraná districts of Brazil at the border of the tropics (James, 1932). Here, we find the typical highland modification of the tropical savanna climate, called by Trewartha (1954) *Aw-Cw*. The average minimum temperature is 63°F, the average maximum, 77°F, and the annual mean approximately 68°F. Cold winds and frosts which occur occasionally in the Paraná district may cause great damage to coffee trees; a few hours of temperature close to freezing may kill the trees or greatly retard their growth.

At or near the Equator, the combination of high temperature and high moisture is undesirable, and direct sunlight at that latitude may be detrimental. Shade is essential for coffee production near the Equator, but is not considered necessary in the Brazilian district near the Tropic of Capricorn (Shaw, 1955). According to Ochse, et al (1961), the effect of shade is indirect, being less essential on the better soils and where atmospheric humidity is fairly high.

Rainfall

Successful coffee production has been possible with as little as 30 inches of rainfall or as much as 100 inches, but 45 to 70 inches annually is considered best. Definite wet and dry seasons are desirable. A dry season aids greatly in picking, drying, pruning, and other operations. Rainfall in the Saõ Paulo area is considered ideally distributed when it includes eight to fourteen inches per month for six months after the first blossom, two to four inches per month for the next three months, and none during the following three months. Heavy rains during the flowering season may reduce the crop considerably. In Colombia, the distribution of rainfall results in two crops, one in fall and one in spring. In most places, one crop is produced, maturing over a period of three to four months (Ripperton, Goto, and Pahau, 1938).

Topography and Soil

Gentle slopes and adequate soil and air drainage are necessary. Coffee trees soon die in flat areas on heavy clay soils. This adaptation has restricted coffee growing mainly to the hilly or rolling uplands, and in some instances to high, level plateaus with deep porous soils. Even steep slopes are used successfully in the Kona district of Hawaii.

The flavor of coffee is influenced greatly by climate and soil. In general, coffee grown at high elevations tends to have a mellow or "soft" flavor as contrasted to the "hard," penetrating flavor of lowland coffee. Much commercial coffee is blended and it is well known that some coffees, especially from certain growing districts, are more desirable than others in their blending qualities.

One of the weaknesses of the coffee industry is the characteristic sharp year-to-year fluctuation in yield. According to Wickizer (1951), this charac-

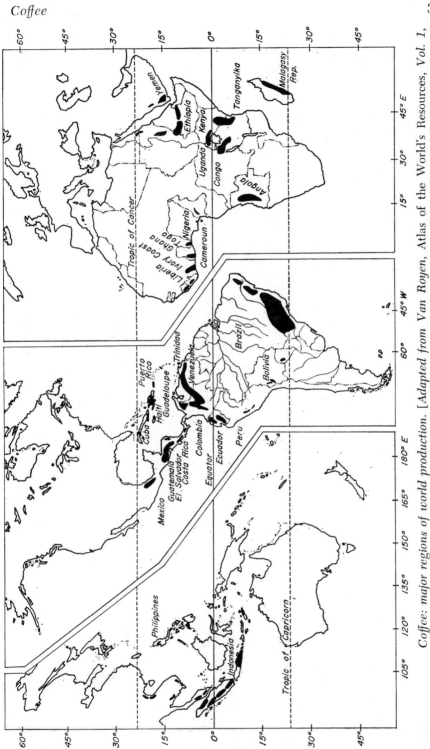

Coffee: major regions of world production. [Adapted from Van Royen, Atlas of the World's Resources, Vol. 1, The Agricultural Resources of the World, (C), 1954, Prentice-Hall, Englewood Cliffs, N. J. and U.S.D.A., Foreign Agricultural Service.]

FIGURE 14-4.

teristic of production is particularly serious in the Saõ Paulo region. A large yield one year will almost invariably be followed by a small yield the next. The magnitude of fluctuation is great, tenfold differences being not uncommon.

World Production and Consumption

Brazil produces approximately half the world's export crop of coffee. Colombia ranks second, with a production of one-third that of Brazil (Figure 14-4). These two countries tend to dominate the production and export market. Other important areas of production include the Caribbean-

TABLE 14-4.   PRODUCTION OF COFFEE IN SELECTED
                        COUNTRIES *

Area and Country	Thousands of Bags of Green Coffee (132.276 lbs. each)		
	1951–1955 average	1959–1960	1960–1961
South America			
Brazil	18,964	44,000	30,000
Colombia	6,330	8,000	8,000
Venezuela	729	750	875
Caribbean Area			
Mexico	1,373	2,025	1,900
El Salvador	1,216	1,575	1,525
Guatemala	1,129	1,600	1,525
Costa Rica	439	905	1,145
Cuba	542	850	800
Nicaragua	362	375	450
Dominican Republic	455	585	500
Africa			
Ivory Coast	1,210	2,578	2,678
Angola	990	1,700	2,000
Uganda	754	1,950	2,130
Republic of Congo	613	1,700	1,600
Ethiopia	613	950	900
Malagasy Republic	634	800	875
Cameroun	180	525	550
Asia			
Indonesia	985	1,500	1,500
India	387	800	850
World	41,015	78,988	65,212

* Data from U.S.D.A. Foreign Agric. Service.

Central American region (Mexico, Central America, and West Indies), and Africa (French West Africa, Angola, Kenya, Uganda, and Tanganyika). Data on world production of coffee are presented in Table 14-4.

The coffee market has lacked stability, a situation highly unsatisfactory to both producers and consumers. Through a period of years, efforts by Brazil to maintain prices on the world market by a valorization scheme were not successful. With the adoption of the Latin American Coffee Agreement in the autumn of 1958 and the International Coffee Agreement in 1960, a greater stability in coffee prices may be expected in the future.

Consumption of coffee, especially in the United States, the Scandinavian countries, and other middle-latitude regions, has increased markedly since World War II. With the advent of the "coffee break," now an established institution in a majority of business and government offices, the trend in increased use appears likely to continue (Brazilian Government Trade Bureau, 1952).

Changes in Brazil's producing districts have been taking place. Production in the Saõ Paulo district has decreased during the past 15 years, whereas production in the newer Paraná area has increased markedly. The Paraná area is close to the coldward limit of production, however, and the frost hazard is greater than in the Saõ Paulo district. It seems likely that Brazil will continue to dominate coffee production because it possesses such a high proportion of the total potential production area (Shaw, 1955). It is unlikely that all of this area will be needed for coffee production in the near future.

Production in Africa could also be increased if the world market required it, but in the West Indies, Venezuela, and Central America, actual production is considered close to potential.

References

1. Bengston, N. A. and Van Royen, Wm. 1950. *Fundamentals of Economic Geography*. Prentice-Hall, New York.
2. Brazilian Government Trade Bureau. 1952. Brazilian Bulletin, Jan. 15, p. 1.
3. Burr, G. O., Hart, C. E., Brodie, H. W., Tanimoto, T., Kortschak, H. P., Tokahashi, D., Ashton, F., and Coleman, R. E. 1957. The sugarcane plant. *Ann. Rev. Plant Phys.* 8: 275–308.
4. Cheesman, E. E. 1939. History of some well known West Indian staples. *Trop. Agr.* 16: 105.
5. Drew, C. G. A. 1956. Green coffee production and distribution. *Trop. Agr.* 33 (3): 190–200.

6. James, Preston E. 1932. Coffee lands of southeastern Brazil. *Geog. Rev.* 22: 225–244.

7. Jonasson, Olof. 1951. Potential areas of cacao production in South America. *Econ. Geog.* 27: 90–93.

8. Jones, C. F. and Morrison, P. C. 1952. Evolution of the banana industry in Costa Rica. *Econ. Geog.* 28: 1–19.

9. Jones, C. F. and Darkenwald, G. G. 1954. *Economic Geography.* Macmillan, New York.

10. Leffingwell, R. J. 1957. Sugar's progress in human relations. *Sugar* 52 (12): 44.

11. Mangelsdorf, A. J. 1950. Sugarcane—as seen from Hawaii. *Econ. Bot.* 4: 150–176.

12. ———. 1959. Genetic aspects of yield decline. Abstract of paper presented at 10th Congress Inter. Soc. Sugarcane Tech. Honolulu, 1959. *Sugar* 54 (8): 40.

13. May, Stacy and Plaza, Galo. 1958. *United Fruit Company in Latin America.* National Planning Assoc.

14. Ochse, J. J., Soule, M. J., Jr., Dijkman, M. J. and Wehlburg, C. 1961. *Tropical and Subtropical Agriculture.* Macmillan, New York.

15. Parsons, J. J. 1957. Bananas in Ecuador. *Econ. Geog.* 33: 201–216.

16. Pemberton, C. E. 1957. The Hawaiian sugar industry. *World Crops.* 9: 237–241.

17. Pope, W. T. 1926. Banana culture in Hawaii. Hawaii Agr. Exp. Sta. Bul. 55.

18. Ripperton, J. C., Goto, Y. B., and Pahau, R. K. 1935. Coffee cultural practices in the Kona district of Hawaii. Hawaii Agr. Exp. Sta. Bul. 75.

19. Shaw, Earl B. 1955. *World Economic Geography.* Wiley, New York.

20. Trewartha, G. T. 1954. *An Introduction to Climate.* McGraw-Hill, New York.

21. Warner, John N. 1954. Hawaii's cane breeding philosophy. *Sugar* 49 (11): 33–35.

22. Wickizer, V. D. 1951. *Coffee, Tea and Cocoa.* Ford Research Institute. Stanford Univ. Press.

Chapter 15

Crops of the Subtropics

The subtropics comprise a number of climatic types, including subtropical humid, *Caf*, dry-summer Mediterranean, *CS*, and West Coast Marine, *Cw*, climates. It follows that a wide variety of crops is grown in these agriculturally favorable climates, including citrus, olives, grapes, vegetables, sugarcane, cotton, cereal grains, and forage crops.

In the humid subtropics of the United States, agriculture was dominated for many years by cotton, although this crop has become less and less important in recent decades. In South America, grazing assumes major importance in the subtropical climates, in Africa sugar is important, and in southeast Asia rice is the dominant crop. To illustrate the distribution of crops in the subtropical regions, rice and cotton will be treated in this chapter.

RICE

Rice is one of the two most important cereals in the world, its total production comparing favorably with that of wheat. It is the principal food crop of nearly half of all the world's people, and is especially important in the tropical and subtropical coastal regions and river basins of eastern and southern Asia. Countries leading in rice production are China, India, Japan, Pakistan, and Indonesia. According to Vavilov (1951), rice originated in India and spread eastward into China by 3000 B.C. Native wild species, including *Oryza sativa spontanea, O. minuta,* and *O. latifolia,* are found growing in the Orient today.

According to Martin and Leonard (1949), rice was planted for the first time in the United States in South Carolina about 1685. The crop spread to North Carolina and Georgia, where it was grown mainly on delta lands until the Civil War period. After 1880, production along the Mississippi River in Louisiana increased considerably, and spread to the Gulf coastal prairies of Louisiana and Texas. By 1905 rice was being cultivated in eastern Arkansas, and by 1912 in the Sacramento Valley in California.

Rice (*Oryza sativa*) is an annual grass, which tillers freely and grows to a height of from two to six feet. The grain is enclosed in the lemma and palea, which constitute a tough hull. The color of unmilled rice varies with variety, but may be white, brown, amber, red, or purple.

In general, rice is classified on the basis of length of grain, into short-, medium-, or long-grain types. A description of important varieties and characteristics of varieties of these three types has been given by Jones, *et al* (1953). The long-grain varieties have long, slender grains and are vitreous in texture. This type of rice usually commands the highest price on the market. The percentage of husk in long grain varieties is higher than in the medium- and short-grain types, but cooking quality is considered superior because the kernels tend to retain their whole-grain shape. Rexoro and Fortuna are typical of the leading long-grained, late-maturing varieties of the southern states.

Short-grain varieties (sometimes called pearl rice) have short, blunt kernels with a starchy texture. Milling quality is higher than in the long-grain type but, when cooked, kernels tend to lose their shape and become sticky and moist. Short-grained varieties are predominant in California, whereas medium- and long-grained sorts are grown widely in Arkansas, Louisiana, and Texas (Jones, *et al*, 1941). Caloro is the most popular short-grained variety and is similar to Japanese varieties. Among medium-grained varieties, Blue Rose, Zenith, Calrose, and Magnolia are important varieties. Preferences for long- or short-grained types appear to be based mainly on custom and usage by people in different parts of the world.

Early-maturing varieties require 120 to 130 days from seeding to maturity, whereas late varieties require 140 or more days. Some varieties show a marked response to day-length. The variety Blue Rose, for example, tends to mature at about the same time when sown over a wide range of planting dates. The late variety Rexoro, however, matures very late when sown late, for a long growing period is necessary regardless of seeding date (Jenkins, 1936).

Adaptation

Rice is unique among cereals in its ability to germinate and grow successfully in water or submerged conditions. The plant can transport oxygen from the leaves to the roots and thus live normally in an aquatic environment (Jones, 1940; Taylor, 1942). It may be considered a facultative hydrophyte. Factors which operate to limit rice production in the United States are unfavorable temperatures, lack of sufficient fresh water for irrigation, and unfavorable soils. For germination, rice needs a minimum temperature of approximately 52° to 54°F; for flowering, 72° to 73°F; and for grain formation, 69° to 70°F (Thomas, 1957). A rather warm tempera-

FIGURE 15-1.

Distribution of rice acreage in the United States in 1954. Each dot represents 1,000 acres. [By permission from Poehlman, Breeding Field Crops, *1959, Henry Holt, New York.]*

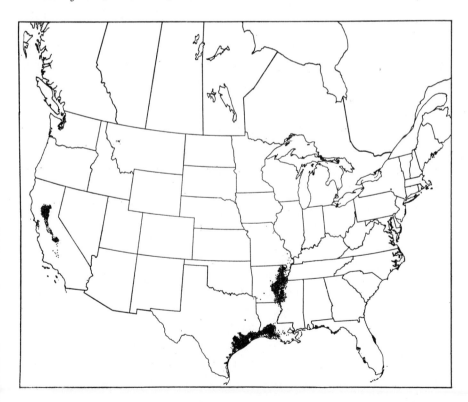

ture, 70°F or above, is needed for the entire growing period, which may extend over a period of four to six months. Rice is grown extensively in the *Caf, Caw, Aw,* and to some extent in the *Cs* climates. In Japan, through selection and breeding, early-maturing varieties have been developed which are adapted as far north as Hokkaido Island, in a *Dbf* climate.

Suitable soils for rice are most important. In Louisiana, the Crowley silt loam, which is underlain at from 1.5 to 5.0 feet by an impervious subsoil, is considered a good soil for rice. In California, the Stockton adobe-clay soil is characteristic of good rice soils. These soils do not lose water rapidly by seepage, which makes the use of irrigation water more efficient. In general culture, the land is flooded to a depth of four to six inches, either after the rice seedlings are six to ten inches tall, or just prior to seeding or transplanting, if the transplanting method is used. The crop is grown under submerged conditions for four or five months, usually until it nears maturity. A deviation from this system in Spain is described by Thomas (1957). Here the rice field is drained and dried out for from four to ten days after being inundated for about three weeks. This alternation of watering and drying is continued until the crop reaches maturity. In California, airplanes are used to sow much of the rice directly on the water surface after the fields are flooded.

There are upland varieties of rice, grown on a relatively small scale, which produce a crop without irrigation in regions of fairly high rainfall. The distribution of rice production in the United States is indicated by Figure 15-1.

World Production of Rice

A highly important crop in many countries of the world, rice is widely distributed, as indicated by production figures in Table 15-1.

Because rice is the staple food crop for such a high proportion of the world's population, it appears likely that production will continue at an increasing level in the near future. Since 1949, the International Rice Commission has given attention to problems of possible mechanization of rice production in wet paddy conditions where the crop has been produced up to now mainly by hand labor. The Food and Agriculture Organization of the United Nations has also studied many local problems in connection with handling irrigation water and management of the rice crop. This work has been done in cooperation with the governments of Burma, Ceylon, India, Japan, the Netherlands, Thailand, and United Kingdom (United Nations, F.A.O. Committee, Inter. Rice Com., 1957). It promises to improve rice growing conditions in many areas where mechanical power

TABLE 15-1. WORLD PRODUCTION OF RICE (rough)*

Area and Country	Acreage (1000 a.) 1950–1954 average	Production in Millions of Pounds		
		1950–1954 average	1958–1959	1959–1960
Asia				
China	59,200	133,730	175,000	155,000
India	75,434	82,150	102,080	99,000
Pakistan	23,226	28,024	26,534	31,817
Japan	7,754	26,317	33,050	33,450
Indonesia	15,939	23,118	26,963	27,500
Burma	10,780	13,900	17,300	18,300
Thailand	13,153	15,281	15,540	15,997
Vietnam	15,939	4,880	9,480	11,685
Philippines	6,264	6,603	8,122	8,100
South Korea	2,550	6,546	7,173	7,145
Taiwan	1,912	4,565	5,499	5,200
Cambodia	2,838	2,821	3,000	3,250
Malaya	836	1,453	1,575	1,990
Ceylon	920	1,223	1,697	1,645
Americas				
Brazil	5,362	7,182	9,206	9,620
United States	2,068	5,002	4,438	5,312
Colombia	404	584	840	930
Mexico	235	370	556	520
Cuba	175	320	497	550
Africa				
Egypt	539	1,829	2,265	3,384
Malagasy Republic	1,705	2,194	1,985	2,750
Europe				
Italy	409	1,881	1,625	1,570
World	257,140	394,974	486,760	480,650

* Data from U.S.D.A. Foreign Agric. Service.

equipment has not been available. Recently a new rice research institute has been established in the Philippines, with the primary objective of greatly improving the basic food supply of that tropical country (Harrar, 1960).

COTTON

Cotton produces the world's most important vegetable fiber. It has been grown as a crop for fiber in India for perhaps 4000 years and was known in Peru as early as 1000 B.C. (Brown and Ware, 1958).

Cotton belongs to the genus *Gossypium* of the *Malvaceae* family. Three major groups are recognized, based on geographic distribution: (1) Asiatic diploid species (n = 13), (2) American diploid species (n = 13), and (3) American and Polynesian amphidiploid species (n = 26) (Stephens, 1947). A number of theories on the origin of the New World amphidiploid cottons have been advanced (Beasley, 1940; Harland, 1941; Hutchinson, Silow and Stephens, 1947). Hutchinson, Silow, and Stephens suggested that Asiatic cottons were carried by an early civilization across the Pacific to the New World in prehistoric times, and that natural hybridization of this cultivated crop with wild American species gave rise to the first amphidiploid. The new species may have spread under cultivation without having to survive indefinitely in competition with native climax vegetation. There is ample evidence that no species of *Gossypium* can survive competition and shading, and will form part of a climax vegetation only in semidesert areas in sparse, xerophytic associations (Hutchinson, Silow, and Stephens, 1947). New World wild cotton species all have spinnable lint, which suggests that they may have been used by man for fiber before the advent of the amphidiploid species. Two centers of origin for American cultivated species were recognized by Vavilov (1951): one for American Upland, *G. hirsutum*, in southern Mexico and Central America, the other for Sea Island types, *G. barbadense*, in the Andean region of Peru, Ecuador, and Colombia. The American species have proved to be remarkably plastic from the genetic standpoint, and a significant range of types, widely adapted geographically, have been developed by breeding (Richmond, 1950).

The cotton plant is usually considered to be an annual, but under tropical conditions where the mean temperature of the coldest months does not fall below 65°F, it behaves as a true perennial. The plant is herbaceous, with a long taproot and an upright stem attaining a height of two to five feet. Two buds are produced at the base of each leaf petiole: the axillary bud, which continues to make vegetative growth, and an extra-axillary bud, which produces the fruiting branch (Hancock, 1941).

Flowers may be arranged on alternate sides of the fruiting branch. There are three large leaflike bracts at the base of the flower, above which is a true calyx consisting of five unequally lobed sepals. The corolla consists of five petals, ranging in color from white to yellow to purple in different varieties. The staminal column bears ten more or less double rows of stamens, and the pistil is made up of three to five carpils. The fruit is the enlarged ovary that develops into a three- to five-loculed ball, usually one and one-half to two inches in length. The cotton seeds are covered with lint hairs (fibers) and usually also have a covering of short fuzz

(Gore, 1935). Cotton fibers are single-cell hairs growing out from certain epidermal cells of the seed (Brown, 1934). Length of fibers (staple length) is influenced by soil fertility and availability of moisture to some extent, but a characteristic length is associated with the genetic makeup of the variety or type of cotton. Staple length is longest in the Sea Island type, next longest in Egyptian, then American Upland long staple, American Upland short staple, and, shortest of all, Asiatic cottons.

Adaptation

Cotton is adapted to the humid subtropics, *Ca*, climate, where the frost-free season is at least 200–210 days, and the summer isotherm about 77°F or more. In latitude, cotton is grown from 32° south to 37° north, except in the Ukraine where it is grown still farther north. The minimum rainfall limit is considered to be about 20 to 25 inches, unless irrigation is practiced. Total autumn rainfall in excess of ten inches is likely to be injurious, and relatively dry, cool conditions at harvest time are much to be preferred.

Cotton planting is delayed in spring until the days and nights are quite warm, with an average temperature of 60° to 62°F. An abundance of sunshine and a moderate amount of moisture is required. Heavy rains at planting time and during early growth stages are undesirable, for a shallow root system may develop. Later, too much rain may cause excessive shedding of leaves, squares, blooms, and bolls. Late in the season, rains stimulate top growth, delay maturity, interfere with picking, and discolor lint.

Eaton (1950) reported that temperature and day-length were important in influencing the type of branching which occurs on the cotton plant. Cool days and cool nights result in mostly vegetative branches, but cool days and hot nights result in mainly fruiting branches. Some varieties respond to day-length, requiring short days for normal fruiting. Other varieties, especially early American Upland cottons and some wild Mexican forms, show no day-length reaction.

Under conditions of moisture stress, vegetative growth may decrease by half, and boll periods and boll sizes may be reduced, but with no appreciable effect on relative fruitfulness (Eaton, 1950). The bolls seem to occupy a favored nutritional position.

In addition to the *Ca* climates, cotton is grown in the subtropical steppe, *BSh*, the Mediterranean, *Cs*, the low-latitude desert, *BWh*, and the tropical savanna, *Aw*, climates.

Soils which were formed under grassland or well-drained, alluvial flood plains are best. Heavy clays tend to delay maturity, and result in greater vegetative growth, which is not desirable from the standpoint of potential insect damage. Level or gently rolling land is preferred because of the rapid trend toward complete mechanization of field operations.

The alluvial soils of the Tennessee, Mississippi, Arkansas, and Red River valleys have furnished excellent cotton lands. The Mississippi Valley region, from the tip of southern Illinois to Louisiana, including the famous Delta area of Mississippi, produces the highest yields per acre in the southeastern states.

In Texas, grasslands of the central and western parts have furnished the best cotton soils. These soils are dark, friable, and high in organic matter and lime. Rainfall, both in total amount and in variability in this steppe climate, constitutes a prime factor in keeping yields lower than in more favorable areas (Jones and Darkenwald, 1954).

The highest yields of cotton in the United States are produced under irrigation in the far west, in the Salt River Valley of Arizona and the San Joaquin of California. Here, the climate is characterized by extremely dry, hot summers and mild winters. According to Trewartha's modified classification, cotton is grown in this region in the Mediterranean, *Cs*, climate, and also in the subtropical steppe and desert climates, *BSh* and *BWh*.

Shaw (1955) has noted the great influence of rivers in contributing fertile soils to many of the world's cotton lands, such as the Mississippi, the Paraná, and the Yangtze and its tributaries. Others of importance primarily for the water they supply for cotton production are the Nile in Egypt and Sudan, the Indus in Pakistan, the Rio Grande in Texas, and the Sacramento and San Joaquin in California.

Irrigation practices vary greatly with the nature of the soil, the amount and distribution of the rainfall, the temperature and humidity of the atmosphere. In general, it is desirable to obtain rapid growth early in the season, before heavy fruiting. In Arizona it was shown by Harris, *et al* (1942, 1947) that plants in plots receiving irrigation soon after planting were stimulated into rapid and extensive vegetative growth prior to heavy flowering; these plots consistently outyielded plots in which the first irrigation was delayed until the plants reached the wilting point.

Insects have played a major role in determining the present distribution of the cotton industry (Gaines, 1950). Cloudy, rainy weather is important in favoring their development, whereas hot, dry weather and cold winters may tend to hold them in check. With the advent of the boll weevil, there was a tendency to extend production north and west, which resulted in a shift from the old cotton belt into the drier areas of Oklahoma and Texas, as well as into the far west, New Mexico, Arizona, and California.

In the southeastern part of the United States, under the old plantation system, each planter carefully selected the seed for planting, and each plantation had its own gin for processing. Later on, public gins became popular and a great mixing of varieties resulted. It was estimated that at one time 1000 varieties were grown in the South.

A campaign to standardize varieties and to establish one-variety communities began in 1931 (Cook, 1932). By 1950 most inferior varieties had disappeared. A few years later it could be said that 87% of all cotton in the United States was planted to only ten varieties, and 67% of the total acreage planted to only three varieties (Westbrook, 1956). This effort has done much to improve the production and quality of the cotton crop.

Fiber Quality and Types

The successful use of cotton in spinning depends on qualities such as length, strength, and fineness of the lint. The length of fiber is closely associated with market value. Instead of the old method of combing out samples and measuring them, a device known as a fibrograph has made possible a rapid method of determining fiber length. Strength of fiber is determined by means of a device known as the Pressley breaker, or a newer device called the Stelometer. For determination of fineness of fiber, the flow of gas through a cotton plug is determined by means of an apparatus called the micronaire (Barker, 1950).

World Cotton Production

The United States produces approximately 40% of the world's cotton distributed approximately as shown in Figure 15-2. Other producing areas in order of importance include the U.S.S.R., India, China, Egypt, Brazil, Pakistan, the East African highlands, Mexico, Turkey, Argentina, and Peru (Table 15-2).

In the U.S.S.R. cotton is grown on the plains and in the valleys on both sides of the Caucasus Mountains and in Asiatic Russia east of the Caspian Sea. Much of this last region has a steppe or desert climate, and according to Michael (1938) cotton is grown farther north in the U.S.S.R. than in any other production area. Irrigation is practiced in much of the cotton-growing region.

In India much of the cotton grown is found in the steppe climate, which is true also for Pakistan. Growing areas in China include the subtropical Yangtze Valley and the plains of Hwang Ho, which have steppe and humid continental climates.

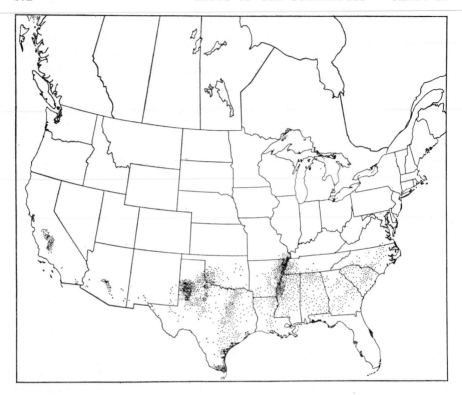

FIGURE 15-2.

Distribution of cotton acreage in the United States in 1954. Each dot represents 10,000 acres. [By permission from Poehlman, Breeding Field Crops, 1959, Henry Holt, New York.]

Brazil has two main areas of production, the northeast steppe and savanna, and the Saõ Paulo region of tropical highland savanna. Peru produces cotton in a low-latitude desert climate under irrigation.

In Africa, Egypt's intensive production comes from low-latitude desert, whereas the east-central African areas of Sudan, Tanganyika, and Uganda are in the tropical savanna climate (Brown, 1952a, 1952b).

Cotton Trends

For 150 years cotton dominated the economics, politics, and social structure of the southern states (Prunty, 1951). It played an important role in the development of world trade, for it led all agricultural exports from the United States for many years. Until after the beginning of World War I,

TABLE 15-2. WORLD PRODUCTION OF COTTON (in 500 pound bales)*

Country	Acreage (1000 a.) 1950–1954 average	Production in Thousands of Bales		
		1950–1954 average	1958–1959	1959–1960
United States	22,861	14,093	14,558	14,553
India	16,463	3,382	3,300	4,000
China	12,740	4,520	8,000	7,500
U.S.S.R.	5,885	4,760	7,300	7,000
Brazil	4,680	1,655	1,700	1,750
Pakistan	3,167	1,321	1,365	1,425
Mexico	1,936	1,333	1,690	1,900
Egypt	1,832	1,705	2,048	2,262
Uganda	1,574	291	300	262
Turkey	1,458	624	850	850
Argentina	1,308	557	415	500
Peru	488	450	525	530
World	81,845	38,832	46,430	47,145

* Data from U.S.D.A. Foreign Agric. Service.

the United States was a debtor nation and the exports of cotton contributed heavily to toward balancing export-import trade. After the war, cotton exports continued until the 1930's, when the best foreign customers no longer had the U. S. dollars for cotton imports. A rapid development in cotton production began to take place in Brazil and Africa. New trade alignments and the marked decline in Europe's export trade in cotton goods resulted in a drastic decline in America's cotton export trade. This decline continued during and following World War II, from which the five major customer countries (for cotton) emerged with little dollar-earning power to import cotton from the United States. The synthetic fiber industry also played a major role in decreasing the use of cotton.

Cotton is still important in world trade because of its great variety of uses. Also, it ships well, keeps well, and has high value per unit of weight. Some of the major importing countries include Great Britain, France, Germany, Italy, Czechoslovakia, Belgium, the Netherlands, the U.S.S.R., and Japan.

Diversification of agriculture in the southern states has greatly changed the importance of cotton in much of that region. Where cotton still is important, greater attention has been given to improving quality and standardizing varieties.

Cotton has been moving west, where Texas and California now lead in total production. With the exceptionally high yields in the Central Valley of California, some of the southeastern producing areas will find it more and more difficult to compete in the future. Mechanization will continue, with less and less labor required to produce cotton in the future. The use of single varieties in large production areas will continue to stabilize yield and quality of lint in those areas (Smith, 1952).

Expansion of cotton production in Brazil and in Mexico is possible, but this depends on more irrigable land becoming available in Mexico and appears rather unlikely in Brazil unless coffee becomes unprofitable. India and China probably will need much of the land available for potential cotton production for food production instead, because of their rapid rate of population increase. The U.S.S.R. is still hoping to expand cotton acreage northward through the use of improved short-season varieties. It would appear that acreage control in the United States will continue because of the unfavorable prospect for any substantial improvement in our export market. Quality of fiber and yield will likely improve even if no greater acreage is devoted to the cotton crop.

References

1. Barker, H. D. 1950. Cotton: Fiber properties and their significance. *Adv. in Agron.* 2. Academic, New York.
2. Beasley, J. O. 1940. The origin of American tetraploid *Gossypium* species. *Amer. Nat.* 74: 285–286.
3. Brown, C. H. 1952a. The Egyptian cotton industry. Part I. *World Crops* 4: 197–200.
4. ———. 1952b. The Egyptian cotton industry. Part II. *World Crops* 4: 244–246.
5. Brown, H. B. 1934. Preliminary studies of length and uniformity of staple of Louisiana cotton varieties. La. Agr. Exp. Sta. Bul. 259.
6. ——— and Ware, J. O. 1958. *Cotton: History, Species, Varieties, Morphology, Breeding, Culture, Diseases, Marketing and Uses.* 3rd Ed. McGraw-Hill, New York.
7. Cooke, F. 1959. World production of cotton. *World Crops.* 11 (6): 235.
8. Cook, O. F. 1932. One-variety cotton communities. U.S.D.A. Bul. 1111.
9. Eaton, E. M. 1950. Physiology of the cotton plant. *Adv. in Agron.* 2: 11–25. Academic, New York.
10. Gaines, J. C. 1950. Cotton: insect pests. *Adv. in Agron.* 2: 32–40. Academic, New York.
11. Gore, U. R. 1935. Morphogenetic studies on the influence of cotton. *Bot. Gaz.* 97: 118–138.
12. Hancock, N. I. 1941. Relative growth rate of the main stem of the cotton plant and its relationship to yield. *Jour. Amer. Soc. Agron.* 33: 590–602.
13. Harland, S. C. 1941. The genetics of cotton. *Jour. Gen.* 42: 1.
14. Harrar, J. G. 1960. International rice research institute. A.I.B.S. Bul. 10 (6): 25–26.

15. Harris, K. and Hawkins, R. S. 1942. Irrigation requirements of cotton on clay loam soils in the Salt River Valley. *Ariz. Agr. Exp. Sta. Bul.* 181.

16. ———, Cords, H. P., and Aepli, D. C. 1947. The irrigation of SXP cotton on clay loam soils in the Salt River Valley. Ariz. Agr. Exp. Sta. Bul. 210.

17. Hutchinson, J. B., Silow, R. A., and Stephens, S. G. 1947. *The Evolution of Gossypium and the Differentiation of the Cultivated Cottons.* Oxford Univ. Press, London.

18. Jenkins, J. M. 1936. Effect of seeding date in the length of the growing period of rice. La. Exp. Sta. Bul. 277.

19. Jones, C. F. and Darkenwald, G. G. 1954. *Economic Geography.* Macmillan, New York.

20. Jones, J. W. 1940. How to grow rice in the Sacramento Valley. U.S.D.A. Farmers Bul. 1240. (revised).

21. Jones, J. W., Adair, C. R., and Beachell, H. M. 1953. Rice varieties and their yields in the United States, 1939–1950. U.S.D.A. Cir. 915.

22. ———, Jenkins, J. W., Nelson, J. M., Carter, L. C., Adair, C. R., Wyche, R. H., Beachell, H. M., Davis, L. L. and King, B. M. 1941. Rice varieties and their comparative yields in the U. S. U.S.D.A. Cir. 612.

23. Martin, J. H. and Leonard, W. H. 1949. *Principles of Field Crop Production.* Macmillan, New York.

24. Michael, L. G. 1938. Cotton growing in the Soviet Union. *Foreign Agr.* 2: 353–382. U. S. Dept Agr., Washington, D. C.

25. Prunty, Merle J. 1951. Recent changes in the southeast United States. *Econ. Geog.* 27: 189–208.

26. Richmond, T. R. 1950. Cotton breeding and improvement. *Adv. in Agron.* 2: 63–74. Academic, New York.

27. Shaw, E. B. 1955. *World Economic Geography.* Wiley, New York.

28. Smith, H. P. 1952. Progress in mechanized cotton production in the U. S. A. *World Crops* 4: 175–178.

29. Stephens, S. G. 1947. Cytogenetics of *Gossypium* and the problems of the origin of New World cottons. *Adv. in Gen.* 1: 431–442. Academic, New York.

30. Taylor, D. L. 1942. Effects of oxygen on respiration, fermentation and growth of wheat and rice. *Sci.* 95: 116–117.

31. Thomas, J. E. 1957. Rice in Spain. *World Crops* 9: 247–250.

32. United Nations, F.A.O. Committee. International Rice Commission. 1957. Rept. on mechanization of rice production. *World Crops* 9: 233–236.

33. Vavilov, N. I. 1951. *The Origin, Variation, Immunity and Breeding of Cultivated Plants.* Ronald, New York.

34. Westbrook, E. C. 1956. One-variety cotton communities. What's New in Crops and Soils. 8: 6.

Chapter 16

Crops of the Intermediate Climates
Maize and Wheat

Two cereal crops, maize* and wheat, will be discussed as examples of crops adapted to the intermediate climates. Maize, a crop of tropical origin, through its great diversity of types and races, has become adapted to a wide range of climates far beyond its original habitat. It has probably reached its greatest potential in the North American corn belt region, located in the humid continental intermediate, *Daf*, climate. Maize is adapted also to portions of the adjacent *Dbf* climate as well as to the subtropical *Caf* and *Cbf* climates. The widespread distribution and prominence of maize as a crop has been brought about, in part by the plant's genetic variability, and in part because of man's ingenuity in developing improved varieties adapted to a wide range of environmental conditions.

Wheat will be discussed as a crop of the dry intermediate climates. Although wheat is widely adapted, from the equator to 60° north latitude, much of the world's production comes from the semiarid or steppe, *BSk* and *BSh* climates. It is well known that wheat does not produce its highest yields in the steppe climate, but, through extensive cultivation and a high degree of mechanization, it may be relatively more efficient than many other crops in those regions. In the United States, Canada and the U.S.S.R. the bulk of the wheat crop is produced in the semiarid, *BSk* climate.

* The word "maize" and "corn" will be used interchangeably in this chapter. Maize is the common name for *Zea mays* in many countries of the world, especially among botanists and geneticists. Corn is the common name for this plant in the United States.

MAIZE (CORN)

Maize, or Indian corn (*Zea mays*), is the greatest contribution of the Americas to the agriculture of the world. Among cereal grain crops, corn ranks third in world production, being surpassed only by wheat and rice. In the United States corn is by far the most important crop in total value. It occupies approximately 20% of the improved farm land and makes up more than 50% of the acreage devoted to all grain crops.

Maize is native to the American tropics, but has attained a truly remarkable total range of adaptation. For centuries, it has been one of the principal food crops in Mexico, Central America, and many of the South American countries. Although many crops were grown by the natives of these areas, including beans, squashes, sweetpotatoes, potatoes, and grain amaranths, none compared with maize in total importance. As pointed out by Weatherwax (1954), the early civilizations of tropical America, those of the Incas of the Peru-Ecuador-Bolivia region, the Mayas of Central America and Yucatan, and the Aztecs of Mexico, all can be considered maize civilizations.

By the time Columbus arrived in America in 1492, maize was being grown widely by the North American Indians. Distribution is believed to have extended from southern North Dakota eastward across to the St. Lawrence Valley and southward to the Gulf of Mexico and the West Indies. A lobe of distribution in the Southwest extended into Arizona, New Mexico, and southern Colorado (Weatherwax and Randolph, 1955). Maize was an important crop to the Mandans of North Dakota, to the Iroquois of New York and the Great Lakes Region, and to the Pueblo Dwellers of the Southwest. It is believed that all major types of maize—flint, flour, dent, sweet, and pop—were known long before the time of Columbus.

Types of Maize

The species *Zea mays* is composed of a number of subspecies of considerable economic interest (Anderson and Cutler, 1942):

1. Pod corn (*Zea mays tunicata*), characterized by the fact that each kernel is enclosed in a pod or husk, and the whole ear is also enclosed in husks.

2. Flour corn (*Zea mays amylacea*), which has soft or floury, instead of vitreous, endosperm.

3. Popcorn (*Zea mays everta*), which has a high proportion of horny endosperm and rather small-sized kernels and ears.

4. Flint corn (*Zea mays indurata*), characterized by starchy endosperm enclosed in a thick layer of horny endosperm; the kernels are large and broad, with rounded tops.

5. Sweet corn (*Zea mays saccharata*), which is characterized by hard, horny endosperm at the sides and back of the kernels, and starchy endosperm extending to the crown of the kernels.

Diversity of Races and Varieties

One of the amazing characteristics of maize is its tremendous genetic diversity and consequent range of adaptation. Studies in Mexico, Guatemala, Colombia, Bolivia, and Peru, conducted by the Rockefeller Foundation, have revealed a wide range of local types and races which developed through the centuries through the combined forces of natural selection and selection by man. According to Wellhausen, Roberts, and Hernandes (1952), there were at least four main factors involved in bringing about the great diversity of maize in Mexico. These were: (1) the most ancient corn of Mexico probably was both a pod corn and a popcorn, (2) at some time during the history of cultivation in Mexico, an influx of exotic races from the south, which hybridized with the indigenous races, resulted in a trend toward increased variation and productivity, (3) introgression of teosinte germplasm into the races of Mexico and Guatemala introduced new characters and new diversity, and (4) the geography of Mexico offers different kinds of isolating factors, conducive to rapid differentiation of cultivated plants.

Over a period of years, 2000 varieties of maize were collected in Mexico, and classified according to their geographic distribution, plant characters, tassel and ear characters, and physiological, genetical, and cytological characters. It was determined by Wellhausen, Roberts, and Hernandes (1952) that there were 31 more or less distinct races of maize, four of which were considered ancient indigenous types which may have arisen from a primitive pod corn. The range of diversity found in the Mexican races of maize is illustrated in Figure 16-1.

A report by Ramirez, *et al* (1960) describes 32 races of maize from a classification of 844 collections in Bolivia. These races varied greatly in plant characteristics and in adaptation to temperature and moisture conditions. In Bolivia, maize is grown at elevations of from 300 to 13,000 feet, and shows a range of extremes in plant height from ten feet or more, with an ear height of seven to eight feet, down to a plant height of 17 inches, and an ear height of about seven inches from the ground. Ear sizes, too,

FIGURE 16-1.

A wide range of diversity is found among the many races of maize in Mexico. Each ear is representative of an individual race having identifiable characteristics and adapted to rather specific environmental conditions. [Courtesy of E. J. Wellhausen, The Rockefeller Foundation.]

range from a length of 14 or 15 inches for the long-season, low-elevation varieties, to a length of two inches for some of the extremely small races of the cool, short-season highlands.

Similar analyses of local collections of maize have been made in Peru by Grobman, *et al* (1960) who indicated that 40 races have been characterized from that country.

In the United States, before the advent of hybrid corn, it is said that more than 1000 varieties were cultivated. In 1936 Jenkins listed varieties of open-pollinated corn for the various agricultural regions and states. These showed a great range from prolific varieties of the southern states to the short-season flints of New England and eastern Canada. In the Corn Belt, many high-yielding varieties of dents were available, of both yellow- and white-kerneled forms.

It is now believed that all the diversity among varieties in the United States represents only a minor part of the diversity of the species. As suggested by Brown and Anderson (1948) maize of the Corn Belt probably resulted from hybridization of northern flints and southern dents. The southern dents, in turn, came from Mexico and are believed to trace to two races of flour corn, possibly modified by introgression of teosinte and derived earlier from four more primitive types.

With the development of hybrid corn, the variety picture changed rapidly in the United States. In 1932 in Iowa there was enough hybrid seed to plant only 0.4% of the state's corn acreage (Hughes, *et al*, 1957). Five years later there was enough hybrid seed to plant 50% of the corn acreage in Iowa. Today practically all of the corn in important corn-producing states is hybrid corn, and in many other countries the use of hybrid corn is increasing rapidly, notably in Latin America, Europe, and the U.S.S.R. The superiority of hybrid corn is based not only on its high yielding ability and relatively wide adaptation, but also on its resistance to lodging. This has facilitated mechanical harvesting, which has been a tremendous boon to the Corn Belt farmer.

Adaptation of Maize

Maize is of tropical origin and is basically a short-day plant, but in its great diversity it is highly variable in response to photoperiod. Most varieties, however, respond to day-length, with a range from equatorial Colombian and Ecuadorean types, adapted to short days, to northern varieties such as Gaspe flint, adapted to long days at 45° or 50° latitude in eastern Canada. Maize is best adapted where the growing season is long and warm, as in the *Caf*, *Daf*, and some of the *Csa*, *Af*, *Aw*, and *BS* climates.

Varieties of corn are grown successfully over a wide range of latitudes, from 58° north to 40° south, including the tropical, subtropical, and intermediate climates. In the tropics the crop is grown from near sea level to 13,000 feet. As was indicated previously, the size of the plant varies greatly.

A particular characteristic related to its environmental requirement is the number of leaves per plant. Kuleshov (1933) made a special study of the Russian maize collections with reference to this characteristic. He found that the number of leaves on the main stem was indicative of the climatic conditions of the habitat. For example, the many samples collected from different environments ranged in average number of leaves from 9 to 44. The Canadian varieties had 9 to 18 leaves, Corn-Belt varieties, 18 to 21 leaves, Transcausian varieties, 11 to 27 leaves, Peruvian varieties, 14 to 33 leaves, and extremely late varieties from Yucatan and southern Colombia, 42 to 44 leaves. The average length of growing season was, according to Kuleshov, correlated with the number of leaves per plant.

In the Corn Belt of the United States, the mean summer temperature of the *Daf* climate ranges from 70° to 75°F, the mean night temperature is 58°F (or more), and the growing season longer than 140 days. The three-month average temperature of 68° to 74°F for June-July-August, appears to be favorable for high yields. Night temperatures do not have to be high, as was noted by Wallace and Bressman (1949), but should be above an average of 55°F. The temperature requirement for germination and growth of corn is about 50°F. Young seedlings, up to the time they are about six inches tall, can often withstand a light frost without injury, but at older stages corn is quite susceptible to freezing temperatures.

High temperatures, too, may be injurious to the corn crop. Zuber and Decker (1956) in Missouri found that during the silking and tasseling period in 1954, the percentage of ears with good seed set dropped from 100 to 32 following three successive days of high temperature (100°F or more). The internal water supply may have been too low to supply silks with enough water to germinate pollen tubes.

Under Iowa conditions, when May temperatures are below normal, yields of corn are likely to be reduced. If June temperatures are normal or just slightly above, high yields usually result. If temperatures are very much above normal, reduction in yields may be expected. July and August temperatures in the central Corn Belt often average too high for best corn yields (Jenkins, 1941; Davis and Harrell, 1942; Hendricks and Scholl, 1943).

In recent years, American varieties of corn have been produced in western Europe in increasing quantities. Performance of the same hybrids in Europe and in the United States has permitted a study of comparative crop ecology and provided further information in their range of adaptation (Andrew, Ferwerde, and Strommen, 1956). Two Wisconsin hybrids, W240 and W255, were grown at Wageningen, Netherlands, and Spooner, Wisconsin, and performance was found to differ in two major respects: (1) yields were approximately 35% greater in the Netherlands, and (2) a much longer growing season was found to be necessary in the Netherlands. The mean summer temperature at the two locations was nearly the same, but the July and August temperatures were slightly lower in the Netherlands. The length of average frost-free season was 48 days longer in the Netherlands than in Wisconsin, but the total temperature accumulation above 50°F was slightly greater in northern Wisconsin.

Moisture Conditions

One of the greatest limiting factors in corn yields, even in the Corn Belt itself, is insufficient moisture. The variability in annual yield of corn is often associated with the precipitation distribution pattern. Annual rainfall and yield, however, were not closely associated in the central Corn Belt in studies by Rose (1936). Drought periods are frequent, however, especially during late July and August. Corn has a rather high efficiency of transpiration, but requires large quantities of water to produce a high yield of dry matter. A most critical period for moisture is at the time of flowering and fertilization. Rainfall most effective in producing corn yield was found to be that which occurred three to five weeks before silking and from silking to three weeks afterward (Shaw and Dale, 1959; Runge and Odell, 1958).

The *Daf* climate of the American Corn Belt, while favorable for corn production, is not by any means to be considered perfect. It was suggested by Jones and Huntington (1935) that some areas of New England, particularly Connecticut, probably had a more favorable climate for corn than was found in the Corn Belt. This idea was based on the fact that in Connecticut there is a more uniform distribution of precipitation the year round. Favorable winter precipitation in Connecticut results in a full reserve of subsoil moisture, whereas the dry winters of the Midwest may at times result in a low subsoil moisture reserve at the time of planting. Seasonal moisture supply may, therefore, have to be greater than normal to insure high yields of corn.

A description of the seasonal conditions favorable for corn in central Iowa has been given by Shaw and Dale (1959). First there should be a good soil-moisture reserve to insure adequate moisture if dry periods develop. May should be slightly warmer than normal, with an average temperature of about 65°F. Precipitation should be approximately 3.5 inches or a little less than normal. June should also be just slightly warmer than the normal of 70°F, with a rainfall of about four inches. For best development of the corn crop, July should average 2° or 3° below the normal of 75°F, with rainfall about 4.5 inches (which is a little above normal). August temperatures are best at normal, 72.5°F, or slightly below normal, with rainfall about one inch above the normal of 3.8 inches. Weather in September should be warmer and drier than the normal of 64°F and four inches of rainfall.

Another frequent hazard to corn production is early frosts. This hazard seems to be greatest in seasons of high rainfall and below-normal temperatures throughout the summer, for this causes a delay in normal development of the crop.

There are several climatic types where corn production is important. Probably the most important are the humid intermediate climate, *Daf*, and the subtropical humid, *Caf*. Because of its great diversity, however, corn is important in other climates, including *Dbf, Csa, Csb*, and *Aw*, as well as the dry climates, *BSh* and *BSk*, under irrigation.

Corn requires well aerated soils, with an abundance of available plant nutrients. Prairie soils are among the most favorable because of their high level of native fertility. Woodland soils may be highly satisfactory, however, when fertilized adequately. Some of the better-producing central Corn Belt soils include the Wabash, Webster, Brookston, Clyde, Tama, Muscatine, Marshall, and Carrington series. Farther east the Miami, Hagerstown, and Maury soils are considered desirable, and farther south the Huntington, Congaree, and Genesee series (Morgan, Gourley, and Ableiter, 1938).

Distribution of Production

In addition to the great center of corn production in the United States, other world centers produce maize in some quantity. In eastern Europe, Rumania and Yugoslavia lead with an acreage between five and ten million in each country. Maize is important also in Bulgaria, Hungary, Italy, Spain, and France. Production of maize in Europe is less mechanized than in the United States, and a larger proportion of the crop produced is used for human food.

Asiatic production centers in the U.S.S.R. and China, but there is a sizable production in Manchuria, India, and Indonesia.

In Africa, the largest producer is the Union of South Africa, followed by French West Africa, Egypt, Angola, and French Morocco.

In South America, Brazil and Argentina are the largest producers. Production in Argentina centers in the Northern Pampa, where annual rainfall, 28 to 40 inches, is adequate. Excess moisture at harvest time, however, results in considerable spoilage and losses in handling the crop. Since most cattle on the Pampa are fattened on alfalfa, much of the maize goes into

TABLE 16-1. WORLD PRODUCTION OF CORN (maize)*

Area and Country	Acreage (1000 a.) 1950–1954 average	Production in Millions of Bushels		
		1950–1954 average	1958	1959
North America				
United States	80,826	3,112	3,801	4,361
Mexico	11,417	141	203	224
Canada	370	20	30	31
South America				
Brazil	12,700	247	290	285
Argentina	4,833	120	215	175
Colombia	1,800	31	34	26
Venezuela	700	13	14	14
Europe				
Rumania	7,350	125	144	250
Yugoslavia	5,950	130	155	265
Italy	3,316	112	145	150
Hungary	2,830	86	115	140
Bulgaria	1,780	28	28	47
France	894	26	66	72
Asia				
China	—	410	—	—
India	8,745	100	120	124
Indonesia	4,940	82	100	110
Philippines	2,764	28	40	42
Turkey	1,581	31	25	24
U.S.S.R.				
(Europe and Asia)	10,400	190	600	425
Africa				
Union of South Africa	7,865	115	144	145
Egypt	1,819	62	69	59
World	223,380	5,655	7,395	7,955

* Data from U.S.D.A. Foreign Agric. Service.

export trade. The Brazilian production of maize is located in the southwestern part near the seacoast, between 23° to 33° latitude.

Mexico produces approximately ten million acres of maize annually, most of which is used for human food. In contrast, United States produces 80 to 90 million acres of corn each year, the bulk of which is grown in the central states and used mainly for livestock feed.

The world's distribution of production is given in Table 16-1 and is shown graphically in Figure 16-2.

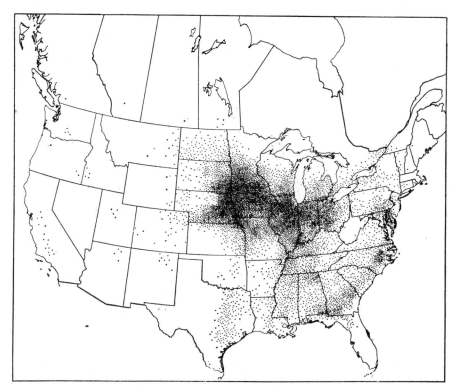

FIGURE 16-2.

Distribution of corn acreage in the United States and Canada in 1954. Each dot represents 10,000 acres. [By permission from Poehlman, Breeding Field Crops, *1959, Henry Holt, New York.]*

WHEAT

Wheat (*Triticum vulgare*) is the most important grain crop in the world. It is grown in at least 50 different countries on a total of 300 million acres each year. Some of the primary production areas are the United States, China, the U.S.S.R., Canada, India, Turkey, Italy, Argentina, France, Australia, and Pakistan. Chief exporters include Argentina, the United States, Canada, and Australia.

The great popularity of wheat is based on several facts: (1) its carbohydrates and proteins are well balanced; (2) it is produced economically with nearly complete mechanization; (3) it can be kept in storage for a long time as whole wheat or as flour; and (4) it can be grown in a wide variety of climates throughout the world (Shaw, 1955).

Origin and Classification of Wheat

According to Vavilov (1951), the common bread wheats originated in two regions: (1) the Caucasus-Turkey-Iraq area, and (2) the Afghanistan-west-central-Asiatic area. Mangelsdorf (1953) accepts the possible origin in the first area, but believes that the evidence of origin of common wheats in the Afghanistan area should preferably be interpreted as a secondary distribution and diversity, instead of origin. Helbaek (1959) favors the Iraq-Turkey-Palestine area as the probable place of origin, whereas Kihara (1959) favors the Afghanistan region. A classification of important species of *Triticum* is given in Table 16-2. Although some of these species are unimportant in agriculture, they are of interest to the student of crop ecology because of their origin and possible relationships to present-day bread wheats.

TABLE 16-2.   CLASSIFICATION OF TRITICUM SPECIES AND CLOSE RELATIVES*

Species	Common name	Chromosome Number (2n)	Genome Formula
T. aegilopoides	Wild einkorn	14	AA
T. monococcum	Einkorn	14	AA
Aegilops speltoides		14	BB
A. caudata		14	CC
A. squarrosa		14	DD
T. dicoccoides	Wild emmer	28	AABB
T. dicoccum	Emmer	28	AABB
T. durum	Durum wheat	28	AABB
T. persicum	Persian wheat	28	AABB
T. polonicum	Polish wheat	28	AABB
T. turgidum	Rivet wheat	28	AABB
T. timopheevi	Timopheevi	28	AAGG
T. compactum	Club wheat	42	AABBDD
T. spelta	Spelt	42	AABBDD
T. sphaerococcum	Shot wheat	42	AABBDD
T. vulgare	Common wheat	42	AABBDD
T. macha	Macha wheat	42	AABBDD

* Adapted from Poehlman, 1959. *Breeding Field Crops.* Holt, N. Y.

It is likely that the tetraploid and hexaploid wheats resulted from earlier diploid wheats and closely related grasses through hybridization and chromosome doubling. It was noted in Chapter 5 that investigations at Jarmo in eastern Iraq showed evidence, both in charred grains and imprints, of two types of wheat in cultivation in the seventh millennium B.C. One of these wheats was similar to wild einkorn, *Triticum aegilopoides,* the other similar to wild emmer, *T. dicoccoides.* Helbaek has noted that this latter type was variable and that some adobe imprints of kernels closely resembled present-day emmer, *T. dicoccum.* There was no evidence of the *vulgare* wheats at the time, and in fact not until the third millennium B.C. In the Egyptian Fayum deposits of approximately 5000 B.C., it is believed that there were scattered evidences of club wheats, but the time and exact place of origin are unknown.

Studies by McFadden and Sears (1946) and Sears (1948) have indicated that a spelt-like hexaploid wheat was produced by crossing a tetraploid emmer with *Aegilops squarrosa* (followed by chromosome doubling). Even though we may not know the exact route through which the hexaploid bread-wheats evolved, we know that they have been in cultivation for at least 5000 years and that countless varieties have developed through natural selection and hybridization. It must not be forgotten that when a plant

FIGURE 16-3.

Distribution of wheat acreage in the United States and Canada in 1954. Each dot represents 10,000 acres. [By permission from Poehlman, Breeding Field Crops, *1959, Henry Holt, New York.]*

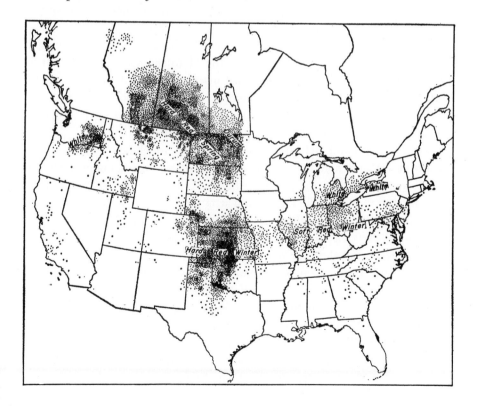

is domesticated man's influence may have resulted in the saving of plant characteristics quite different from those necessary for survival in the wild condition. In most instances, man took these plants to new environments, at least to environments differing in some degree from those where the plants were originally collected.

Another method of classification of wheats is based upon world market requirements. At the present time, seven classes are recognized: (1) Hard Red Spring, (2) Durum, (3) Red Durum, (4) Hard Red Winter, (5) Soft Red Winter, (6) White wheat, and (7) Mixed wheat (Clark and Quisenberry; Salmon and Reitz, 1957). Distribution of production in the United States and Canada by types and growing regions is shown in Figure 16-3.

Adaptation

Wheat is a crop widely adapted throughout the world, from near the equator to 60° north latitude and 40° south latitude. It seems likely that it originated in a relatively dry area, for it is fairly well adapted to steppe, (*BSk*), climates, where it is extensively grown in the United States, Canada, and the U.S.S.R. It should be emphasized, however, that wheat can be grown in many other climates, for it does well where there is a relatively cool, moist growing season, followed by a dry warm season for ripening. As Shaw (1955) has indicated, it is grown in the Egyptian desert climate with irrigation; it is a dominant crop in the Mediterranean climate of Italy; it produces high yields in the west-coast marine climate of Belgium and the Netherlands; it grows well in the humid continental, cool-summer climate of Michigan and New York; it produces a great export crop in Argentina in the humid subtropical climate of the Great Pampa.

On the other hand, wheat is poorly adapted to climates that are continually moist and hot. Diseases may cause severe losses under such conditions, and harvesting and storing a high quality of grain are difficult.

Because of its wide adaptation, wheat is grown in such diverse latitudes that it is harvested somewhere every month of the year. Figure 16-4 illustrates how effective this situation is with regard to marketing newly-harvested wheat all the year round.

The versatility of wheat is increased by having both fall (winter) and spring-sown types. Winter wheat in the United States is grown mainly south of 42° latitude, except in the milder winter areas of Michigan, New York, and the Pacific Northwest. It is planted in September and October and is harvested the following year in early summer.

Spring wheat is planted in early spring and requires from 90 to 100 days or more to reach maturity. In the United States, spring wheat is grown

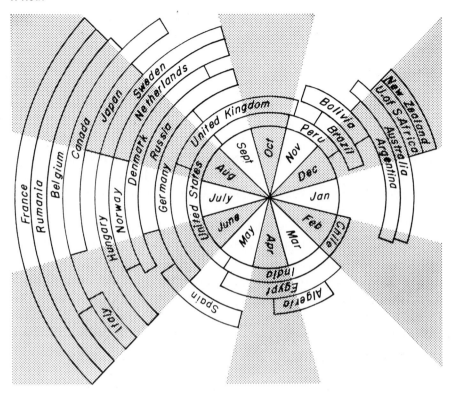

FIGURE 16-4.

Approximate time of harvesting wheat in selected countries throughout the world.

north of the winter wheat belt, Minnesota, North Dakota, South Dakota, Montana, and Washington being the leading states. From there the spring wheat belt extends into the Canadian provinces, particularly Manitoba, Saskatchewan, and Alberta, as far north as the growing season will allow maturity of early varieties. This limit may be approximately at the 57°F isotherm for the three summer months.

The quality of wheat depends on the variety and on environment. High protein varieties, with extensible gluten desired for making bread, is grown in the BSk climate, or on the border of the BSk and Daf, in the Great Plains region. Soft wheats, suitable for short fermentation processes, such as are used with flours in the cake and biscuit trade, are grown in moist climates, such as the cool summer Dbf climate of Michigan and New York, or the Mediterranean climates of Europe. For most people, the best flours for baking bread are from blends of soft and hard wheats. This blending practice is highly important in maintaining the position of wheat in international trade (Jones and Darkenwald, 1954).

World Production of Wheat

Production and consumption balance in only a few of the countries that grow wheat. Nearly 700 million bushels are exported annually, making wheat one of the world's most important commodities. The largest producers of wheat include the U.S.S.R., the United States, and China. Both the U.S.S.R. and the United States have large export supplies, but China needs all she can produce. India and Pakistan too use all locally grown wheat and import additional quantities. Australia, Argentina, and Canada together produce about as much wheat as is produced in the United States, and must export a great share of the product. A distribution of the world's annual production is shown in Table 16-3.

It has been emphasized by Shaw (1955) that great surpluses of wheat have been produced in the steppe lands, especially in the U.S.S.R., the United States, Canada, Australia, and, to a lesser extent, Argentina. Here are found extensive level lands, mechanized agriculture, and fertile, grassland soils. The highest yields of wheat do not come from these areas, but from Northwest Europe in the Low countries.

Population density is low in many of the steppe wheat-producing areas. Water is usually a limiting factor and production is accompanied by a considerable risk. Particularly in the U.S.S.R., Canada, and the United States, the chances of crop failure in the spring wheat belt is always great. Such areas are risky for any kind of crop production, however, unless water for irrigation is available when dry phases of the climatic cycle occur. In the Dust Bowl days of the 1930's and to a more limited extent in the 1950's, excessive wind erosion took place. It is at these times that we recognize the glaring lack of good ecological land use, for many of these lands should never have been plowed, but instead left in native grassland.

At present, it has been estimated that the world is using only one-eighth of the land physically adapted to wheat production, but in several of the large producing countries we are faced with large surpluses. The export market for wheat has been on the decline since about 1951. In spite of the rapid increase in the world's population, there is likely to be an overabundance of wheat on the world's market in the future. This prospect is made still more serious because of the trend in the United States, and in other countries having relatively high income levels, toward a decreasing per capita use of wheat in the diet.

TABLE 16-3. WORLD PRODUCTION OF WHEAT*

Area and Country	Acreage (1000 a.) 1950–1954 average	Production in Millions of Bushels		
		1950–1954 average	1958	1959
North America				
United States	63,361	1,094	1,462	1,128
Canada	26,129	538	372	414
Mexico	1,647	22	46	48
South America				
Argentina	11,871	216	245	215
Chile	1,933	37	41	40
Europe				
France	10,916	315	353	425
Italy	12,085	288	360	311
Spain	10,470	155	167	176
West Germany	2,728	110	136	166
United Kingdom	2,263	95	101	104
Poland	3,725	70	86	92
Rumania	6,710	109	110	147
Hungary	3,400	73	55	70
Yugoslavia	4,800	85	90	151
Bulgaria	3,525	70	74	75
Asia				
China	—	890	890	
India	24,422	252	290	365
Turkey	13,514	214	240	225
Pakistan	10,364	130	137	144
U.S.S.R.				
(Europe and Asia)	111,500	1,240	2,300	
Africa				
Egypt	1,631	49	52	53
Algeria	4,267	42	42	42
Morocco	3,496	35	40	37
South Africa	3,020	23	23	26
Oceana				
Australia	10,716	182	215	199
World	447,380	6,980	8,700	8,140

* Data from U.S.D.A. Foreign Agric. Service.

References

1. Anderson, Edgar and Cutler, H. C. 1942. Races of *Zea Mays* 1: their recognition and classification. *Ann. Mo. Bot. Gard.* 29.
2. Andrew, R. H., Ferwerde, F. P., and Strommen, A. M. 1956. Maturation and yield of corn as influenced by climate and production technique. *Agron. Jour.* 48: 231–236.
3. Brown, W. L. and Anderson, E. 1948. The southern dent corns. *Ann. Mo. Bot. Gard.* 35: 255–268.
4. Clark, J. A. and Quisenberry, K. S. 1948. Distribution of the varieties and classes of wheat in the United States in 1944. U.S.D.A. Circ. 761.
5. Commodity Yearbook. 1959.
6. Crop Production—Annual Summary by States. 1958. Crop Reporting Board, Agr. Marketing Service, U.S.D.A.
7. Davis, F. E. and Harrell, G. D. 1942. Relation of weather and its distribution to corn yields. U.S.D.A. Tech. Bul. 806.
8. Grobman, A., Cerrate, A., Manrique, A., Paulette, M., Salhuana, W., and Scheuch, F. 1960. Breeding potential of corn germplasm of Peru. Paper presented at Annual Meeting of American Society of Agronomy, Chicago, Ill., Dec. 5–9.
9. Helbaek, H. 1959. Domestication of food plants in the Old World. *Sci.* 130: 365–371.
10. Hendricks, W. A. and Scholl, J. C. 1943. The joint effects of temperature and precipitation on corn yields. N. C. Agr. Exp. Sta. Tech. Bul. 74.
11. Hughes, H. D. and Henson, E. R. 1957. Revised by Hughes, H. D., Metcalfe, D. S. and Johnson, I. J. *Crop Production—Principles and Practices*. Macmillan, New York.
12. Jenkins, M. T. 1936. Corn Improvement. U.S.D.A. Yearbook, Washington, D. C.
13. ———. 1941. Influence of climate and weather on growth of corn. U.S.D.A. Yearbook, Washington, D. C.
14. Jones, C. F. and Darkenwald, G. G. 1954. *Economic Geography*. Macmillan, New York.
15. Jones, D. F. and Huntington, E. 1935. The adaptation of corn to climate. *Jour. Amer. Soc. Agron.* 27: 261–270.
16. Kihara, H. 1959. Japanese expeditions to the Hindu Kush. Proc. 1st. Inter. Wheat Gen. Symp., Aug. 11–15, 1958. Winnipeg.
17. Kuleshov, N. N. 1933. World's diversity of phenotypes of maize. *Jour. Amer. Soc. Agron.* 25: 688–700.
18. McFadden, E. S. and Sears, E. R. 1946. The origin of *Triticum spelta* and its free-threshing hexaploid relatives. *Jour. Her.* 37 (3): 81–89.
19. Mangelsdorf, Paul C. 1953. *Wheat. Sci. Amer.* July.
20. Morgan, M. F., Gourley, J. H., and Ableiter, J. K. 1938. The soil requirements of plants. Soils and Men. U. S. Dept. Agr. Yearbook.
21. Poehlman, J. M. 1959. *Breeding Field Crops*. Holt, New York.
22. Ramirez, R., Timothy, D. H., Diaz B., Efrain, and Grant, U. J. 1960. *Races of Maize in Bolivia*. Nat'l. Acad. Sci., Nat'l Res. Coun., Public. 747.
23. Rose, J. K. 1936. Corn yield and climate in the corn belt. *Geog. Rev.* 26: 88–102.
24. Runge, E. C. A. and Odell, R. T. 1958. The relation between precipitation,

temperature and the yield of corn on the Agronomy South Farm, Urbana, Illinois. *Agron. Jour.* 50:448–454.

25. Salmon, S. C. and Reitz, L. P. 1957. Distribution of the varieties and classes of wheat in the U. S. in 1954. U.S.D.A. Handbook 108.

26. Sears, E. R. 1948. The cytology and genetics of the wheats and their relatives. *Advances in Genetics.* 2: 230–270.

27. Shaw, E. B. 1955. *World Economic Geography.* Wiley, New York.

28. Shaw, R. H. and Dale, R. F. 1959. Climate and corn yields in Iowa. Weekly Weather and Crop Bulletin XLVI (19): 7–8.

29. Vavilov, N. I. 1951. *The Origin, Variation, Immunity, and Breeding of Cultivated Plants.* Ronald, New York.

30. Wallace, H. A. and Bressman, E. N. 1949. *Corn and Corn Growing.* 5th ed. Wiley, New York.

31. Weatherwax, Paul. *Indian Corn in Old America.* Macmillan, New York.

32. ———— and Randolph, L. F. 1955. History and origin of corn. In *Corn and Corn Improvement.* Ed. by G. F. Sprague. Academic, New York.

33. Wellhausen, E. J., Roberts, L. M., and Hernandes X., E. 1952. *Races of Maize in Mexico.* Bussey Inst., Harvard Univ., Cambridge.

34. Yearbook of Food and Agriculture Statistics. 1957. F.A.O. of the United Nations. Rome.

35. Zuber, M. S. and Decker, W. L. 1956. Effects of 1954 drouth on corn. Mo. Agr. Exp. Sta. Res. Bul. 604.

Crops of the Intermediate Climates: Apple

Probably no crop illustrates to better advantage than the deciduous orchard tree the importance of adaptation to climatic conditions over a wide continental area. Of the deciduous orchard fruits, the apple is of greatest importance. Actually the principal deciduous fruit-growing regions on the North American continent are determined mainly on the basis of apple growing, but species such as peaches will not thrive in all apple-growing regions because of their sensitivity to low temperatures (Childers, 1961). With the exception of a few of the plums, the apple will grow the farthest north of the principal deciduous fruits.

Although it is grown widely, through a considerable range of latitude and other environmental conditions, Chandler (1957) has estimated that more than 90% of the area of the United States is unsuited for commercial production of apples.

The common apple, *Malus sylvestris,* is believed to be a collection of clones derived from hybrids of *Malus sylvestris* and other *Malus* species native to western Asia where there still are forests of wild apple species (Vavilov, 1951). The crop has been cultivated for more than 2000 years in Europe, and was introduced into America by the early settlers.

In most orchard fruits, the term **variety** may be more accurately described as a **clone,** which includes all of the progeny of an individual, propagated vegetatively. Sexual seedlings of the apple, for example, are unlike each other and unlike the parental clone, but still resemble the parent more than they do other varieties (Chandler, 1957). Pome fruits have a haploid chromosome number of 17. A number of good apple varieties are triploid, but it is believed that these triploids are not sterile because the ancestral haploid number was seven. According to Crane and Lawrence (1952), a so-called diploid apple variety is partly tetraploid and partly hexaploid, and a triploid is partly hexaploid and partly nonaploid.

The apple is a highly heterozygous species and over a period of years excellent clonal varieties, which originated as seedlings, including some from specific crosses, have been selected and increased. In general, trees of these clones bear much better than the average tree of the species and much better than the average of its seedlings. In apple breeding, superior seedlings are occasionally found, especially from crosses of good varieties, and some of these have been developed into new varieties.

ADAPTATION OF THE APPLE

The northern limits of latitude for deciduous fruits are determined by killing winter nights or long, cold periods that kill the roots if the soil is not protected by snow or other cover. Extremely hardy rootstocks may help to extend the range a little, especially when the most hardy varieties are being grown.

If the climate is modified by large bodies of water or by proximity to mountain barriers, the northern limits probably will depend on the ability of a variety to ripen in short, cool summers. In North America, apples are grown as far north as Nova Scotia and British Columbia; in Denmark, as far north as 54° to 58°; in Sweden to 55° to 60°, and in Norway still farther north (Nilsson, 1947).

The lowest latitude for commercial deciduous fruit production is determined by the amount of winter chilling required to break the rest period. If the rest period is not completely broken, poor opening and delayed opening of the buds result, with a consequent poor crop of fruit (Chandler and Tufts, 1934; Weinberger, 1954). In the case of the apple, the southern limit of adaptation may actually be determined by other factors, including hot, humid summer weather with accompanying greater disease and insect hazards.

The rest period of deciduous trees is that period during dormancy when the above-ground portion will not grow even though temperature, moisture, and other environmental conditions are favorable. This rest period is highly important, for the plant cannot be forced into growth by warm spells in winter. The apple tree goes into the rest period slowly and emerges from it slowly, more so than other fruit trees. However, the earlier it goes into the rest period, the earlier it will emerge from it in spring. Apple buds require winter chilling to open normally in spring. When grown closer to the Equator than approximately 33° latitude, apple buds may fail to open, or may blossom unevenly. This results in weak growth of the whole tree and a poor setting of fruit (Childers, 1961).

Freeze damage to apple trees may include different kinds of injury. Greatest losses probably come from freezing of flowers or young fruits. Often buds begin to swell, and a portion of the flower and fruit tissue becomes tender and remains so until the fruit is one-half inch in diameter. Completely open flowers may be killed or badly damaged at 26° to 28°F and seeds in young fruits may be killed by temperatures of 28° to 30°F. Following the death of seeds, the fruit soon falls off. Flowers damaged by frost at temperatures not lower than 26°F often show considerable recovery with, at times, a nearly normal fruit set (Knowlton, 1936).

Hardiness of tissues differs greatly in winter and summer. The cambium and newly developed cells on either side are easily killed by a freeze when in active-growing condition. During the period November 11 to 15, 1940, in the Missouri River Basin, drastic freeze damage to deciduous fruits and other vegetation occurred. At Ames, Iowa, the temperature was 51°F at 8 A.M., November 11. By noon there was a 50-mile-an-hour wind and the temperature dropped to 9°F by evening. Minima for the next four days were 4°, −2°, 2°, and −2°F, with the result that thousands of fruit trees were killed (Pickett and Lantz, 1942). In midwinter, however, matured cambium is quite resistant to freezing (followed in order by bark, sapwood, and pith) and probably cannot be frozen by temperatures considerably lower than those occurring in the orchards in most winters (Childers, 1961). In roots, the cambium is the tissue most susceptible to freezing, being more susceptible than bark, sapwood, and pith. The root system in general is not as hardy as the above-ground portion. Roots of the apple may be killed at temperatures ranging from 5° to 19.4°F, but in fruit-growing regions root temperatures seldom reach that low level if there is any snow cover.

Environmental effects are of importance also in relation to color and texture of the fruit. Abundant sunshine favors good coloring of fruit, occasioned in part at least by the effect of ultraviolet rays (White, 1953; Shoemaker and Teskey, 1959). An increase in leaf area results in an increase in color until exceedingly heavy foliage causes too much natural shading of fruit (Schrader and Marth, 1931). In the hot, dry atmosphere of the Pacific slope, especially below 35° latitude, red color tends to be dull or poor. Flesh flavor and texture are also influenced by environment. One variety, Red Astrachan, is said to be rather sour when grown at 39° latitude in Missouri.

In New York, at 43°, the flavor is tart, but pleasant, and at 59° in Sweden, the flavor is considered excellent (Chandler, 1957).

The McIntosh variety, which has a rather high flavor and skin color when grown in northern areas with cool nights, tends to have poor color and inferior flesh texture when grown farther south under warm nights. An early variety, June Red, on the other hand, produces fruit of fine red color in the Mississippi Valley with warm nights. In general, apples of the Pacific slope region, even in the northern portion, tend to have a firmer texture, a tougher, more waxy skin, and less flavor than those grown in the northeastern part of the United States under humid conditions (Tukey, 1957; Chandler, 1957; Childers, 1961).

Soils for deciduous fruits should be deep and well aerated. Especially in areas where summers are hot and the atmosphere dry, trees will not yield their best crops unless the root system penetrates to five or six feet or more. Under cool, humid conditions, rooting depth is not as important. Young orchards may grow fairly well on shallow soils, if rains are frequent or irrigation water plentiful, but, as the trees grow older, deep rooting is essential if satisfactory water relations and normal growth are to be maintained.

A wide range of soil reaction is tolerated by fruit trees. Some excellent apple orchards in New England have a pH as low as 4.5, whereas high-yielding peach, plum, and apricot orchards in the western states are located on soils with a pH of 7.5 to 8.0. The optimum pH for apple trees may be from about 6.5 to 6.8 (Shoemaker and Teskey, 1959).

Soil fertility is probably not as critical for deciduous fruit trees as it is for most field crops. Many orchards are benefited by application of nitrogen, but the amount to apply is often difficult to determine. Nitrogen favors growth, but too much causes delayed maturity, poor color, and poor quality of fruit. Phosphorus is usually not as limiting as it would be for crops like alfalfa or corn. Trees have the ability to obtain phosphorus perhaps more efficiently than most crops because of the great extent of their root systems. Phosphorus absorbed when the trees do not need all of it for growth may be available at a later time when needed. Potassium is often deficient in orchard soils, especially in soils containing large quantities of calcium and magnesium. Also, on poorly aerated soils with a high percentage of fine clay particles, potassium may not become available in sufficient quantities for normal growth.

Poor aeration in soils may be a serious problem in growing deciduous fruits. On impervious, poorly aerated soils roots grow slowly and may never fully occupy the available space (Oskamp, 1932). Slower root growth results in limited water supply to the leaves and the top portion of the tree grows slowly. If the soil is well aerated, branches of the tree are likely to be more upright and the shoots thicker than those on trees in wet, poorly aerated soil. Poor aeration tends to result in slow spring growth and often in a heavy drop of fruits, owing possibly to a lack of moisture during brief periods of high transpiration rate (Chandler, 1957). Fruits, too, may suffer by having a duller color and poor keeping qualities. Root injury caused by poor aeration, lack of oxygen, and high CO_2 content is considerably greater at high soil temperatures than at cool temperatures.

Artificial drainage appears to be highly essential on all soils which tend to be wet, waterlogged in the spring, and poorly aerated. Although the apple has sometimes been considered tolerant of wet soils, many orchards have shown great injury from such conditions, possibly because of a tendency to locate orchards on wet soils (Boynton, 1954).

The apple tree is able to absorb nitrogen in the form of both nitrates and ammonia at low temperatures, 32° or 33°F, and to change it into organic nitrogen. In many areas with a normal snow cover in winter, nitrogen absorption goes on during the winter season, but it has been found that little upward movement into the branches takes place when no leaves are present (Batjer, *et al*, 1943; Boynton, 1950).

DISTRIBUTION IN NORTH AMERICA

Although apples are grown in most states of the United States and in all of southern Canada, Shoemaker and Teskey (1959) have suggested that there are but two principal regions of commercial production. These are (1) the eastern region, including the Northeastern States, the Great Lakes and Ohio Basin, the North Central and Central Atlantic States, Nova Scotia, Quebec, and Ontario, and (2) the western region, with production mainly in Washington, California, Oregon, and British Columbia. Most horticulturists, however, have subdivided these regions, especially the eastern region, into a number of sections differing considerably in climatic aspects of great importance to the adaptation of deciduous fruits (Figure 17-1). Chandler (1957) and Childers (1961) have given a detailed account of some of the important climatic features as related to fruit production and these features will be mentioned.

Northeastern Section

This area, extending from Michigan to Maine, and south into northern Ohio and central Pennsylvania, produces more than 30% of the United

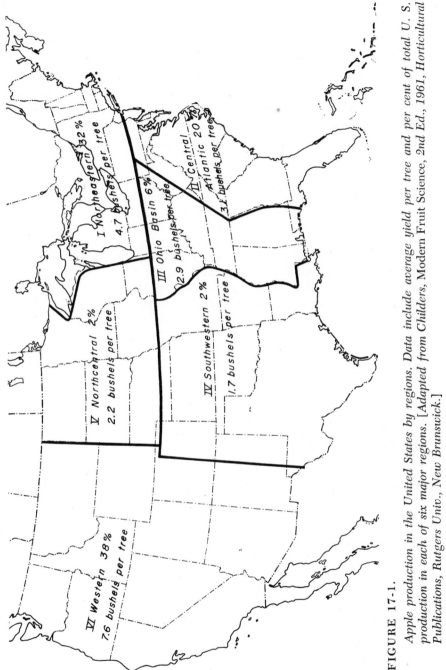

FIGURE 17-1.

Apple production in the United States by regions. Data include average yield per tree and per cent of total U. S. production in each of six major regions. [Adapted from Childers, Modern Fruit Science, 2nd Ed., 1961, Horticultural Publications, Rutgers Univ., New Brunswick.]

States crop. Temperatures during the growing season are fairly cool, the June-through-August means ranging from 65° to 70°F. In the northern portion of this region, including southern Ontario and Quebec, varieties maturing in 140 to 150 days after flowering must be grown. McIntosh, Cortland, Northern Spy, Wealthy, Delicious, and Dutchess are popular varieties across the region. In Nova Scotia, at 44° latitude, the climate is so moderate, because of the Atlantic Ocean's influence, that rather nonhardy varieties such as Baldwin and Gravenstein are not injured by winter temperatures. Toward the southern part of the region, varieties requiring 155 to 160

FIGURE 17-2.

    Fruit production in Michigan. Lake Michigan and westerly winds modify the climate and influence the kinds of crops grown. Fruit production in western Michigan is much greater than for the entire state of Wisconsin located on the windward side of the lake. Critical frost dates are indicated. [Redrawn by permission from Miller, Parkins and Hudgins, Geography of North America, *1954, Wiley, New York.]*

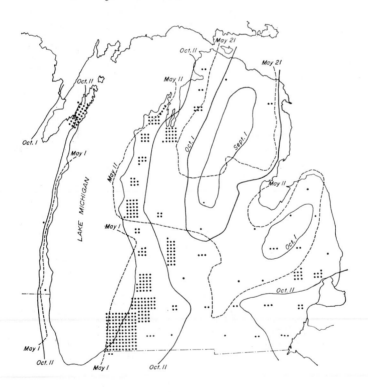

days after blooming may be grown. Winesap and Rome Beauty are common in this area (Childers, 1961).

The rainfall across Michigan, northern Ohio, and western New York averages from 30 to 35 inches annually, about half of it coming during the growing season, with no regular annual periods of drought. Farther east, the precipitation may average from 35 to 45 inches per year. The combined effect of the Great Lakes and the Atlantic Ocean in producing an important moderating effect on the temperature results in a favorable environment for deciduous fruit production. In the spring, because of the influence of latitude, the Great Lakes and the Atlantic Ocean, spring advance is slow, and frost hazard is less than in many other fruit-growing areas (Figure 17-2). At times, cool weather may limit pollination, causing losses in production.

Central Atlantic Section

This section produces one-fifth of the total apple crop. Average summer temperatures range from 70° to 75°F, with some areas at 2000 feet or more elevation in the Appalachians ranging from 65° to 75°F. Few apples are grown in the southern part of the region, except at higher altitudes. Winters are too warm in most of North and South Carolina to completely break the rest period of many good varieties, and the opening of buds in the spring will tend to be delayed. This delay in bud opening may be enough to reduce the crop considerably, so only varieties with short chilling requirements are successful (Chandler, 1957).

In the northern part of the Central Atlantic section varieties requiring 160 to 165 days for maturity are grown. In the entire region varieties such as York Imperial, Stayman Winesap, Delicious, Rome Beauty, Grimes Golden, and Jonathan are popular.

Ohio Basin Section

Only 6% of the United States apple crop is produced in this region. The June-through-August temperature averages about 75°F. Rainfall along the Ohio River varies from 40 to 50 inches annually, but droughts are much more frequent than in the Northeastern region. Length of growing season is similar to that of the Central Atlantic section. Common varieties include Golden Delicious, Delicious, Rome Beauty, Grimes Golden, Jonathan, and Winesap, to name a few.

Southwestern Section

This is not an important apple area, probably because of high summer temperatures, averaging 75° to 80°F for the three summer months. Rainfall in Arkansas, most of Missouri, and eastern Kansas tends to be sufficient, but much of the region is subject to frequent drought and lower rainfall than is desirable. Jonathan seems to be the leading variety, but Golden Delicious, Delicious, Ben Davis, and Winesap are also common.

Northcentral Section

Apples are relatively unimportant in this region, and are limited mainly to areas not too far from Lake Michigan (Wisconsin), the Mississippi River (Minnesota and Iowa), and the Missouri River (eastern Nebraska and western Iowa). Cold is the limiting influence. With increasing latitude, danger from cold winter nights increases. Winters are dry, and cold winds are not infrequent, especially in the western part of the region. Here, we sense the transition zone between the more humid east and the drier region to the west. Köppen's climatic classification showed a lack of critical differentiation between the eastern and western portions of the Midwest's *Daf* climate. Thornthwaite's differentiation into humid and subhumid regions corresponds more adequately with the actual climatic conditions as indicated by the adaptation and successful production of deciduous fruits.

In Wisconsin and in southern Iowa, McIntosh, Wealthy, Cortland, Delicious, and Jonathan varieties are grown. Special cold-resistant varieties, such as Harlson in Minnesota and Joan and Secor in Iowa, have shown improved adaptation in the region.

Western Section

Thirty-eight percent of the commercial apple crop is grown in this region. Here are found higher yields per acre than in other apple regions, especially in Washington where yields average more than seven bushels per tree. It should be noted that, in general, spring begins early in the Pacific slope region, and apple varieties which have a relatively long growing season ripen much farther north than they would in the eastern states. Special districts in this large area are recognized, and a few will be mentioned.

The Wenatchee district lies in northcentral Washington in the Columbia River Valley and along its tributaries. Orchards are planted on bench lands which have sufficient elevation to provide good air drainage. Spring frosts are rarely a factor, and summer temperatures are favorable, June to August being 65° to 70°F. Rainfall is low, and 30 to 35 inches of water annually may be applied in irrigation. The Yakima, Washington, district is south of the Wenatchee district and environmental conditions are similar. Spring frost hazard is probably greater, however, and irrigation problems are greater because of relatively shallow soils.

The Delicious variety accounts for 50% of the production in the state of Washington. Other varieties include Winesap, Jonathan, Rome Beauty, and Golden Delicious.

The Hood River district in Oregon is famous for its apples. Summer temperatures are relatively cool, 65°F on the average. Yellow Newton and Delicious are the most important varieties.

Three California districts are of importance in apple production. North of San Francisco, where precipitation averages 40 inches annually, the relatively nonhardy Gravenstein variety is one of the most important. In another district south of San Francisco, where annual rainfall is 25 to 30 inches, yellow varieties are favored because foggy weather does not promote good coloring in red apples. A third district is located east of Los Angeles at 2500 to 3000 feet elevation, where there is sufficient cold to break the rest period. In this area, with an annual rainfall of 20 inches, Rome Beauty, Winesap, and Delicious varieties are produced.

In the intermountain region of Idaho and Utah, apple growing districts are located at elevations of 2000 to 4000 feet, where summer temperatures average about 70°F.

From this discussion it can be seen that deciduous fruit trees, apples in this instance, have rather specific tolerances to climatic conditions, particularly temperature. It is evident that the modifying influences of the Great Lakes and Atlantic Ocean in the eastern part of the United States are clearly reflected in the adaptation of the apple as a crop. The great central portion of the country from the Rocky Mountains to the Mississippi River produces less than five percent of the total crop. In the central and northern portions of this great grassland region, primary limiting factors appear to be extremely low temperatures in winter, frequency of dry, cold winds, and lack of winter precipitation. Actually, the danger from cold damage is greater at 38° latitude in the Mississippi Valley than at 45° in Nova Scotia, where the Atlantic Ocean tempers the severity of the winter climate, or at a latitude of 45° on the West Coast, where air temperatures are higher because of the influence of the Pacific Ocean and the high mountain barriers to polar air movement (Chandler, 1957). As far as spring frost is concerned, the risk is probably as great at 36° to 39° in the Mississippi Valley as in any other area in the country.

In the southern part of the central region, in addition to possible spring frost damage, high summer temperatures and frequency of drought contribute greatly to the limited adaptation of apples and other deciduous fruits.

APPLE PRODUCTION

Average annual production of apples in the United States for the period 1949 to 1958 was 112 million bushels. Average production by state for this same period and for the year 1960 is given in Table 17-1.

TABLE 17-1. COMMERCIAL CROP OF APPLES IN THE MORE IMPORTANT PRODUCTION AREAS OF THE UNITED STATES*

State	Production in Thousands of Bushels		
	1949–1958 Average	1959	1960
Washington	26,355	23,650	22,000
New York	17,494	19,500	17,300
Michigan	9,354	12,800	10,500
Virginia	9,506	10,900	10,200
California	8,727	10,900	9,300
Pennsylvania	6,346	7,500	5,700
West Virginia	4,484	5,700	4,600
Ohio	3,088	2,750	3,150
New Jersey	2,828	3,700	2,500
Oregon	2,492	2,200	2,150
Illinois	2,641	2,300	2,100
Massachusetts	2,548	2,700	2,050
North Carolina	1,329	1,500	2,000
Indiana	1,468	1,525	1,580
Wisconsin	1,217	1,340	1,200
Maryland	1,185	1,600	1,130
New Hampshire	1,185	1,630	1,120
Maine	1,030	1,430	1,060
Missouri	912	750	825
Vermont	897	860	940
United States	112,456	121,787	106,380

* Data from U.S.D.A. Crop Reporting Board, 1960.

Greatest annual production is in Washington, followed by New York, Michigan, Virginia, California, and Pennsylvania. These six states produce more than three-fourths of the country's total commercial apple crop.

World production of apples, as reported by the Foreign Agricultural Service, United States Department of Agriculture, is given in Table 17-2.

TABLE 17-2. WORLD PRODUCTION OF APPLES*

Country	Production in Millions of Bushels (48 pounds each)			
	1947–1956 Average	1957	1958	1959
Argentina	12.5	13.0	21.3	21.0
Australia	10.8	12.9	11.0	12.1
Austria	9.7	3.4	19.8	7.8
Belgium and Luxemburg	12.7	5.8	8.3	6.9
Canada	14.7	15.9	16.7	15.3
France	18.9	8.2	29.1	18.7
West Germany	62.3	18.7	106.9	39.0
Italy	37.7	44.6	74.8	81.8
Japan	19.0	37.1	36.1	38.5
Netherlands	14.3	6.5	17.6	12.7
Switzerland	20.5	5.1	34.9	17.4
United Kingdom	23.5	20.2	28.4	24.8
United States	108.2	118.5	126.6	118.2
Yugoslavia	7.2	4.9	14.1	12.7
World	412.1	360.2	581.4	460.0

* Data from Commodity Yearbook, 1960 and U.S.D.A. Foreign Agric. Service.

References

1. Batjer, L. P., Magness, J. R. and Regeimbal, L. O. 1943. Nitrogen intake of dormant apple trees at low temperatures. *Proc. Amer. Soc. Hort. Sci.* 42: 69.
2. Boynton, D. 1950. McIntosh apple trees, N response. Cornell Univ. Memoir 290.
3. ———. 1954. Apple nutrition, p. 1 in *Fruit Nutrition,* Rutgers Univ. Press, New Brunswick.
4. Chandler, W. H. 1957. *Deciduous Orchards.* Lea and Febiger, Philadelphia, Pa.
5. ——— and Tufts, W. P. 1934. Influence of rest period on opening of buds of fruit trees in spring and on development of flower buds of peach. *Proc. Amer. Soc. Hort. Sci.* 30: 180–186.
6. Childers, N. F. 1961. *Modern Fruit Science.* 2nd ed. Hort. Publ., Rutgers Univ., New Brunswick, N. J., Printed by Somerset Press, Somerville, N. J.
7. Crane, M. B. and Lawrence, W. J. C. 1952. *The Genetics of Garden Plants.* 4th ed. Macmillan, New York.
8. Commodity Yearbook. 1960. Commodity Research Bureau, Inc., New York.
9. Crop Production. 1960. Annual Summary. U.S.D.A., Agr. Mktg. Serv., Washington, D. C
10. Knowlton, H. E. 1936. Effect time of thinning on apple size. *Proc. Amer. Soc. Hort. Sci.* 34: 116–119.

11. Nilsson, F. 1947. Fruit growing in Sweden. Hort. Abs. 16, Abs. No. 1268, 1946, and 17, Abs. No. 1162, 1947.

12. Oskamp, J. 1932. Rooting habits of deciduous fruits on different soils. *Proc. Amer. Soc. Hort. Sci.* 29: 236–238.

13. Pickett, B. S. and Lantz, H. L. 1942. Survival of apple trees in 200 varieties after an early winter freeze. *Proc. Amer. Soc. Hort. Sci.* 40: 212.

14. Schrader, A. L. and Marth, P. C. 1931. Light intensity as a factor in development of apple color and size. *Proc. Amer. Soc. Hort. Sci.* 28: 552–555

15. Shoemaker, J. S. and Teskey, B. J. E. 1959. *Tree Fruit Production.* Wiley, New York.

16. Tukey, L. D. 1957. Effect of night temperature on growth of McIntosh apples. *Proc. Amer. Soc. Hort. Sci.* 68: 32–43.

17. Vavilov, N. I. 1951. *The Origin, Variation, Immunity and Breeding of Cultivated Plants.* Ronald, New York.

18. Weinberger, J. H. 1954. Effect of high temperature during the breaking of the rest of Sullivan Elberta peach buds. *Proc. Amer. Soc. Hort. Sci.* 63: 157–162.

19. White, D. G. 1953. Promotion of red color of apples. *Proc. Amer. Soc. Hort. Sci.* 61: 180–184.

Crop Productivity and the Ecological Optimum

Complex interactions among factors of a plant's environment and between the environmental factors and the plant itself make difficult an accurate analysis of the relationships involved. Experiments under controlled conditions are adding greatly to our knowledge of the specific requirements for temperature, moisture, light, and nutrients, but crops must still be grown where the environment is only partially controlled by man, and where the interacting effects of many factors plus their variability from day to day and season to season are great indeed.

From the time the tiny seedling emerges from the soil until its final product of seed, forage, or fiber is harvested, it is subjected to a long series of changing environmental conditions. At certain stages of development, the environmental requirements are such that one factor may be critical; at subsequent stages, another factor may be critical. Some tropical climates have a monotonous uniformity, whereas the continental intermediate climates are extremely variable. Crops such as wheat and barley have a wide range of tolerance to environmental changes, as evidenced by the extent of their distribution over wide ranges of latitude and altitude.

Ecologists and agronomists have searched for methods by which the relationships between conditions of the environment and productivity of the crop can be expressed. One of the first of these was correlation between the magnitude of certain factors of the environment and the final yield. Correlation studies, however, have not been as fruitful as might be hoped. In the Corn Belt states, Rose (1936) studied the relationship between climatic factors and the yield of corn. At the eastern border of this region, temperatures in the early part of the growing season tended to be too low for optimum growth, whereas on the southern boundary of the Corn Belt, temperatures were too high. In the middle of the Corn Belt region, correlations between single climatic factors, such as temperature or rainfall, and the final yield of the crop, were uniformly low. Multiple correlations, in which several environmental factors were involved, were usually higher. Near the marginal areas for moisture, however, as in Nebraska, the correlation between total rainfall and yield was much higher than it was in Illinois or Iowa.

In central South Dakota, Pengra (1946) found that over a 25-year period the autumn and winter rainfall the preceding year was just as important in determining final yield of small grains as was the current seasonal rainfall. With corn, a full season crop, seasonal rainfall was somewhat more important.

In the Great Plains region, Mathews and Brown (1938) found that a minimum of 7.37 inches of precipitation was necessary to produce any yield of wheat. With that minimum as a base, each .51 inch of additional rainfall resulted in an approximate increase of one bushel per acre yield. In the southern part of the region, in areas with 13 inches annual precipitation (or less), wheat failed four-fifths of the years. Even with 19 to 20 inches of precipitation in the Great Plains region, the rainfall is so erratic that a crop failure is expected in at least one out of four years.

METEOROLOGICAL EQUIVALENTS

If data on both weather conditions and varietal yields of crops are available for long periods of time, an evaluation of the comparative degree of adaptation of specific crop varieties to local environments may be made. Such a method, known as the **meteorological equivalent method,** is described by Azzi (1956). The first step is to determine the amount of an individual meteorological factor necessary for the plant's normal development. The meteorological equivalent may be defined in thermic or pluviometric terms as the degrees of temperature or the millimeters of precipitation which distinguish normal from abnormal conditions. Abnormal conditions may be either the excess or deficiency of an environmental factor. For wheat in Italy, normal rainfall conditions lie between 40 and 116 mm for the month just preceding heading of the plants.

Azzi recorded data from an extensive network of stations, together with conditions of development of the crop, every ten days. Based on 500,000 reports of weather and crop-development data, the effect of a single factor, rainfall, was presented as a function of all other factors acting on yield under most varied conditions (Figure 18-1).

To obtain a drought equivalent for wheat, all years were divided into two groups: (1) years of excellent yields, and (2) years of poor yields. Plotted by years and magnitude of precipitation, values are indicated either for below-normal yield or for above-normal yield. When many of such points have been located on the chart, the values can be grouped into three groups. The top group contains only values for yields above normal, and the lower group contains only values for yields below normal, but the central group contains both above-normal and below-normal values. If this group is divided horizontally so that there are as many values above normal yield as below normal yield, this line on the precipitation scale represents the drought equivalent.

There is some degree of similarity between Azzi's "meteorological equivalents" and the method reported by Barger and Thom (1949a, 1949b) for characterizing drought intensity and evaluating drought hazard for different locations in Iowa. This method in-

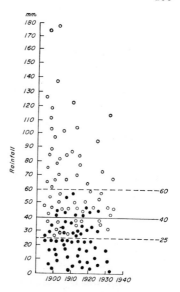

FIGURE 18-1.

Equivalent of drought for wheat in the month before heading. Abundant harvests only were observed with 60 mm. of rainfall in month before heading (small open circles); poor yields occurred with rainfall below 25 mm.; in intermediate area factor compensation or interaction is believed to influence yield. [*Adapted from* Agricultural Ecology, *Azzi, 1956, Constable, London.*]

volved measuring rainfall requirements of an average corn crop in selected counties in Iowa, and provided an estimate of the minimum amount of rainfall needed during a given number of consecutive weeks. The drought hazard, or probability of getting less than this amount, was estimated and the estimate indicated that southern counties were more likely to suffer drought than were northern and central sections. Also, the western part of Iowa appeared to have a greater drought problem than did the eastern part of the state.

Azzi extended the use of the method of meteorological equivalents to a consideration of temperature and other environmental factors.

COMPARATIVE AGRICULTURAL POTENTIAL

A somewhat different, and a more geographical, approach was proposed by Visher (1955). Based upon many detailed local studies of environmental conditions and yield of crops, certain generalizations were made. A provisional classification of the world's regions as to their agricultural potential was first established (Figure 18-2). Eighty different regions were ranked according to three criteria: (1) percentage of the land under agriculture, (2) average rank of the cropland, and (3) average suitability for choice crops. Seven criteria were used to determine suitability: (1) average topographic suitability for crops, (2) average soil quality, (3) average warmth adequacy, (4) average precipitation adequacy, (5) suitability of precipitation time-distribution, (6) weather dependability, and (7) accessibility of markets for the region's agricultural products.

A rating for each of these seven criteria was given: 0 = lacking, or nearly so; 1 = poor, little or low; 2 = medium, average or fair; 3 = above average, good; 4 = superior, excellent, or large. A summarization of scores gives the generalized evaluation of the region (Table 18-1 and Figure 18-3).

FIGURE 18-2.

World agricultural regions for the evaluation of production potential. [*Adapted from Visher*, Econ. Geog. 31:82–86, 1955.]

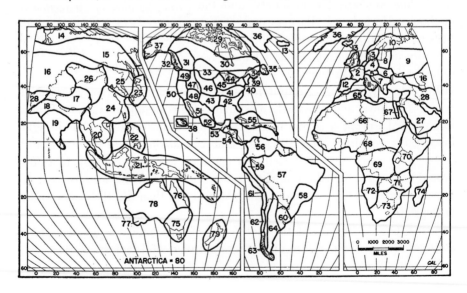

Regions	Topographic Suitability	Soil Adequacy	Warmth Adequacy	Precipitation Adequacy	Precipitation Distribution	Weather Reliability	Market Accessibility	Total Score	Tenth Score
EUROPE									
1. British Isles	3	3	3	4	3	4	4	24	I
2. France	3	3	3	3	3	3	4	22	I
3. North Sea Borders (part)	4	3	2	4	3	4	4	24	I
4. Germany	3	2	3	4	3	3	4	22	I
5. Switzerland and Austria	2	2	2	4	3	3	4	20	II
6. Other Central Europe	2	2	3	3	3	3	4	20	II
7. The Balkans	1	2	3	2	2	2	3	15	VI
8. Poland, etc.	3	2	2	3	3	2	3	18	III
9. Russia proper	4	3	2	2	3	2	2	18	III
10. Subarctic Europe	2	0	0	2	1	1	1	7	IX
11. Italy	2	2	3	2	2	2	4	17	IV
12. Spain and Portugal	3	2	3	2	2	2	3	17	IV
13. Iceland	1	0	1	2	1	1	2	8	IX
ASIA									
14. Tundra	1	0	0	2	1	1	0	5	X
15. Taiga	2	1	1	2	1	1	1	9	IX
16. Steppe	3	3	2	1	2	1	1	13	VII
17. Tibet	1	0	1	1	1	1	0	5	X
18. North India	3	3	4	2	3	2	3	20	II
19. Other India	2	2	4	2	3	2	2	17	IV
20. S. E. Asia	2	2	4	2	3	2	2	17	IV
21. East Indies	2	2	4	3	3	2	2	18	III
22. Philippines	2	2	4	3	3	2	2	18	III
23. Japan	1	2	3	4	3	3	3	19	II
24. China proper	3	3	3	2	3	2	2	18	III
25. Manchuria	2	2	2	2	3	2	2	15	VI
26. Mongolia	2	2	2	1	2	1	1	11	VIII
27. Syria-Arabia	2	2	3	1	1	1	1	11	VIII
28. Other S. W. Asia	2	2	3	1	1	1	1	11	VIII
NORTH AMERICA									
29. Tundra	1	0	0	2	1	1	0	5	X
30. Taiga	2	1	1	2	1	1	1	9	IX
31. W. Canadian Mountains	1	2	2	2	2	2	1	12	VIII
32. N. Pacific Coast	1	1	2	3	2	4	3	16	V
33. Springwheat Belt	3	3	2	2	3	2	2	17	IV
34. S. E. Canada	2	2	2	3	3	3	3	18	III
35. Newfoundland	1	1	1	3	2	2	2	12	VIII
36. Greenland	0	0	0	1	1	1	1	4	X
37. Alaska	1	1	1	1	1	1	1	7	IX
38. Hawaii	2	3	4	2	3	3	2	19	II
39. New England	2	2	3	3	3	4	4	21	I
40. Mid-Atlantic States	2	2	3	3	3	3	4	20	II
41. The Upper South	2	2	3	2	3	3	3	18	III
42. E. Gulf Coast and Florida	3	2	4	2	2	2	3	18	III

411

TABLE 18-1. (Continued)

Regions	Topographic Suitability	Soil Adequacy	Warmth Adequacy	Precipitation Adequacy	Precipitation Distribution	Weather Reliability	Market Accessibility	Total Score	Tenth Score
43. Texas	3	2	3	2	2	2	2	16	V
44. Great Lakes Region	3	2	3	3	3	3	4	21	I
45. The Midwest	4	4	3	3	3	3	4	24	I
46. Central Great Plains	4	4	2	2	4	2	2	20	II
47. W. Mountains and Plateaus	2	2	2	2	2	2	2	14	VII
48. Arid South-West	2	2	3	1	2	1	2	13	VII
49. The N. W. States	2	2	3	2	2	3	3	17	IV
50. California proper	2	3	4	2	2	2	3	18	III
51. Arid Mexico	2	2	3	1	1	1	1	11	VIII
52. Mexican Plateau	2	2	2	1	2	1	2	12	VIII
53. Mexico, Humid Lowlands	3	1	3	2	3	3	1	16	V
54. Central America	2	1	3	3	3	3	1	16	V
55. West Indies	3	2	3	3	3	2	3	19	II
SOUTH AMERICA									
56. Northern S. America	2	1	3	3	2	2	2	15	VI
57. Amazon Lowland	2	1	3	3	2	2	1	14	VII
58. Brazilian Plateau	2	2	3	3	3	3	1	17	IV
59. Andes Mts. and Plateau	1	1	1	2	2	1	1	9	IX
60. River Platte Region	4	4	3	3	3	3	2	22	I
61. N. Chile-W. Peru	2	2	3	1	1	1	1	11	VIII
62. Central Chile	3	3	3	2	2	2	1	16	V
63. Southern Chile	1	2	2	3	3	3	1	15	VI
64. Patagonia	2	2	2	1	1	1	1	10	VIII
AFRICA									
65. North Africa	2	2	4	2	1	2	3	16	V
66. The Sahara	2	1	3	1	1	2	1	11	VIII
67. Nile Egypt	4	4	4	0	0	2	3	17	IV
68. Sudan and West Africa	3	2	3	2	2	1	2	15	VI
69. Congo Basin	2	1	3	3	3	2	1	15	VI
70. E. African Uplands	2	2	3	2	3	2	1	15	VI
71. S. African Plateaus	2	2	3	2	2	2	1	14	VII
72. Arid S. W. Africa	2	2	3	0	0	1	0	8	IX
73. South Africa	2	3	3	2	2	2	2	16	V
74. Madagascar	2	2	3	2	2	2	1	14	VII
AUSTRALIA									
75. S. E. Australia	2	3	3	2	2	2	2	16	V
76. N. E. Australia	2	2	4	2	2	2	1	15	VI
77. S. W. Australia	3	3	3	2	2	2	1	16	V
78. Arid Australia	2	2	2	1	1	1	0	9	IX
79. New Zealand	2	2	3	2	2	3	1	15	VI
80. Antarctica	0	0	0	1	1	1	0	3	X

* From Visher—Econ. Geog. 31(1), 1955.

† Criteria are regional average of (1) topographic suitability for agriculture, (2) soil quality, (3) warmth adequacy, (4) precipitation adequacy, (5) precipitation time-distribution suitability for agriculture, (6) weather dependability, including storms, and (7) accessibility to markets for agricultural products.

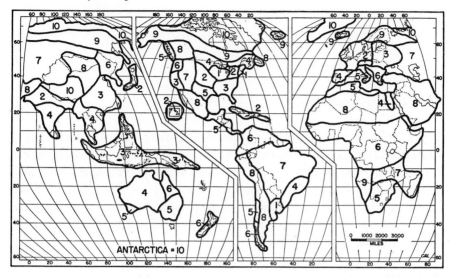

FIGURE 18-3.

Agricultural potentials of the world regions based on 7 criteria of evaluation. 1 = highest average; 10 = lowest average. [Adapted from Visher, Econ. Geog. 31:82–86, 1955.]

On this basis, the best crop lands are in western Europe, northeastern United States, the Platte River region of South America, Northern India, and Japan. The poorer lands include the deserts that cannot be irrigated, and the polar and subpolar regions.

Visher does not claim that this method of evaluation has no faults. He simply presents it as a step in the direction of gaining a more adequate knowledge of all parts of the world. This should be useful in any consideration of productivity and environmental relationships.

LAND-USE CAPABILITY

A considerable degree of similarity may be noted between Visher's "comparative agricultural potential" and the land-use classification developed by the Soil Conservation Service of the U. S. Department of Agriculture. Graham (1944) suggested that "for effective land utilization in an area consideration must be given to the landscape as an ecological complex which prescribes the use which man can make of the land." He noted that land-use classification should relate to the physical capacity of the land to produce given crops for an indefinite period without exhaustion or waste of the land resources. Tilled crops may be the highest use of certain classes of land but, for some poor swampy areas, the highest use may be muskrats or other wildlife.

LAND-USE CLASSES

A practical and valuable classification of land may be made according to **use-capabilities.** The classification is based on natural characteristics, slope, soil, and biological conditions, ignoring economic aspects or managerial skill of operation. Eight classes are recognized for rural use, and it is logical that urban, industrial, and recreational areas should also be classified on the basis of use capability. These eight classes as outlined by Graham (1944) and Steele (1951) are as follows.

1. Suitable for cultivation without special practices for prevention of serious erosion, although fertilizers and simple crop rotations may be used. This land is of very good productivity, easy to work, deep, and fairly well supplied with plant nutrients.

2. Suitable for cultivation with simple practices such as contour cultivation, strip cropping, growing protective cover crops, or simple water management. This is good land but it has deficiencies which limit its use or require attention year after year.

3. Suitable for cultivation only with complex or intensive practices such as terracing, though a combination of remedies may be needed. It is moderately good land for cultivation, but limited more than the previous class because of natural features. It can be used regularly for crops only with intensive treatments and by using the best farming methods. Slopes may demand erosion control, may be undesirably dry, or wet enough to require drainage.

4. Suitable for cultivation only with intensive practices and limited use such as cultivation in small plots or in long rotations with only occasional crops. This land is not suitable for regular cultivation, because of steepness and danger of erosion. It might be cultivated one year in six, being used for hay or pasturage in the other years.

5. Suitable for permanent pasture or woodland without special practices: land only slightly susceptible to deterioration when the range is fully grazed or the forest widely cut. Usually nearly level and not subject to erosion, this land is not suitable for cultivation because of wetness, climate, or such permanent obstructions as rocky outcrops. The soil is deep and has few limitations for grazing or forestry use.

6. Suitable for permanent pasture or woodland with some restriction in

use: land moderately susceptible to deterioration, so that grazing must be done by rotation, or logging with due care, and special conservation practices may have to be employed.

7. Suitable for permanent pasture and woodland only with severe restrictions in use: land highly susceptible to deterioration, so grazing must be only occasional and tree cutting highly selective. Great care must be taken to prevent erosion.

8. Suitable for wildlife with or without special practices. It is productive of useful wild plants, fur, game birds, mammals, or fish. Such land is usually very rough or wet or susceptible to erosion. It may possibly be too arid or too steep to be used for grazing or forests.

The preceding classification of land into capability classes depends to some extent on floristic and vegetational features or effects, giving it a phytogeographical basis. For a given climatic regime it may provide an indication of comparative productivity, particularly without considerable modification by man. Where a crop is reasonably well adapted, as far as climate is concerned, a comparison of the first two classes, for example, should indicate readily where consistently higher yields would be likely. Figure 18-4 illustrates the relation of land-capability classes to safe land use.

It has been emphasized by Nunns (1958) that the term "land-capability" means principally that certain lands can be put to broader uses more effec-

FIGURE 18-4.

Relation of land use capability classes to most effective land use. [Adapted from Steele, The Measure of Our Land, *1951, Govt. Printing Office, Washington, D. C.]*

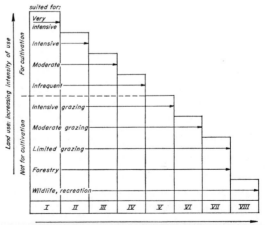

tively and with fewer conservation practices than others. It does not follow that such a classification necessarily indicates relative or absolute capabilities of net returns from various uses. An economic classification of land which should be helpful in predicting potential profitable returns from agriculture has been developed at Cornell University, and has been discussed by Nunns.

ECOLOGICAL CONCEPT OF PRODUCTIVITY

This concept, discussed at length by Odum (1959), suggests that **primary productivity** of an ecological system may be defined as the rate at which energy is stored by photosynthetic and chemosynthetic activity of producer organisms (green plants) in the form of organic substances which can be used as food materials. Two kinds of primary productivity must be distinguished: (1) gross primary productivity is the total rate of photosynthesis including the organic matter used up in respiration during the period of measurement; (2) net primary productivity is the rate of storage of organic matter in plant tissues in excess of respiration. The rates of energy storage at the tropic levels of consumer and decomposer organisms are known as **secondary productivities,** and are less and less at successive levels. Consumers use only food materials already produced; therefore there is only one kind of secondary production.

Odum has emphasized that in this concept of productivity the time element is important. Biological productivity is continuous in time, so that it is necessary to express it in terms of productivity per day or per year. Standing biomass or standing crop at any given time is not the same as productivity. The productivity of an ecological system cannot be determined merely by counting and weighing the organisms which happen to be present at a given moment. With cultivated crops, of course, good estimates of net productivity may be obtained from standing crop data, but in many situations the size of the standing crop may bear little relation to productivity. A highly productive pasture being grazed by livestock, for example, would be likely to have a smaller standing crop of grass than a less productive pasture which is not being grazed at the time of measurement. Here, we find consumption occurring at the same time as production, a situation common to many ecological systems.

A summary of estimates of net productivity, on both an annual and a daily basis, of crops, forests, deserts, and other ecosystems in which it is possible to use a harvest method, has been prepared by Odum and is presented as Table 18-2.

TABLE 18-2. ANNUAL NET PRIMARY PRODUCTIVITY OF VARI-
OUS CULTIVATED AND NATURAL ECOSYSTEMS AS
DETERMINED BY USE OF HARVEST METHODS*

	Net Primary Production Grams per Square Meter		
Ecosystems	Per Year	Per Day	
Cultivated Crops			
Wheat, world average	344	0.94	(2.3)
Wheat, average in area of highest yields (Netherlands)	1250	3.43	(8.3)
Oats, world average	359	0.98	(2.4)
Oats, average in area of highest yields (Denmark)	926	2.54	(6.2)
Corn, world average	412	1.13	(2.3)
Corn, average in area of highest yields (Illinois)	1011	2.77	(5.6)†
Rice, world average	497	1.36	(2.7)
Rice, average in area of highest yields (Italy and Japan)	1440	3.95	(8.0)
Hay, U. S. average	420	1.15	(2.3)
Hay, average in area of highest yields (California)	940	2.58	(5.2)
Potatoes, world average	385	1.10	(2.6)
Potatoes, average in area of highest yields (Netherlands)	845	2.31	(5.6)
Sugar beets, world average	765	2.10	(4.3)
Sugar beets, average in area of highest yields (Netherlands)	1470	4.03	(8.2)
Sugar cane, world average	1725	4.73	(4.7)
Sugar cane, average (Hawaii)	3430	9.40	(9.4)
Mass algae culture, best yields under intensive culture outdoors (Tokyo)	4530	12.4	(12.4)
Noncultivated Ecosystems			
Giant ragweed, fertile bottomland (Oklahoma)	1440	3.95	(9.6)
Tall Spartina salt marsh, Georgia	3300	9.0	(9.0)
Forest, pine plantation, average during years of most rapid growth, England	3180	6.0	(6.0)
Forest, deciduous plantation, England, comparable to above pine plantation	1560	3.0	(6.0)
Tall grass prairies, Oklahoma and Nebraska	446	1.22	(3.0)
Short grass grassland, 13 in. rainfall (Wyoming)	69	0.19	(0.5)
Desert, 5 in. rainfall (Nevada)	40	0.11	(0.2)
Seaweed beds (Nova Scotia)	358	1.98	(1.0)

* From Odum. 1959. *Fundamentals of Ecology*. 2nd ed. Saunders, Philadelphia.

† Values in parentheses are rates for growing season only. Net primary production for Illinois was added to Odum's table.

It is of considerable interest to note the importance of both time and space in these data. A marked superiority in net productivity of a pine forest over a deciduous forest under the same climatic conditions in England is obviously due to the pine's longer growing season, for the daily production during the deciduous forest's growing season was the same. Differences between long-season and short-season cultivated crops are apparent, as are also the differences between average yields and highest yields obtained. Sugarcane, which continues growth all the year round, has an extremely high net primary productivity.

The importance of space is suggested by the comparison between average yields of most staple crops in the United States and yields from these crops in the small countries of northwest Europe or Japan. We are fully aware of this when we lump production of a given crop into a unit bounded by state lines. Heterogeneous areas are thus included and the high yields of specific favorable areas tend to be obscured.

It is Odum's belief that man has not increased maximum primary productivity beyond that which occurs in man's absence. A summarization of world distribution of primary productivity (Table 18-3) helps to bring out that concept. It appears that open oceans and dry lands are very low in productivity. Also, the kind of producer organisms and the media (air, fresh water, or salt water) do not necessarily determine basic productivity; it is controlled rather by raw materials: sun energy and ability of local communities as a whole to utilize and regenerate materials for continuous reuse. Land systems may not be inherently different from aquatic systems, if light, water, and nutrient conditions are similar. Cultivated crops appear to have the same order of magnitude of productivity as natural "crops" on similar sites. Coral reefs, for example, may have just as high a level of primary productivity as crops under intensive cultivation. As Odum has pointed out, efficient agriculture tends to channel primary productivity into specific secondary levels of direct use to man, but does not necessarily increase primary productivity. In specific situations man, through the use of water and fertilizers, has increased primary productivity where those factors were limiting. On the other hand, he has also reduced primary productivity on many acres

TABLE 18-3.   DISTRIBUTION OF PRIMARY GROSS PRODUCTIVITY: The Range of Values Found in Major Environments of the World *

Types of Ecosystems	Range of Average Gross Productivity (gms./m²/day)
Deserts and semiarid grasslands.	less than 0.5
Open oceans (probably also deep lakes).	less than 1.0
Continental shelf ocean waters, shallow lakes and ponds, average forests, moist grasslands, ordinary agriculture.	0.5 to 5.0
Coral reefs, estuaries, some mineral springs, semiaquatic and terrestrial communities on alluvial plains, evergreen forests, and intensive agriculture.	5.0 to 20.0
Maximum rates which may be maintained for short periods in the more productive natural and cultivated ecosystems.	up to 60.0

* From Odum. 1959. *Fundamentals of Ecology.* 2nd ed. Saunders, Philadelphia.

of semiarid lands and forestlands through exploitation harvest and through failure to recognize all of the important phases of biochemical cycles which are necessary to proper functioning of natural ecosystems.

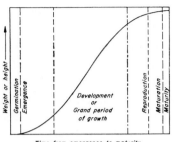

ECOLOGICAL OPTIMUM

FIGURE 18-5.

Growth curve of annual plants under optimum conditions. [Redrawn from Klages, Wyo. Agr. Exp. Sta. Bul. 367, 1960.]

Another approach to the evaluation of the relationship between environment and crop yields is the concept of **ecological optimum,** as developed by Klages (1930, 1934). To develop this concept we must first consider the idealized growth curve of annual plants as indicated in Figure 18-5. Such a symmetrical curve is attained only under ideal conditions, seldom realized under field cultivation.

The exact shape of the growth curve is determined by the intensity of environmental factors. Klages (1934) showed growth curves for Ceres spring wheat for two successive years (Figure 18-6). In 1932, the curve was more or less symmetrical, with a steep slope rising at an average rate of 11.01 cm per week. In 1931, the growth curve lacked symmetry and rose at the rate of only 5.95 cm per week. The limiting factor in this instance was said to be temperature.

To be well adapted, a crop should exhibit a vegetation rhythm in harmony with the climatic rhythm. Usually this refers to moisture available at a given time, or temperature, or occasionally some other factor or factors. Poor adaptation is indicated by a depressed growth curve, or a leveling out because of an unfavorable level of some factor or factors.

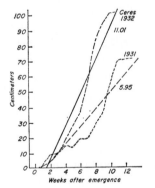

FIGURE 18-6.

Growth curves for Ceres spring wheat at Brookings, South Dakota, in 1931 and 1932. [Redrawn from Klages, Wyo. Agr. Exp. Sta. Bul. 367, 1960.]

The theoretical ecological optimum, as defined by Schimper (1903), consists of the summation of the various harmonic optima. Harmonic optimum refers to the most favorable intensity of any one function in relation to the other functions of the plant. Summation of harmonic optima suggests not only the location of an average point but also the relative importance of each of the various plant functions in their relation to the growth and behavior of the entire organism (Klages, 1942).

In the Palouse area of Washington and Idaho, winter wheat, because of its start in the previous autumn, matures earlier in the season than spring wheat. Developmental phases in relation to decreasing moisture supply, as the season advances, are more in harmony with moisture needs and as a result the yields of winter wheat on dry land are higher than yields of spring wheat (Klages, 1960).

On the basis of the idealized growth curve, it is obvious that the ecological optimum could hardly be realized by a constant set of external conditions. Different requirements for the three principal phases—seedling growth, grand period of growth, and reproduction—require different intensities of moisture, temperature, light, and nutrients. The ecological optimum, therefore, would correspond rather to a type of climate in which the various phases of development proceed under changing conditions with the advance of the season.

A quantitative approach to the concept of ecological optimum was developed by Klages (1930, 1934) using yield data on cereal grains and corn in the upper Mississippi Valley and in South Dakota. He reasoned that, considering the whole range of adaptation of a given crop, there should be areas of consistently high yields, with low variability from year to year. This situation approaches the ecological optimum for that crop, and areas near the periphery of the range represent poorer adaptation, where greater risks are encountered in the production of that crop. Average yields and coefficients of variability in yield were computed by Klages (1930, 1934) over a 37-year period for corn, oats, wheat, barley, and rye. For corn, highest average yield and lowest variability were found in the heart of the Corn Belt, with a tendency for yields to decrease in all directions. For oats, the area of ecological optimum appeared to be somewhat to the north of the heart of the Corn Belt, where cooler summers prevail.

Using Klages' method, tables were prepared showing up-to-date values of the average yield and variability of a number of important crops. Although long-time yield data are needed for such a purpose, the author has used data for ten-year periods with considerable success. A comparison of such data with those obtained by Klages over a 37-year period shows little difference for practical usage.

Yields for a ten-year period, 1951 to 1960, were used with coefficients of variability in yield for that period. The data for corn are reported in Table 18-4. The data refer only to those states important in corn production and a few others so located as to help in showing a particular trend in yield per acre or the variability in yield.

TABLE 18-4. CORN ACREAGE, YIELD PER ACRE AND VARIABILITY, FOR PERIOD 1951–1960

State	Acres (000 omitted) Average 1951–1960	Yield in Bushels per Acre										Ten-year Average	C.V. (%)
		1951	1952	1953	1954	1955	1956	1957	1958	1959	1960		
New York	673	44.0	47.0	44.0	42.0	47.5	49.0	51.0	50.0	50.0	52.0	47.8	7.2
Pennsylvania	1,306	46.0	49.0	42.0	46.0	46.0	56.0	43.0	65.5	60.0	62.0	51.6	16.6
Ohio	3,618	48.0	53.0	55.0	62.0	59.0	60.0	54.0	60.0	63.0	68.0	58.2	9.9
Indiana	4,770	53.0	50.0	51.5	53.5	56.0	62.0	59.0	63.0	62.0	68.0	57.8	10.2
Illinois	9,123	55.0	58.0	54.0	49.5	56.0	68.0	64.0	69.0	67.0	68.0	60.8	11.7
Michigan	1,915	51.5	50.0	45.5	44.0	46.5	51.0	49.5	56.0	56.0	53.0	49.3	10.0
Wisconsin	2,658	43.0	58.0	58.5	57.5	50.0	61.0	58.5	52.5	65.0	57.5	56.2	11.0
Minnesota	5,848	39.5	50.5	48.0	50.5	49.0	57.5	56.5	54.5	49.0	52.5	50.8	10.1
Iowa	10,889	43.5	64.0	53.0	52.5	48.5	51.0	62.0	65.5	65.0	62.0	56.7	13.9
Missouri	3,951	34.0	41.0	33.5	16.5	40.0	48.0	44.0	56.0	55.0	53.0	42.1	28.7
North Dakota	1,272	18.5	19.5	22.0	21.0	22.5	23.5	26.5	18.5	16.5	24.0	21.2	14.3
South Dakota	3,946	22.0	28.0	34.5	29.0	21.0	28.0	33.0	27.0	19.5	32.5	27.4	19.0
Nebraska	6,356	26.5	37.0	28.0	28.0	18.0	22.0	46.0	51.5	48.5	50.5	35.6	35.6
Kansas	1,999	24.0	22.0	21.5	19.0	21.0	21.0	29.0	42.0	41.5	45.0	28.6	35.7
Virginia	862	43.0	33.0	27.0	33.0	38.0	48.0	26.5	53.0	46.0	49.0	39.7	23.9
North Carolina	2,038	31.0	25.5	27.0	24.0	34.0	41.0	32.5	44.0	43.0	50.0	35.2	25.1
South Carolina	1,052	20.0	15.0	19.5	10.5	28.0	21.0	26.0	31.0	27.0	33.5	23.2	31.2
Georgia	2,840	16.0	12.0	20.0	10.5	24.0	24.0	26.0	32.0	28.5	32.0	22.5	34.3
Kentucky	1,880	37.5	28.0	35.5	31.0	41.0	46.0	41.0	49.0	47.0	49.0	40.5	18.4
Tennessee	1,735	30.0	20.0	29.5	21.5	35.0	32.5	31.0	39.0	40.0	40.0	31.8	22.2
Alabama	2,244	19.0	11.0	22.0	13.0	30.0	25.0	26.0	32.0	28.0	28.0	23.4	30.3
Mississippi	1,538	21.5	16.0	22.0	17.0	30.0	25.0	25.0	30.5	31.0	25.5	24.4	21.8
Texas	1,882	18.5	18.5	16.5	16.0	24.0	15.0	23.5	24.5	28.0	22.0	20.6	21.0

From these data, it may be seen that the Corn Belt is the area which most nearly approaches the ecological optimum for corn production. Within the Corn Belt there is a considerable range of yield and variability. For the ten-year period, 1951 to 1960, highest yields were obtained in Illinois. Ohio, Indiana, Iowa, and Wisconsin had only slightly lower yields. Highly fertile soils, a warm, long growing season, and a rather dependable summer rainfall pattern contribute to high yields in the Corn Belt region. Slightly higher coefficients of variability were obtained in Iowa than in several other Corn Belt states, owing possibly to the greater probability of adequate rainfall in the eastern part of the Midwest. Winter precipitation is more favorable in this area than it is farther west, which practically insures adequate subsoil moisture in the spring. This is not always true of Iowa where dry autumns and winters may, in some years, result in a shortage of moisture in the soil profile at the time of spring planting. The pattern of rainfall in summer is not particularly different, but average winter precipitation is greater in Indiana and Ohio than it is in Iowa.

In all directions from the Corn Belt, there is a gradual falling off in yield and often a higher variability in yield. Certain notable exceptions may be pointed out. There are high yields of corn in some areas of the Middle Atlantic region, the Delta area of Mississippi, and small areas in the Pacific Coast states.

Yields of wheat, a crop of extremely wide adaptation, are of considerable interest. Winter wheat is of much greater importance in the United States than spring wheat. This is in part because winter wheat matures early in the summer. This gives it an advantage over spring wheat for at least two reasons. It can take greater advantage of previous fall and winter rains, thus escaping some of the effects of drought, and, by maturing early, may also escape greater potential losses from insect and disease attacks. From the data in Table 18-5 it appears that there are two areas which most nearly approach the ecological optimum for winter wheat in the United States: (1) the midwestern-northeastern area, including Michigan, Illinois, Indiana, Ohio, and Pennsylvania, and (2) the Pacific Northwest area, including Washington, Oregon, and Idaho. It is noteworthy that the great wheat states, Kansas, North Dakota, and Nebraska, are characterized by considerably lower yields and by much higher variability.

It should be emphasized here that there is actually no large area in the United States that approaches the ecological optimum for wheat as nearly as more favorable areas such as the Denmark-Netherlands-Belgium region in Europe. Here wheat yields average 50 bushels or more per acre. Yields per acre are relatively high also in United Kingdom, Sweden, Germany, and New Zealand.

For spring wheat, the most favorable area appears to be in the Pacific Northwest, in Idaho, Oregon, and Washington, where yields are much higher and more dependable than in the great spring wheat areas of North Dakota, South Dakota, and Montana (Table 18-6).

In the production of oats, the picture is not too dissimilar to that for wheat. Wisconsin has had the highest yields during the ten-year period studied, and a belt of fairly high yields extends eastward across Illinois, Ohio, and New York (Table 18-7).

Barley is of much less total importance as a crop than either wheat or oats. The story of the migration pattern of barley as a crop has been emphasized by Weaver (1943a, 1943b, 1950). The importance of climatic factors as they influence malting quality and the prevalence of major barley diseases are at once apparent. States in which barley was a major crop a few years ago, such as New York and Wisconsin, are no longer great producers. Distribution of barley production, yield per acre, and variability in yield, are given in Table 18-8. Highest yields have been produced in Arizona under irrigation. Other states with high average yields include Utah, Pennsylvania, California, Wisconsin, Virginia, Washington, and Oregon.

In cotton production, the shift from the old Cotton Belt westward is sharply evident. Average acreage harvested over the past ten years and yield of lint per acre by years are shown in Table 18-9.

Highest yields were produced in the Far West under irrigation in Arizona, California, and New Mexico. In the old Cotton Belt, several states have relatively high average yields, including Tennessee, Missouri, Mississippi, Louisiana, and Arkansas. Year-to-year variability is relatively high in most states, the lowest coefficient of variability being present in Louisiana, Tennessee, and Arizona. In states like Kentucky and Virginia, where cotton was of great importance in the early American colonial period, the crop has dwindled to a minor position.

A development of ecological significance in crop distribution has been the recent growth of the alfalfa seed industry. Since 1947 the rapid increase in alfalfa production and the changing pattern in seed production give a unique picture in crop adaptation. Since *Lygus* bugs and other injurious insects have been controlled with modern insecticides, and since supplemental colonies of bees have been used to aid in pollination (or production areas located in areas where wild bees are plentiful), seed production in the Pacific coastal region has developed rapidly. In California the increased production is concentrated in the Central Valley; in Washington it is in the eastern part of the state, particularly in some of the newly developed irrigation districts watered from the Grand Coulee Dam. Wild bees constitute the principal pollinating agency in Washington, but honeybees (moved in

TABLE 18-5.   WINTER WHEAT ACREAGE, YIELD PER ACRE AND VARIABILITY, FOR PERIOD 1951–1960

State	Acres (000 omitted) Average 1951–1960	Yield in Bushels per Acre										Ten-year Average	C.V. (%)
		1951	1952	1953	1954	1955	1956	1957	1958	1959	1960		
Pennsylvania	662	22.5	22.5	24.0	28.0	26.0	27.0	26.0	30.0	26.5	29.5	26.2	10.0
Ohio	1,713	18.0	24.5	29.0	27.5	29.0	26.0	22.0	31.0	24.5	35.0	26.6	18.0
Indiana	1,337	16.5	24.0	28.0	30.5	29.0	30.0	25.5	32.0	26.0	33.0	27.4	17.5
Illinois	1,713	19.0	23.0	27.0	29.0	33.0	37.0	21.0	31.5	26.0	29.0	27.6	20.2
Michigan	1,146	25.0	25.5	29.5	30.0	29.5	30.0	29.0	38.0	32.0	31.5	30.0	12.0
Missouri	1,453	17.0	22.0	20.5	18.0	31.0	30.0	23.0	28.0	25.0	28.5	24.3	20.5
Nebraska	3,399	14.5	22.5	22.5	20.0	25.0	19.0	27.0	33.0	20.0	28.5	23.4	22.4
Kansas	10,052	13.0	21.0	12.5	17.5	15.0	15.5	19.0	27.5	20.0	28.0	18.9	28.8
Oklahoma	4,493	9.5	18.5	12.0	15.0	8.0	16.0	12.5	26.0	19.5	25.5	16.2	38.0
Texas	2,736	9.0	11.5	8.5	9.5	9.5	12.5	14.5	22.0	17.5	22.5	13.7	38.6
Montana	1,701	21.5	18.0	21.0	23.5	27.0	20.5	24.5	27.0	25.0	22.0	23.0	12.7
Idaho	712	22.0	22.5	27.0	27.0	27.5	28.0	32.0	30.5	32.0	26.5	27.5	12.5
Colorado	2,172	14.0	17.5	15.5	10.0	13.5	11.0	24.5	25.5	22.0	27.0	18.0	34.6
Washington	1,879	28.5	28.5	30.5	34.0	28.5	29.5	38.0	37.0	38.5	34.0	32.7	12.6
Oregon	752	30.0	28.0	28.5	28.5	26.5	31.5	37.0	35.0	36.0	33.5	31.4	11.8
California	514	17.0	21.0	19.0	20.0	21.0	21.0	22.0	22.0	23.5	22.0	20.8	8.8

TABLE 18-6. SPRING WHEAT ACREAGE, YIELD PER ACRE AND VARIABILITY, FOR PERIOD 1951–1960

State	Acres (000 omitted) Average 1951–1960	Yield in Bushels per Acre										Ten-year Average	C.V. (%)
		1951	1952	1953	1954	1955	1956	1957	1958	1959	1960		
Minnesota	835	18.3	14.4	15.9	12.1	19.0	24.0	22.6	31.4	23.0	27.5	20.8	28.9
North Dakota	7,668	13.9	10.2	9.9	9.0	15.1	17.2	18.7	23.0	15.2	19.8	15.2	30.3
South Dakota	2,256	14.6	7.4	8.4	9.4	10.5	9.0	18.3	21.0	7.5	16.7	12.3	40.4
Montana	3,134	14.5	13.0	19.0	14.0	21.0	17.4	15.4	18.5	14.7	16.7	16.4	15.5
Idaho	587	29.5	31.5	30.0	33.5	37.5	38.0	43.0	39.0	41.0	38.5	36.2	13.0
Washington	387	24.0	23.5	24.5	28.0	22.0	29.5	33.0	23.0	31.0	25.5	26.4	14.2
Oregon	155	23.5	28.0	26.5	28.5	27.0	31.0	30.0	27.5	28.0	30.0	28.0	7.6

TABLE 18-7. OATS ACREAGE, YIELD PER ACRE AND VARIABILITY, FOR PERIOD 1951–1960

State	Acres (000 omitted) Average 1951–1960	Yield in Bushels per Acre										Ten-year Average	C.V. (%)
		1951	1952	1953	1954	1955	1956	1957	1958	1959	1960		
New York	663	48.0	37.0	39.0	37.5	41.0	44.0	33.0	52.0	54.0	52.0	43.8	16.8
Pennsylvania	749	42.0	29.0	37.0	43.0	42.0	38.0	39.0	43.5	44.0	42.5	40.0	11.4
Ohio	1,152	41.0	37.0	42.0	46.5	51.0	43.0	38.0	52.0	46.0	63.0	46.0	16.9
Indiana	1,152	37.0	35.5	36.5	44.0	51.0	45.0	34.0	51.0	38.0	59.0	43.1	19.4
Illinois	2,842	40.0	37.0	37.0	42.0	56.0	47.0	39.0	55.0	41.0	51.0	44.5	16.3
Michigan	1,189	40.5	33.5	35.0	39.0	44.0	34.0	39.5	51.0	41.0	51.0	40.8	15.4
Wisconsin	2,748	49.5	45.0	41.5	44.0	49.0	46.0	52.5	58.0	50.0	47.0	48.2	9.5
Minnesota	4,509	43.0	39.0	31.5	35.0	41.0	39.0	42.0	54.0	45.0	49.0	41.8	15.6
Iowa	5,261	33.5	35.0	25.5	38.5	44.5	29.5	42.0	47.0	43.5	40.5	38.0	18.3
Missouri	1,080	23.0	22.0	25.5	41.5	36.0	31.0	32.0	32.0	26.5	35.0	30.4	20.4
North Dakota	1,850	29.0	23.0	30.5	24.0	28.0	29.0	32.5	39.0	24.5	33.5	29.3	16.7
South Dakota	3,164	37.0	26.5	25.5	28.5	25.5	20.0	35.0	39.0	20.0	41.0	29.8	25.8
Nebraska	1,800	28.6	19.0	18.5	29.0	26.0	12.0	33.5	35.0	25.0	35.5	26.2	29.7
Kansas	880	18.0	20.5	21.5	32.5	27.5	21.5	30.5	26.0	24.0	34.0	25.6	21.2
Oklahoma	581	16.0	21.0	21.5	25.0	17.0	19.0	20.0	30.5	24.5	29.0	22.4	21.6
Texas	1,278	15.0	25.5	27.0	23.0	17.5	18.0	21.5	30.0	23.0	26.0	22.6	20.8

TABLE 18-8. BARLEY ACREAGE, YIELD PER ACRE AND VARIABILITY, FOR PERIOD 1951–1960

State	Acres (000 omitted) Average 1951–1960	Yield in Bushels per Acre										Ten-year Average	C.V. (%)
		1951	1952	1953	1954	1955	1956	1957	1958	1959	1960		
Pennsylvania	191	34.5	37.0	39.0	44.0	37.0	38.0	38.0	40.0	30.0	42.0	38.0	10.2
Wisconsin	79	33.0	35.0	35.0	36.0	35.0	36.0	35.0	43.5	38.0	35.5	36.2	7.9
Minnesota	1,034	27.5	25.0	25.5	25.5	24.5	29.0	25.0	36.0	29.0	33.5	28.0	14.0
Missouri	247	21.5	25.0	29.5	28.0	27.5	27.0	22.0	26.0	27.0	32.0	26.6	12.0
North Dakota	3,029	22.5	19.0	23.5	22.5	22.5	23.5	22.0	28.0	20.0	24.5	22.8	10.8
South Dakota	533	23.5	15.5	17.0	20.0	18.0	15.5	23.0	30.5	13.5	30.0	20.6	29.0
Nebraska	222	22.0	20.0	19.0	18.0	20.0	12.0	31.0	27.5	22.0	29.0	22.0	29.0
Kansas	501	13.0	15.5	14.0	21.5	18.5	18.0	22.0	27.0	26.0	26.0	20.2	25.6
Virginia	106	32.0	34.0	33.0	39.0	35.0	40.0	31.0	34.5	38.0	39.0	35.6	9.0
Oklahoma	297	11.0	17.5	19.0	19.0	13.0	14.5	18.5	29.0	22.0	24.0	18.8	28.4
Texas	207	11.5	14.5	19.5	16.5	14.0	16.0	21.0	23.0	19.5	22.0	17.8	21.5
Montana	1,207	27.5	28.0	27.0	26.0	30.0	28.5	26.5	31.0	27.5	23.5	27.6	7.6
Idaho	485	32.0	37.0	32.0	32.5	32.0	32.5	35.0	35.0	31.5	29.0	32.8	6.8
Wyoming	117	33.0	32.0	28.0	24.0	28.0	27.0	37.0	37.0	31.0	32.0	30.9	13.7
Colorado	418	23.5	28.5	27.0	20.0	26.5	25.5	30.5	30.0	29.0	33.0	27.4	13.7
Arizona	167	50.0	55.0	55.0	52.0	60.0	60.0	59.0	58.0	56.0	61.0	56.6	6.5
Utah	161	44.0	44.0	44.0	40.0	40.5	46.0	45.0	41.0	45.0	43.0	43.2	4.8
Washington	507	36.0	36.0	38.0	36.0	25.0	35.0	41.0	31.5	38.5	36.0	35.3	12.4
Oregon	479	30.0	37.0	37.0	36.0	32.0	37.5	35.5	34.0	36.0	35.5	35.0	6.8
California	1,735	30.0	36.0	34.0	36.5	37.5	37.0	40.0	36.5	39.0	40.0	36.6	8.2
Michigan	92	34.0	29.0	31.5	35.0	34.0	31.0	33.5	45.0	34.0	35.0	34.2	12.4

TABLE 18-9. COTTON ACREAGE, YIELD OF LINT PER ACRE AND VARIABILITY, FOR PERIOD 1951–1960

State	Acres (000 omitted) Average 1951–1960	Lint Yield in Pounds per Harvested Acre										Ten-year Average	C.V. (%)
		1951	1952	1953	1954	1955	1956	1957	1958	1959	1960		
North Carolina	502	376	380	278	316	350	393	321	465	395	288	356	16.0
South Carolina	704	389	292	281	281	375	364	329	409	353	364	344	13.0
Georgia	919	317	249	262	285	376	336	333	447	381	371	336	18.1
Tennessee	616	334	374	354	408	523	484	427	492	620	555	457	20.4
Alabama	1,073	299	285	285	297	478	371	346	403	412	424	360	18.9
Mississippi	1,788	329	380	410	387	570	486	388	407	514	491	436	17.2
Missouri	412	302	400	386	478	502	592	281	447	610	548	455	24.9
Arkansas	1,527	295	337	358	381	545	506	416	433	568	493	433	21.3
Louisiana	623	391	405	407	400	454	501	380	390	481	483	429	10.6
Oklahoma	829	150	108	205	154	281	175	234	375	292	349	232	38.6
Texas	7,578	166	175	233	244	281	278	295	387	334	329	272	25.7
New Mexico	226	415	519	497	736	688	811	619	818	782	686	657	21.4
Arizona	457	705	727	743	968	981	1,113	1,035	980	893	941	909	15.3
California	970	640	624	632	786	774	897	1,035	1,049	1,055	992	848	21.2

TABLE 18-10. ALFALFA SEED ACREAGE, YIELD PER ACRE AND VARIABILITY, FOR PERIOD 1951–1960

State	Acres (000 omitted) Average 1951–1960	Yield in Pounds per Acre										Ten-year Average	C.V. (%)
		1951	1952	1953	1954	1955	1956	1957	1958	1959	1960		
Ohio	4,890	42	46	50	49	48	60	50	50	50	45	49	9.6
Michigan	18,100	33	41	40	38	50	45	50	55	60	55	47	18.6
Wisconsin	10,050	40	48	60	50	60	55	50	65	75	55	56	17.6
Minnesota	21,900	51	47	35	55	60	53	50	47	65	85	55	24.3
North Dakota	57,200	38	42	37	40	50	33	36	45	45	60	43	18.6
South Dakota	151,200	26	65	45	70	55	47	40	55	55	75	53	27.4
Nebraska	96,500	41	90	90	90	95	80	65	80	63	85	78	21.6
Kansas	112,200	60	110	95	120	130	92	75	105	75	125	99	23.8
Oklahoma	59,000	96	115	92	125	100	105	125	180	125	140	120	21.6
Texas	22,800	135	150	110	120	130	120	145	180	125	150	136	15.0
Montana	71,000	62	84	74	115	110	95	105	85	85	100	92	18.1
Idaho	33,100	150	180	185	150	190	175	185	210	275	370	207	32.5
Wyoming	20,850	60	87	180	120	140	110	120	85	87	80	107	32.7
Colorado	19,600	85	100	115	125	135	150	135	150	130	130	126	16.4
Utah	53,400	185	180	230	210	185	190	170	180	210	185	192	9.5
New Mexico	5,700	265	290	275	295	330	365	215	275	280	225	282	15.7
Arizona	27,600	215	225	200	190	140	235	220	195	200	190	201	13.2
Washington	23,700	540	525	595	460	520	550	420	410	430	400	485	14.2
Oregon	8,050	220	280	315	250	400	390	330	350	380	500	342	24.0
California	140,800	325	460	455	440	480	415	460	390	380	365	417	12.1

for the purpose) are of great importance in California. Seed yields by states from the Midwest to the West Coast are given in Table 18-10. Highest yields of seed have been produced in the West Coast region, Washington, California, and Oregon. The intermountain region has been in an intermediate position, whereas the northcentral states (where 20 million acres of alfalfa are grown for forage) have produced the poorest seed yields of all areas. The basic reasons for the development of this pattern of production appear to be two: (1) the dry summer season in the western areas, and (2) more adequate pollination.

It is obvious that all of the methods suggested in this chapter for expressing the relationship between the environmental conditions in a region and the approach to maximum productivity leave much to be desired. In most areas of the United States, for example, sufficient data on both yields of specific varieties and meteorological conditions over a long period of time simply are not available. Varieties have been changed too often and weather data are not sufficiently specific to permit the most effective use of a method such as Azzi's meteorological equivalents.

The ecological optimum approach of Klages, with some refinements, would appear to have considerable practical usefulness. Its weaknesses are in the generalizations which are made in taking data from political and not ecological areas, and in the paucity of weather data on a sufficiently detailed basis for precise study of climatic and crop yield relationships. These weaknesses can be corrected and, with political boundaries ignored, specific areas of similar yield and variability can be delineated. The "ecological optimum" approach would appear to have merit, particularly in view of the growing trend toward more concentrated production of corn (in Corn Belt areas) on more level areas of high potential productivity, with less regard for traditional crop rotation patterns. This implies a careful selection of fields where corn production may be emphasized, and should imply as well a careful selection of areas where high-yielding forage crops such as alfalfa can be produced most efficiently. This trend represents a logical approach to more effective ecological use of our land resources.

References

1. Azzi, G. 1956. *Agricultural Ecology.* Constable, London.
2. Barger, G. L. and Thom, H. C. S. 1949a. A method for characterizing drought intensity in Iowa. *Jour. Amer. Soc. Agron.* 41: 13–19.
3. ———. 1949b. Evaluation of drought hazard. *Jour. Amer. Soc. Agron.* 41: 519–526.

4. Crop Production—Annual Summaries 1949 to 1960 inclusive. Agr. Mktg. Serv., Crop Rep. Board, U. S. Dept. of Agric., Washington, D. C.
5. Graham, E. H. 1944. *Natural Principles of Land Use*. Oxford Univ. Press, London.
6. Klages, K. H. W. 1930. Geographical distribution of variability in the yield of field crops in the states of the Mississippi Valley. *Ecol.* 11: 293–306.
7. ———. 1934. Geographical distribution of variability in the yields of cereal crops in South Dakota. *Ecol.* 12: 334–345.
8. ———. 1942. *Ecological Crop Geography*. Macmillan, New York.
9. ———. 1960. Crop adaptation in relation to the economic use of water. Wyo. Agr. Exp. Sta. Bul. 367.
10. Mathews, O. R. and Brown, L. A. 1938. Winter wheat and sorghum production in the Southern Great Plains under limited rainfall. U. S. Dept. Agr., Cir. 477.
11. Nunns, F. K. 1958. The classification of rural land. In *Yearbook of Agriculture*, Govt. Print. Off., Washington, D. C. pp. 362–370.
12. Odum, E. P. 1959. *Fundamentals of Ecology*. Saunders, Philadelphia.
13. Pengra, R. F. 1946. Correlation analyses of precipitation and crop yield data for the subhumid areas of the Northern Great Plains. *Jour. Amer. Soc. Agron.* 38: 848–850.
14. Rose, J. K. 1936. Corn yield and climate in the Corn Belt. *Geog. Rev.* 26: 88–102.
15. Schimper, A. F. W. 1903. *Plant Geography on a Physiological Basis*. Clarendon, Oxford.
16. Steele, J. G. 1951. The measure of our land. Soil Cons. Serv., Govt. Print. Off., Washington, D. C.
17. Visher, S. S. 1955. Comparative Agricultural potentials of the world's regions. *Econ. Geog.* 31: 82–86.
18. ———. 1943a. Barley in the United States: a historical sketch. *Geog. Rev.* 33: 56–73.
19. ———. 1943b. Climatic relations of American barley production. *Geog. Rev.* 33: 569–588.
20. Weaver, John C. 1950. *American Barley Production*. Burgess, Minneapolis.

Index

Absolute humidity, 134

Acer saccharum (saccharophorum), adaptation limits, 41–42

Achillea borealis, soil ecotypes, 83

Acidic rocks, 43

Adaptation: definition of, 46; importance of response to photoperiod, 241; of world crops, 18; principles of, 3; relationship to selection, 4; to desiccation of tissues, 46

Adaptation of crops, versatility or perfection, 50

Adaptations: fate of, 63; morphological, 46; physiological, 46

Adaptive value, 49–50; of resistance, 54–55

Adaptive worth, 51

Adiabatic cooling, 138

Adverse factors, 46

Aegilops spp., in wheat fields in Thrace, 99

Aegilops spelfoides, 386

Aegilops squarrosa, 386–387

Aerobic metabolism, reduction with too much soil moisture, 167

Africa: banana production, 350–351; cacao production, 345, 347

Aggregation of soil, effect on aeration, 253, 279

Agricultural commodities, export countries, 11

Agricultural economy, 4; relation to population density, 7

Agricultural potential, comparative, in world's regions, 410–413

Agricultural production, with advanced technology, 288

Agricultural products, export of, 4

Agro-ecological groups of plants, 98–99

Agropyron smithii, drought resistance of, 164

Air movement, 247–261, 337–338; high and low pressure relationships, 255

Air pollutants, chemical nature of, 249–250

Air pollution: causes of, 248–250; disasters from, 248; smog, 249

Air temperature, geographic distribution of, 182

Alaska, rainfall, mist and dew, 43

Albedo, reflection coefficient, 144–145

Alder (*Alnus glutinosa*), nitrogen fixation by, 304

Alfalfa: competition with companion crop, 4; damage by SO_2 fumes, 249; depth of roots aid in avoiding moisture stress, 165; hardening process, 204; heaving conditions, 202; in Mexico, 185; seed production and genetic shift, 59; transpiration rhythm, 153

Alfalfa seed: approach to ecological optimum, 429–430; pollination insects essential, 423, 430; shift of producing regions to the west, 423, 429–430

Algae culture, 127; primary productivity rate, 417

Allele, 51

Alluvial soils, 269; natural fertility of, 14

Alnus incana, races of, in Finland, 83

Alpine bluegrass, 66

Alpine pastures, limits of, 185

Alpine vegetation—at timberline in Sierras, 70

Altitude, temperature effects of, 42, 183–185, 190

Altitudinal limits, effects of temperature and wind, 199

Amaranthus leucocarpus, as a food crop, 109

Amaranthus viridis, 40

Anaerobic environment, in wet soils, 167

Anaerobic respiration, of roots, 254

Ancestral plants, 88

Anemometer, 256

Angiosperms, first appearance of, 22

Angle of incidence, variation with latitude, 225

Animals as biotic factors, 307

Animal proteins in diets, 11

432